Mathematics for Machine Technology

Fifth Edition

Instructor's Guide

Robert D. Smith

THOMSON

DELMAR LEARNING   Australia Canada Mexico Singapore Spain United Kingdom United States

THOMSON

DELMAR LEARNING

Instructor's Manual to accompany *Mathematics for Machine Technology*, 5th Edition

By Robert D. Smith

Vice President, Technology and Trades SBU:

Alar Elken

Editorial Director:

Sandy Clark

Acquisitions Editor:

James Gish

Development:

Jennifer Luck

Marketing Director:

Cynthia Eichelman

Marketing Coordinator:

Mark Pierro

Production Director:

Mary Ellen Black

Production Manager:

Larry Main

Senior Project Editor:

Christopher Chien

Art/Design Specialist:

Cheri Plasse

Editorial Assistant:

Marissa Maiella

Library of Congress Cataloging-in-Publication Data:
Card Number:

ISBN: 1-4018-1649-5

NOTICE TO THE READER

CONTENTS

TO THE INSTRUCTOR

The primary objective in the design of *Mathematics for Machine Technology* is to present those mathematical concepts and practical application of concepts which are generally required by skilled employees in the machine trades and related occupations. Presentation of concepts and their solutions is immediately followed by realistic industry-related applications. The applications progress from the simple to those whose solutions are relatively complex. The contents of this text range from general arithmetic processes to complex right and oblique triangle applications, compound-angle problems, and computer numerical control. An understanding of mathematical concepts through realistic trade applications is stressed in all topics presented.

Throughout the text, the student is required to work with illustrations, tables, and charts such as those found in machine trade handbooks and on engineering drawings. Student activities are similar to those actually required on the job. In Section 1—Common Fractions and Decimal Fractions, general arithmetic processes are presented with many practical applications.

Following the text units on common fractions, both customary and metric units of measure are presented in the topics, examples, and problems. Upon completion of the text, students should be equally familiar and proficient with both systems of measure as they relate to machine trade applications. An ample number of customary and metric problems are given. Content may be selected and problems assigned based on the degree of emphasis to be placed on each system.

The scientific calculator is introduced in the Preface. Further instruction and examples are given throughout the text wherever calculator applications are appropriate to the material presented. Calculator information and sequencing in examples and practical applications have been updated and expanded in this editon. The use of the calculator is left as an option to the instructor. Naturally, students may be permitted to solve problems using calculators at the discretion of the instructor. It is felt that the individual instructor is best able to identify student needs and the computational skills developed with his/her unique group of students.

Section 2—Linear Measurement: Customary (English) and Metric was developed to enable students to use customary and metric units with equal facility when computing tolerances, clearances, and interferences.

The content in Section 3—Fundamentals of Algebra was selected and developed to provide the learner an adequate base for working with handbook formulas and for subsequent computations required in practical geometry and trigonometry applied problems. It is felt that the algebra concepts presented are those actually needed for the vast majority of situations encountered on the job. Therefore, concepts such as types of factoring, complex fractional equations, systems of equations, and quadratic equations were purposely excluded from the text.

In Section 4—Fundamentals of Plane Geometry, Section 6—Trigonometry, Section 7—Compound Angles, and Section 8—Computer Numerical Control, concepts and applications are presented which require analyses and computations which are often necessary when planning and machining parts from engineering drawings. The procedures are typical of those required in calculating working dimensions, expressing equivalent angular measure and linear measure, and computing check or inspection dimensions. The content in the plane geometry section emphasizes principles and applications related to lines, angles, polygons, and circles which are required in laying out, machining, and inspecting parts. A new Section 5—Geometric Figures: Areas and Volumes, has been added. A survey of instructors using the fourth edition suggested including areas and volumes of basic plane and solid geometric figures. Machine technology applied problems involving material quantities, costs, and weights are emphasized.

The more complex right triangle and oblique triangle problems require the application of a combination of algebra and geometry principles as well as trigonometry concepts in their solutions. As the complexity of problems increases, a greater proportion of time and effort is required in their analyses. It is important that the student be given direction in completely "thinking through" a problem before writing computations. The following method of solution must be emphasized to the student and continually reinforced.

Analyze the problem before writing computations.

- Relate given dimensions to the unknown and determine whether other dimensions in addition to the given dimensions are required in the solution.

- Determine the auxiliary lines which are required to form right triangles which contain dimensions that are needed for the solution.

- Determine whether sufficient dimensions are known to obtain required values within the right triangles. If enough information is not available for solving a triangle, continue the analysis until enough information is obtained.

- Check each step in the analysis to verify that there are no gaps or false assumptions.

Write the computations.

Student understanding and the application of logical step-by-step procedures are stressed throughout the content dealing with compound angles. Visualization of the components which make up a specific compound-angle situation is emphasized. It is crucial that students study and understand the procedures given in the text examples when solving various types of compound angle problems. When solving problems, students should be required to apply the procedures of sketching components in rectangular solids and showing and identifying axes, surfaces, and angles which are required in their solutions. Only after having achieved these analytical and visualization skills should the student be permitted to use the given formulas which follow.

Emphasis should be placed on student understanding, analysis, and procedural steps in the solutions of complex plane trigonometry, compound angle, and computer numerical control problems.

An Achievement Review is included at the end of each section of the text. Each Achievement Review is designed to sample all topics, concepts, and applied problems presented within a section. An Achievement Review may also be used as a Placement Test prior to any student involvement with the content of the section. Upon evaluation of students' performances on an Achievement Review, the instructor may conclude that students have previously achieved sufficient mastery of some or all of the content within a section. It may be possible to omit a section entirely. Where specific student strengths and weaknesses are identified, the instructor may elect to omit certain section concepts and concentrate on only the concepts in which deficiencies were identified.

Section One
Common Fractions and Decimal Fractions

1. A $= \dfrac{3}{32}$

B $= \dfrac{7}{32}$

C $= \dfrac{12}{32} = \dfrac{3}{8}$

D $= \dfrac{10}{32}$

E $= \dfrac{27}{32}$

F $= \dfrac{32}{32} = 1$

2. Piece 1: $\dfrac{16}{64} = \dfrac{1}{4}$

Piece 2: $\dfrac{12}{64} = \dfrac{3}{16}$

Piece 3: $\dfrac{32}{64} = \dfrac{1}{2}$

Piece 4: $\dfrac{4}{64} = \dfrac{1}{16}$

3. a. $\dfrac{1}{16}$

b. $\dfrac{3}{16}$

c. $\dfrac{7}{16}$

d. $\dfrac{5}{16}$

e. $\dfrac{16}{16} = 1$

f. $\dfrac{1}{32}$

g. $\dfrac{1}{48}$

3. h. $\dfrac{3}{64}$

i. $\dfrac{1}{160}$

j. $\dfrac{1}{256}$

4. a. $\dfrac{1}{2}$

b. $\dfrac{1}{2}$

c. $\dfrac{1}{2}$

d. $\dfrac{1}{2}$

e. $\dfrac{5}{2}$

f. $\dfrac{3}{2}$

g. $\dfrac{7}{2}$

h. $\dfrac{9}{2}$

5. a. $\dfrac{3}{4}$

b. 3

c. $\dfrac{3}{5}$

d. 6

e. $\dfrac{1}{4}$

f. $\dfrac{7}{3}$

g. 3

5. h. $\dfrac{13}{3}$

i. $\dfrac{1}{6}$

j. $\dfrac{2}{15}$

6. a. $\dfrac{8}{32}$

b. $\dfrac{24}{32}$

c. $\dfrac{44}{32}$

d. $\dfrac{14}{32}$

e. $\dfrac{42}{32}$

f. $\dfrac{304}{32}$

g. $\dfrac{394}{32}$

h. $\dfrac{84}{32}$

7. a. $\dfrac{6}{8}$

b. $\dfrac{21}{36}$

c. $\dfrac{24}{60}$

d. $\dfrac{51}{42}$

e. $\dfrac{100}{45}$

f. $\dfrac{84}{18}$

7. g. $\dfrac{56}{128}$

h. $\dfrac{78}{48}$

i. $\dfrac{210}{16}$

8. a. $\dfrac{8}{3}$

b. $\dfrac{15}{8}$

c. $\dfrac{27}{5}$

d. $\dfrac{27}{8}$

e. $\dfrac{169}{32}$

f. $\dfrac{59}{7}$

g. $\dfrac{31}{3}$

h. $\dfrac{40}{5}$

i. $\dfrac{201}{2}$

j. $\dfrac{319}{64}$

k. $\dfrac{395}{8}$

l. $\dfrac{6541}{16}$

9. a. $1\dfrac{2}{3}$

b. $10\dfrac{1}{2}$

9. c. $1\dfrac{1}{8}$

d. $21\dfrac{3}{4}$

e. 8

f. $1\dfrac{3}{124}$

g. $3\dfrac{31}{32}$

h. $3\dfrac{12}{15} = 3\dfrac{4}{5}$

i. $16\dfrac{2}{3}$

j. $14\dfrac{11}{16}$

k. $128\dfrac{1}{2}$

l. $6\dfrac{17}{64}$

10. a. $\dfrac{20}{8}$

b. $\dfrac{54}{16}$

c. $\dfrac{117}{15}$

d. $\dfrac{228}{18}$

e. $\dfrac{632}{64}$

f. $\dfrac{1984}{128}$

UNIT **1**   (*continued*)

11.

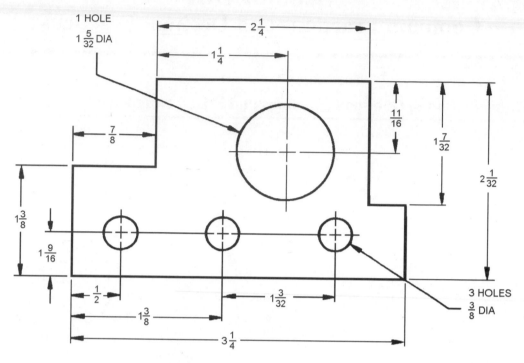

Note: All dimensions are in inches

UNIT **2**   Addition of Common Fractions and Mixed Numbers

1. 12

2. 30

3. 48

4. 20

5. $\dfrac{6}{12}, \dfrac{9}{12}, \dfrac{5}{12}$

6. $\dfrac{7}{16}, \dfrac{6}{16}, \dfrac{8}{16}$

7. $\dfrac{18}{20}, \dfrac{5}{20}, \dfrac{12}{20}, \dfrac{4}{20}$

8. $\dfrac{12}{64}, \dfrac{14}{64}, \dfrac{17}{64}, \dfrac{48}{64}$

9. A $= \dfrac{1''}{2} + \dfrac{9''}{16} = 1\dfrac{1''}{16}$

    B $= \dfrac{3''}{8} + \dfrac{35''}{64} = \dfrac{59''}{64}$

    C $= \dfrac{31''}{32} + \dfrac{1''}{8} + \dfrac{15''}{32} = 1\dfrac{9''}{16}$

    D $= \dfrac{1''}{4} + \dfrac{7''}{16} = \dfrac{11''}{16}$

    E $= \dfrac{59''}{64} + 1\dfrac{9''}{16} + \dfrac{11''}{16} = 3\dfrac{11''}{64}$

    F $= \dfrac{11''}{64} + \dfrac{5''}{16} + \dfrac{21''}{64} = \dfrac{13''}{16}$

10. length $= \dfrac{17''}{32} + \dfrac{63''}{64} + \dfrac{3''}{8} = 1\dfrac{57''}{64}$

     width $= \dfrac{1''}{4} + \dfrac{7''}{16} + \dfrac{21''}{32} = 1\dfrac{11''}{32}$

     height $= \dfrac{29''}{64} + \dfrac{9''}{16} + \dfrac{5''}{32} + \dfrac{1''}{2} = 1\dfrac{43''}{64}$

11. A $= \dfrac{1''}{4} + 1\dfrac{7''}{16} + \dfrac{19''}{32} + 2\dfrac{9''}{32}$

    B $= 2\dfrac{1''}{32} + 1\dfrac{27''}{32} = 3\dfrac{7''}{8}$

    C $= 3\dfrac{7''}{8} + \dfrac{3''}{8} = 4\dfrac{1''}{4}$

    D $= 1'' + \dfrac{1''}{4} + 1\dfrac{1''}{8} + \dfrac{7''}{32} = 2\dfrac{19''}{32}$

    E $= \dfrac{5''}{8} + 2\dfrac{3''}{4} = 3\dfrac{3''}{8}$

    F $= \dfrac{9''}{32} + 1\dfrac{3''}{64} = 1\dfrac{21''}{64}$

    G $= 3\dfrac{3''}{8} + 1\dfrac{21''}{64} = 4\dfrac{45''}{64}$

UNIT **2**   *(continued)*

12. $A = \dfrac{3''}{32} + 1\dfrac{5''}{64} = 1\dfrac{11''}{64}$

$\quad B = \dfrac{3''}{32} + 1\dfrac{1''}{16} + \dfrac{1''}{8} = 1\dfrac{9''}{32}$

$\quad C = 1\dfrac{11''}{64} + 1\dfrac{9''}{32} = 2\dfrac{29''}{64}$

12. $D = 2\dfrac{29''}{64} + \dfrac{1''}{4} + \dfrac{9''}{32} = 2\dfrac{63''}{64}$

13. $1h + 2\dfrac{3}{4}h + \dfrac{5}{6}h + \dfrac{3}{10}h + \dfrac{2}{5}h = 5\dfrac{17}{60}h$

UNIT **3**   Subtraction of Common Fractions and Mixed Numbers

1. a. $\dfrac{11}{32}$ c. $\dfrac{13}{25}$ e. $\dfrac{23}{64}$

   b. $\dfrac{1}{4}$ d. $\dfrac{31}{64}$ f. $\dfrac{29}{48}$

2. $A = \dfrac{5''}{8} - \dfrac{7''}{32} = \dfrac{13''}{32}$

$\quad B = \dfrac{63''}{64} - \dfrac{3''}{4} = \dfrac{15''}{64}$

$\quad C = \dfrac{15''}{16} - \dfrac{1''}{2} = \dfrac{7''}{16}$

$\quad D = \dfrac{29''}{32} - \dfrac{1''}{2} = \dfrac{13''}{32}$

3. $A = \dfrac{3''}{4} - \dfrac{17''}{32} = \dfrac{7''}{32}$

$\quad B - \dfrac{25''}{32} - \dfrac{3''}{16} - \dfrac{19''}{32}$

$\quad C = \dfrac{49''}{64} - \dfrac{3''}{8} = \dfrac{25''}{64}$

$\quad D = \dfrac{1''}{2} - \dfrac{5''}{16} = \dfrac{3''}{16}$

$\quad E = \dfrac{23''}{32} - \dfrac{9''}{32} = \dfrac{7''}{16}$

$\quad F = \dfrac{7''}{8} - \dfrac{15''}{32} = \dfrac{13''}{32}$

4. $A = 1\dfrac{7''}{8} - 1\dfrac{11''}{32} = \dfrac{17''}{32}$

$\quad B = 3\dfrac{9''}{64} - 1\dfrac{7''}{8} = 1\dfrac{17''}{64}$

$\quad C = 5\dfrac{1''}{4} - 3\dfrac{9''}{64} - 1\dfrac{3''}{8} = \dfrac{47''}{64}$

$\quad D = 1\dfrac{3''}{8} - \dfrac{23''}{64} = 1\dfrac{1''}{64}$

4. $E = \dfrac{1''}{1} - \dfrac{9''}{61} = \dfrac{7''}{61}$

$\quad F = \dfrac{7''}{16} - \dfrac{1''}{4} = \dfrac{3''}{16}$

$\quad G = \dfrac{7''}{16} - \dfrac{5''}{32} = \dfrac{9''}{32}$

5. $A = 2\dfrac{3''}{8} - 1\dfrac{29''}{32} = \dfrac{15''}{32}$

$\quad B = 1\dfrac{29''}{32} - 1\dfrac{1''}{4} = \dfrac{21''}{32}$

$\quad C = 1\dfrac{1''}{4} - \dfrac{13''}{16} = \dfrac{7''}{16}$

$\quad D = 2\dfrac{17''}{32} - 2\dfrac{1''}{16} = \dfrac{15''}{32}$

$\quad E = 1\dfrac{3''}{8} - 1\dfrac{3''}{32} = \dfrac{9''}{32}$

$\quad F = \dfrac{13''}{16} - \dfrac{1''}{2} = \dfrac{5''}{16}$

$\quad G = 2\dfrac{1''}{32} - \dfrac{13''}{16} = 1\dfrac{7''}{32}$

$\quad H = 1\dfrac{17''}{32} - 1\dfrac{1''}{64} = \dfrac{33''}{64}$

$\quad I = 2\dfrac{23''}{32} - 2\dfrac{1''}{8} = \dfrac{19''}{32}$

6. a. $2\dfrac{1''}{61} - 1\dfrac{3''}{32} - \dfrac{59''}{61}$

   b. $3\dfrac{1''}{4} - 2\dfrac{1''}{64} = 1\dfrac{15''}{64}$

   c. $3\dfrac{1''}{4} - 1\dfrac{3''}{32} = 2\dfrac{5''}{32}$

   d. $2\dfrac{3''}{16} - 1\dfrac{5''}{8} = \dfrac{9''}{16}$

   e. $3\dfrac{1''}{2} - 2\dfrac{3''}{16} = 1\dfrac{5''}{16}$

   f. $3\dfrac{1''}{2} - 1\dfrac{5''}{8} = 1\dfrac{7''}{8}$

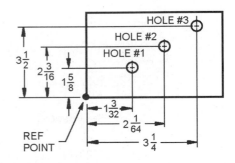

Note: All dimensions are in inches

UNIT 4 Multiplication of Common Fractions and Mixed Numbers

1. a. $\dfrac{1}{9}$ d. $\dfrac{3}{10}$

   b. $\dfrac{1}{8}$ e. $\dfrac{27}{2}$ or $13\dfrac{1}{2}$

   c. $\dfrac{65}{512}$ f. $\dfrac{1}{8}$

2. $A = 6 \times \dfrac{7''}{64} = \dfrac{21''}{32}$

   $B = 6 \times \dfrac{9''}{16} = 3\dfrac{3''}{8}$

   $C = 2 \times \dfrac{3''}{8} = \dfrac{3''}{4}$

   $D = 5 \times \dfrac{7''}{32} = 1\dfrac{3''}{32}$

   $E = 5 \times \dfrac{3''}{16} = \dfrac{15''}{16}$

3. a. $\dfrac{55}{64} \times \dfrac{29''}{32} = \dfrac{1595''}{2048}$

   b. $\dfrac{1}{8} \times \dfrac{7''}{32} = \dfrac{7''}{256}$

4. a. $A = \dfrac{1}{8} \times \dfrac{7''}{16} = \dfrac{7''}{128}$

     $B = \dfrac{17}{24} \times \dfrac{7''}{16} = \dfrac{119''}{384}$

   b. $A = \dfrac{1}{8} \times \dfrac{3''}{8} = \dfrac{3''}{64}$

     $B = \dfrac{17}{24} \times \dfrac{3''}{8} = \dfrac{17''}{64}$

   c. $A = \dfrac{1}{8} \times \dfrac{15''}{16} = \dfrac{15''}{128}$

     $B = \dfrac{17}{24} \times \dfrac{15''}{16} = \dfrac{85''}{128}$

   d. $A = \dfrac{1}{8} \times \dfrac{21''}{32} = \dfrac{21''}{256}$

     $B = \dfrac{17}{24} \times \dfrac{21''}{32} = \dfrac{119''}{256}$

   e. $A = \dfrac{1}{8} \times \dfrac{3''}{4} = \dfrac{3''}{32}$

     $B = \dfrac{17}{24} \times \dfrac{3''}{4} = \dfrac{17''}{32}$

4. f. $C = \dfrac{1}{8} \times \dfrac{1''}{4} = \dfrac{1''}{32}$

   g. $C = \dfrac{1}{8} \times \dfrac{3''}{32} = \dfrac{3''}{256}$

   h. $C = \dfrac{1}{8} \times \dfrac{1''}{20} = \dfrac{1''}{160}$

   i. $C = \dfrac{1}{8} \times \dfrac{1''}{28} = \dfrac{1''}{224}$

   j. $C = \dfrac{1}{8} \times \dfrac{3''}{16} = \dfrac{3''}{128}$

5. a. $10\dfrac{1}{2}$ d. $6\dfrac{13}{32}$

   b. $25\dfrac{43}{64}$ e. $\dfrac{201}{256}$

   c. $11\dfrac{9}{16}$ f. $37\dfrac{1}{3}$

6. $20 \times \left(3\dfrac{3''}{16} + \dfrac{3''}{32}\right) = 65\dfrac{5''}{8}$

UNIT 5 Division of Common Fractions and Mixed Numbers

1. $\dfrac{8}{7}$ 3. $\dfrac{8}{25}$

2. $\dfrac{4}{1}$ 4. $\dfrac{1}{6}$

5. $A = \dfrac{1}{2} \div \dfrac{1}{12} = 6$ threads

   $B = \dfrac{15}{16} \div \dfrac{1}{9} = 8\dfrac{7}{16}$ threads

   $C = \dfrac{1}{4} \div \dfrac{1}{14} = 3\dfrac{1}{2}$ threads

   $D = \dfrac{7}{8} \div \dfrac{1}{8} = 7$ threads

   $E = \dfrac{5}{8} \div \dfrac{1}{11} = 6\dfrac{7}{8}$ threads

   $F = \dfrac{13}{32} \div \dfrac{1}{16} = 6\dfrac{1}{2}$ threads

   $G = \dfrac{9}{16} \div \dfrac{1}{5} = 2\dfrac{13}{16}$ threads

6. $\dfrac{3}{4} \div \dfrac{3}{64} = 16$ revolutions

7. $\dfrac{15}{16} \div \dfrac{3}{16} = 5$ cuts

8. Set A: $15\dfrac{5''}{16} \div 7 = 2\dfrac{3''}{16}$

   Set B: $2\dfrac{3''}{32} \div 2 = 1\dfrac{3''}{64}$

   Set C: $5\dfrac{5''}{8} \div 3 = 1\dfrac{7''}{8}$

   Set D: $3\dfrac{15''}{32} \div 3 = 1\dfrac{5''}{32}$

   Set E: $7\dfrac{7''}{8} \div 4 = 1\dfrac{31''}{32}$

9. $3\dfrac{3}{4} \div \dfrac{1}{64} = 240$ revolutions

10. $27\dfrac{1}{4} \times 12 = 327''$

   $327'' - \dfrac{5''}{16} = 326\dfrac{11''}{16}$

   $326\dfrac{11''}{16} \div 2\dfrac{3''}{16} = 149\dfrac{12}{35}$

   $= 149$ complete pieces

11. $3\dfrac{1}{4}$ feet $\div 4\dfrac{1}{16} = \dfrac{4}{5}$ foot

12. $42\dfrac{1''}{2} \div \left(1\dfrac{7''}{8} + \dfrac{3''}{32}\right) = 21\dfrac{37}{63}$

   $= 21$ complete posts

13. $110\dfrac{1}{2}$ lb $\div 23\dfrac{1}{4} = 4\dfrac{70}{93}$ lb

14. a. $2\dfrac{1''}{4} \div 10 = \dfrac{9''}{40}$

   b. $7\dfrac{37''}{64} \div 24\dfrac{1}{4} = \dfrac{5''}{16}$

   c. $2\dfrac{7''}{16} \div 6\dfrac{1}{2} = \dfrac{3''}{8}$

   d. $1\dfrac{1''}{2} \div 15 = \dfrac{1''}{10}$

   e. $6\dfrac{3''}{10} \div 12\dfrac{3}{5} = \dfrac{1''}{2}$

UNIT 6   Combined Operations of Common Fractions and Mixed Numbers

1. a. $\dfrac{7}{16}$ d. $28\dfrac{1}{2}$ g. $12 - 9 + 2\dfrac{3}{4} = 5\dfrac{3}{4}$ j. $20\dfrac{1}{3} + \dfrac{16}{29} = 20\dfrac{77}{87}$

   b. $2\dfrac{1}{16}$ e. $32\dfrac{1}{8} + 1\dfrac{41}{64} = 33\dfrac{49}{64}$ h. $11\dfrac{1}{2} \div \dfrac{1}{2} + 5\dfrac{3}{8} = 23 + 5\dfrac{5}{8} = 28\dfrac{3}{8}$

   c. $5\dfrac{33}{50}$ f. $\dfrac{7}{9} \times 4\dfrac{1}{2} = 3\dfrac{1}{2}$ i. $11\dfrac{1}{2} \div 2\dfrac{5}{8} = 4\dfrac{8}{21}$

2. a. $1\dfrac{1}{2}$ c. $\dfrac{15}{34}$ e. $3\dfrac{7}{8} \div 4\dfrac{9}{16} = \dfrac{62}{73}$

   b. $\dfrac{31}{40}$ d. $\dfrac{7}{6} \div 3\dfrac{3}{4} = \dfrac{14}{45}$ f. $5\dfrac{1}{4} \div \dfrac{16}{9} = 2\dfrac{61}{64}$

3. a. $B = 6\dfrac{3''}{4} - \left(1\dfrac{3''}{8} + \dfrac{1''}{2}\right) = 6\dfrac{3''}{4} - 1\dfrac{7''}{8} = 4\dfrac{7''}{8}$

     $E = 7\dfrac{9''}{8} - \left(1\dfrac{3''}{8} + \dfrac{12''}{16}\right) = 7\dfrac{3''}{8} - 2\dfrac{5''}{16} = 5\dfrac{1''}{16}$

   b. $A = 5\dfrac{37''}{64} - \left(3\dfrac{13''}{16} + 1\dfrac{5''}{8}\right) = 5\dfrac{37''}{64} - 5\dfrac{7''}{16} = \dfrac{9''}{64}$

     $G = 1\dfrac{5''}{8} + 4\dfrac{3''}{8} + \dfrac{3''}{4} = 6\dfrac{3''}{4}$

   c. $C = 7\dfrac{1''}{32} - \left(5\dfrac{1''}{8} + \dfrac{27''}{32}\right) = 7\dfrac{1''}{32} - 5\dfrac{31''}{32} = 1\dfrac{1''}{16}$

     $D = \dfrac{7''}{16} + 4\dfrac{3''}{32} + 1\dfrac{1''}{16} = 5\dfrac{19''}{32}$

   d. $B = 5\dfrac{31''}{32} - \left(\dfrac{5''}{8} + 1\dfrac{7''}{16}\right) = 5\dfrac{31''}{32} - 2\dfrac{1''}{16} = 3\dfrac{29''}{32}$

     $E = 7\dfrac{15''}{16} - \left(1\dfrac{7''}{16} + \dfrac{7''}{8}\right) = 7\dfrac{15''}{16} - 2\dfrac{5''}{16} = 5\dfrac{5''}{8}$

   e. $A = 6\dfrac{1''}{32} - \left(3\dfrac{3''}{4} + 1\dfrac{11''}{16}\right) = 6\dfrac{1''}{32} - 5\dfrac{7''}{16} = \dfrac{19''}{32}$

     $G = 1\dfrac{11''}{16} + 4\dfrac{61''}{64} + \dfrac{25''}{32} = 7\dfrac{27''}{64}$

   f. $D = \dfrac{11''}{16} + 4\dfrac{3''}{16} + \dfrac{63''}{64} = 5\dfrac{55''}{64}$

4. $3\dfrac{1''}{16} - 2 \times \dfrac{5''}{32} = 2\dfrac{3''}{4}$

5. $1\dfrac{3''}{4} + 1\dfrac{7''}{8} + 2\dfrac{5''}{16} + 1\dfrac{11''}{32} + 3 \times \dfrac{1''}{8} + 8 \times \dfrac{1''}{32} = 7\dfrac{29''}{32}$

6. $A = 3\dfrac{5''}{8} - \left(\dfrac{29''}{32} + \dfrac{11''}{16}\right) = 3\dfrac{5''}{8} - 1\dfrac{19''}{32} = 2\dfrac{1''}{32}$

     $B = \dfrac{11''}{16} - \left(\dfrac{3''}{8} \div 2\right) = \dfrac{11''}{16} - \dfrac{3''}{16} = \dfrac{1''}{2}$

     $C = 2\dfrac{3''}{4} - \left(3\dfrac{7''}{8} + \dfrac{7''}{8} + \dfrac{7''}{16}\right) = 2\dfrac{3''}{4} - 2\dfrac{3''}{16} = \dfrac{9''}{16}$

     $D = 3\dfrac{1''}{8} - \left(\dfrac{13''}{16} + \dfrac{11''}{16} + \dfrac{7''}{16}\right) = 3\dfrac{1''}{8} - 1\dfrac{15''}{16} = 1\dfrac{3''}{16}$

UNIT 6 (*continued*)

7. Distance in 1 min $= 150 \times \frac{1}{32} = \frac{150}{32}$ inches per minute; $1\frac{1}{4}$ feet = 15 inches; $15 \div \frac{150}{32} = 3\frac{1}{5}$ min

8. $\left(47\frac{1''}{2} - 19\frac{7''}{8}\right) \div 2 = 27\frac{5''}{8} \div 2 = 27\frac{5''}{8} \div 2 = 13\frac{13''}{16}$

9. $\frac{3''}{4} + 2 \times \frac{1''}{16} + \frac{1''}{64} = \frac{57''}{64}$

10. $A = 1\frac{3''}{4} - \left(\frac{11''}{16} + \frac{17''}{32}\right) = 1\frac{3''}{4} - 1\frac{7''}{32} = \frac{17''}{32}$ 　　　 $E = \frac{1''}{4} + 7 \times \frac{15''}{32} = \frac{1''}{4} + 3\frac{9''}{32} = 3\frac{17''}{32}$

　　　$B = \frac{17''}{32} + \frac{3''}{16} + \frac{3''}{16} = \frac{29''}{32}$ 　　　 $F \longrightarrow = \frac{3''}{4} \times 2\frac{1''}{2} = 1\frac{7''}{8}$

　　　$C = \frac{7''}{16} - \frac{3''}{16} = \frac{1''}{4}$ 　　　 $G = 3\frac{1''}{8} - \left(2\frac{1''}{2} + \frac{1''}{4}\right) = 3\frac{1''}{8} - 2\frac{3''}{4} = \frac{3''}{8}$

　　　$D = \frac{1''}{4} + \frac{9''}{32} + 5 \times \frac{9''}{16} = \frac{1''}{4} + \frac{9''}{32} + 2\frac{13''}{16} = 3\frac{11''}{32}$

11. $1 - \left(\frac{19''}{20} + \frac{1''}{50}\right) = 1 - \frac{97}{100} = \frac{3}{100}; \frac{3}{100} \times 125\,\text{lb} = 3\frac{3}{4}\,\text{lb}$

12. $15'' - \left(2\frac{1''}{2} + 1\frac{3''}{4} + 1\frac{7''}{8} + \frac{5''}{16} + 4 \times \frac{1''}{8}\right) = 15'' - 6\frac{15''}{16} = 8\frac{1''}{16}$

UNIT 7 Computing with a Calculator: Fractions and Mixed Numbers

(All solutions to problems are given within the unit.)

UNIT 8 Introduction to Decimal Fractions

1. A = 0.3
   B = 0.5
   C = 0.8
   D = 0.92
   E = 0.04

2. A = 0.03
   B = 0.05
   C = 0.07
   D = 0.083
   E = 0.008

3. A = 0.0025
   B = 0.006
   C = 0.007
   D = 0.0073
   E = 0.0004

4. 0.001
5. 0.01
6. 10
7. 10
8. 0.01
9. 0.1
10. 0.01
11. 100
12. 10,000
13. 0.001
14. sixty-four thousandths
15. seven thousandths

16. one hundred thirty-two thousandths
17. thirty-five ten-thousandths
18. one hundred eight thousandths
19. one and five tenths
20. ten and thirty-seven hundredths
21. sixteen and seven ten-thousandths
22. four and twelve ten-thousandths
23. thirteen and one hundred three thousandths
24. 0.0084
25. 0.3
26. 43.08
27. 4.00005
28. 0.0035

29. 10.2
30. 5.0001
31. 20.71
32. 0.9
33. 0.0007
34. 0.17
35. 0.43
36. 0.061
37. 0.0999
38. 0.073
39. 0.01973
40. 0.47375

UNIT 9 Rounding Decimal Fractions and Equivalent Decimal and Common Fractions

1. 0.632
2. 0.12
3. 0.240
4. 0.017
5. 0.04
6. 0.90

7. 0.7201
8. 0.001
9. 0.000
10. 0.10
11. 0.6875
12. 0.8750

13. 0.6250
14. 0.7500
15. 0.6667
16. 0.9091
17. 0.0800
18. 0.7344

19. 0.2188
20. 0.5000
21. 0.5714
22. 0.3750
23. $\dfrac{1}{3} = 0.3333$

24. $17 - \left(2\dfrac{1}{2} + 3\dfrac{1}{16} + 2\dfrac{3}{4} + 3\dfrac{15}{16} + 2\dfrac{1}{8} + 5 \times \dfrac{1}{8}\right) = 17 - 15 = 2, \dfrac{2}{17} = 0.1176$ CHECK.

25. a. 6 feet = 72 inches $\dfrac{9}{72} = \dfrac{1}{8} = 0.125$

    b. $6' - 0' = (3' - 3' + 6'')$ $72'' - 48'' = 24'', \dfrac{24}{39} = 0.6154$

26. $\dfrac{7}{8}$
27. $\dfrac{1}{8}$
28. $\dfrac{2}{5}$
29. $\dfrac{3}{4}$
30. $\dfrac{3}{5}$
31. $\dfrac{11}{16}$
32. $\dfrac{67}{100}$

33. $\dfrac{3}{1000}$
34. $\dfrac{1}{125}$
35. $\dfrac{251}{500}$
36. $\dfrac{99}{100}$
37. $\dfrac{7}{16}$
38. $\dfrac{2113}{10,000}$
39. $\dfrac{8717}{10,000}$

40. $\dfrac{1}{2000}$
41. $\dfrac{3}{100}$
42. $\dfrac{3}{32}$
43. $\dfrac{237}{1000}$
44. $\dfrac{9}{20}$
45. $\dfrac{9}{200}$
46. $\dfrac{9}{2000}$

47. $\dfrac{0.875}{1.000} = \dfrac{875}{1000} = \dfrac{7}{8}$
48. $\dfrac{0.38}{1.00} = \dfrac{38}{100} = \dfrac{19}{50}$

49. a. $\dfrac{2.50}{10.00} = \dfrac{25}{100} = \dfrac{1}{4}$

    b. $\dfrac{5.625}{10.000} = \dfrac{5625}{10,000} = \dfrac{9}{16}$

    c. $\dfrac{1}{10}$

    d. $\dfrac{0.375}{10.000} = \dfrac{375}{10,000} = \dfrac{3}{80}$

    e. $\dfrac{3.75}{10.00} = \dfrac{375}{1000} = \dfrac{3}{8}$

UNIT 10 Addition and Subtraction of Decimal Fractions

1. a. 15.775
    b. 0.14095
    c. 1.295
    d. 5.129
    e. 381.357

    f. 4.444
    g. 94.2539
    h. 0.1101
    i. 5.7787
    j. 328.963

2. A = 0.2″ + 0.47″ = 0.67″

    B = 0.67″ + 1.51″ = 2.18″

    C = 0.375″ + 0.24″ + 0.362″ = 0.977″

    D = 0.452″ + 0.257″ = 0.709″

    E = 0.709″ + 0.35″ + 0.247″ = 1.306″

    F = 0.977″ + 1.306″ = 2.283″

3. 3.000″ + 0.500″ + 0.250″ + 0.125″ + 0.100″ + 0.1007″ + 0.1001″ = 4.1758″

4. 6.25 mm + 3.18 mm + 0.137 mm = 9.57 mm

5. (Other combinations may total certain thicknesses.)

    a. 0.010″ + 0.004″

    b. 0.015″ + 0.010″ + 0.008″

    c. 0.015″ + 0.006″

    d. 0.015″ + 0.012″ + 0.008″ + 0.003″

    e. 0.008″ + 0.003″

    f. 0.015″ + 0.012″ + 0.010″ + 0.003″ + 0.002″

    g. 0.015″ + 0.012″ + 0.002″

    h. 0.015″ + 0.012″ + 0.010″ + 0.008″ + 0.004″

UNIT **10** (*continued*)

6. a. 0.113   d. 0.001   g. 0.081
   b. 0.306   e. 0.021   h. 4.697
   c. 1.522   f. 22.089   i. 2.000

7. A = 22.80 mm − 9.98 mm = 12.82 mm
   B = 55.27 mm − 28.25 mm = 27.02 mm
   C = 22.80 mm − 16.22 mm = 6.58 mm
   D = 42.80 mm − 22.80 mm = 20.00 mm
   E = 23.26 mm − 12.68 mm = 10.58 mm
   F = 30.65 mm − 23.26 mm = 7.39 mm

8. a. 0.952″ − 0.402″ = 0.550″
   b. 2.232″ − 0.952″ = 1.280″
   c. 2.232″ − 0.625″ = 1.607″
   d. 3.695″ − 2.232″ = 1.463″
   e. 3.695″ − (2.232″ + 0.827″) = 0.636″

UNIT **11**   Multiplication of Decimal Fractions

1. a. 0.0563   c. 6
   b. 3.3   d. 1.6718

2. a. Working Depth = 0.6366 × 0.3925″ = 0.2499″
      Clearance = 0.05 × 0.3925″ = 0.0196″
      Tooth Thickness = 0.5 × 0.3925″ = 0.1963″
   b. Working Depth = 0.6366 × 0.1582″ = 0.1007″
      Clearance = 0.05 × 0.1582″ = 0.0079″
      Tooth Thickness = 0.5 × 0.1582″ = 0.0791″
   c. Working Depth = 0.6366 × 0.8069″ = 0.5137″
      Clearance = 0.05 × 0.8069″ = 0.0403″
      Tooth Thickness = 0.5 × 0.8069″ = 0.4035″
   d. Working Depth = 0.6366 × 1.2378″ = 0.7880″
      Clearance = 0.05 × 1.2378″ = 0.0619″
      Tooth Thickness = 0.5 × 1.2378″ = 0.6189″

2. e. Working Depth = 0.6366 × 1.5931″ = 1.0142″
      Clearance = 0.05 × 1.5931″ = 0.0797″
      Tooth Thickness = 0.5 × 1.5931″ = 0.7966″

3. Dia A = 37.937 mm − 2(3.087 mm) = 31.763 mm
   Dia B = 31.763 mm − 2(6.282 mm) = 19.199 mm
   Dia C = 31.763 mm − 2(9.458 mm) = 12.847 mm
   Dia D = 37.937 mm − 2(7.683 mm) = 22.571 mm
   Dia E = 22.571 mm − 2(7.915 mm) = 6.741 mm

4. a. x = 0.382″ × 32 = 12.224″
   b. x = (8.06 mm × 55) + (3.20 mm × 54) + (2 × 3.75 mm)
        = 623.36 mm   CHECK   623.6 ✓
   c. x = 0.125″ × 25 = 3.125″
   d. x = 0.866″ × 1.938″ = 1.678″

UNIT **12**   Division of Decimal Fractions

1. a. 1.597   d. 10,000.000   g. 135.53
   b. 2.56   e. 11.367   h. 0.0062
   c. 0.0100   f. 4.29

2. a. Linear Pitch $= \dfrac{3.1416}{6.75} = 0.4654''$

      Whole Depth $= \dfrac{2.157}{6.75} = 0.3196''$

   b. Linear Pitch $= \dfrac{3.1416}{2.75} = 1.1424''$

      Whole Depth $= \dfrac{2.157}{2.5} = 0.8628''$ .7844
      2.75

2. c. Linear Pitch $= \dfrac{3.1416}{7.25} = 0.4333''$

      Whole Depth $= \dfrac{2.157}{7.25} = 0.2975''$

   d. Linear Pitch $= \dfrac{3.1416}{16.125} = 0.1948''$

      Whole Depth $= \dfrac{2.157}{16.125} = 0.1338''$

3. A = 70.52 mm ÷ 6 = 11.75 mm
   B = 41.40 mm ÷ 7 = 5.91 mm
   C = 24.92 mm ÷ 2 = 12.46 mm
   D = 43.78 mm ÷ 4 = 10.95 mm

UNIT **12** *(continued)*

4. a. Pitch Dia = $\frac{45}{4}$ = 11.2500″

   Addendum = $\frac{1}{4}$ = 0.2500″

   Dedendum = $\frac{1.1570}{4}$ = 0.2893″

   b. Pitch Dia = $\frac{75}{6}$ = 12.5000″

   Addendum = $\frac{1}{6}$ = 0.1667″

   Dedendum = $\frac{1.1570}{6}$ = 0.1928″

   c. Pitch Dia = $\frac{44}{8}$ = 5.5000″

   Addendum = $\frac{1}{8}$ = 0.1250″

   Dedendum = $\frac{1.1570}{8}$ = 0.1446″

4. d. Pitch Dia = $\frac{54}{3}$ = 18.0000″

   Addendum = $\frac{1}{3}$ = 0.3333″

   Dedendum = $\frac{1.1570}{3}$ = 0.3857″

5. 473.75 mm ÷ (14.60 mm + 3.12 mm) = 26.7 = 26 complete bushings

6. 3.120 ÷ 0.015 = 208.00 revolutions

7. 4.725 mm ÷ 75 = 0.063 mm

8. 1.25 × 60 = 75, 75 ÷ 0.02 = 3750 pieces

9. 0.902″ − 7.7 − 0.128″

10. 0.718 ÷ 0.0625 = 11.5 threads

11. 54.44 mm + 1.4142 = 38.50 mm

UNIT **13** Powers

1. 39.304

2. 1

3. 100,000,000

4. $\frac{8}{27}$

5. $\frac{8}{3}$ or $2\frac{2}{3}$

6. $\frac{3}{64}$

7. 4.41

8. 778.41

9. 64

10. 1.56 sq in

11. 532.23 mm²

12. 0.03 sq in

13. 114.49 mm²

14. 0.00 sq in

15. $\frac{9}{16}$ sq in

16. $\frac{49}{64}$ sq in

17. $14\frac{1}{16}$ sq in

18. $\frac{169}{256}$ sq in

19. $189\frac{1}{16}$ sq in

20. 0.02 cu in

21. 8741.82 mm³

22. 60.70 cu in

23. 2744 mm³

24. 0.00 cu in

25. $\frac{1}{27}$ cu in

26. $\frac{343}{512}$ cu in

27. $3\frac{3}{8}$ cu in

28. $759\frac{409}{512}$ cu in

29. $\frac{27}{64}$ cu in

30. 3.14 × 262.44 mm² = 824 mm²

31. 3.14 × 243.36 mm² = 764 mm²

32. 3.14 × 0.0049 sq in = 0 sq in

33. 3.14 × 86.1184 sq in = 270 sq in

34. 3.14 × 152.5225 mm² = 479 mm²
    Note: 3.14 ÷ 6 = 0.52333

35. 0.52333 × 0.274625 cu in = 0.1 cu in

36. 0.52333 × 274.625 mm³ = 143.7 mm³

37. 0.52333 × 0.4219 cu in = 0.2 cu in

38. 0.52333 × 1259.712 mm³ = 659.3 mm³

39. 0.52333 × 351.89582 mm³ = 1842 mm³

40. 3.14 × 25 mm² × 3.2 mm = 251 mm³

41. 3.14 × 2.25 sq in × 2.3 in = 16 cu in

42. 3.14 × 5.0625 sq in × 3 in = 48 cu in

43. 3.14 × 0.49 sq in × 6.7 in = 10 cu in

44. 3.14 × 60.9961 mm² × 6.72 mm = 1287 mm³

45. 0.2618 × 10.24 sq in × 4 in = 11 cu in

46. 0.2618 × 9 sq in × 5 in = 12 cu in

47. 0.2618 × 112.36 mm² × 13.10 mm = 385 mm³

48. 0.2618 × 98.01 mm² × 6.20 mm = 159 mm³

49. 0.2618 × 0.1369 sq in × 0.96 in = 0 cu in

50. A_1 = 3.14 × (21.87 mm)² = 1501.8523 mm²
    A_2 = 3.14 × (9.38 mm)² = 276.2710 mm²
    A_3 = 1501.8523 mm³ − 276.2710 mm² = 1226 mm²

UNIT **13**   (*continued*)

51. $A_1 = (19.60\ mm)^2 = 384.16\ mm^2$

    $A_2 = 3.14 \times (4.20\ mm)^2 = 55.3896\ mm^2$

    $A_3 = 384.16\ mm^2 - 55.3896\ mm^2 = 329\ mm^2$

52. $A_1 = (12.60\ mm)^2 = 158.76\ mm^2$

    $A_2 = (8.70\ mm)^2 = 75.69\ mm^2$

    $A_3 = (21.20\ mm)^2 = 449.44\ mm^2$

    $A_4 = 158.76\ mm^2 + 75.69\ mm^2 + 449.44\ mm^2 = 684\ mm^2$

53. $V_1 = 3.14 \times (0.85\ in)^2 \times 1.22\ in = 2.7678\ cu\ in$

    $V_2 = 3.14 \times (0.60\ in)^2 \times 1.22\ in = 1.3791\ cu\ in$

    $V_3 = 2.7678\ cu\ in - 1.3791\ cu\ in = 1\ cu\ in$

54. $V_1 = 0.2618 \times (1.30\ in)^2 \times 0.50\ in = 0.2212\ cu\ in$

    $V_2 = 3.14 \times (0.65\ in)^2 \times 6.87\ in = 9.1141\ cu\ in$

    $V_3 = 0.2212\ cu\ in + 9.1141\ cu\ in = 9\ cu\ in$

55. $V_1 = (8.20\ in)^3 = 551.368\ cu\ in$

    $V_2 = (14.5\ in)^3 = 3048.625\ cu\ in$

    $V_3 = 551.368\ cu\ in + 3048.625\ cu\ in$
       $= 3559.993\ cu\ in$

    $V_4 = 551.368\ cu\ in + 3048.625\ cu\ in$
       $= 3599.993\ cu\ in$

    $V_5 = 0.0975\ lb\ /\ cu\ in \times 3599.993\ cu\ in$
       $= 350.9993\ lb$

    $V_6 = $ Total weight $= 350.9993\ lb \times 15$
       $= 5264.99\ lb,\ 5265\ lb$

UNIT **14**   Roots

1. 6

2. $\dfrac{2}{3}$

3. $\dfrac{2}{9}$

4. $4\dfrac{1}{6}$

5. $\dfrac{3}{4}$

6. 3

7. 12

8. 3

9. 4

10. a. 15 mm
    b. 11 mm
    c. 8 mm
    d. 9 in
    e. 7 in

11. a. 6 mm
    b. 4 in
    c. 8 in
    d. 10 mm
    e. 1 in

12. a. $R = \sqrt{\dfrac{50.24\ sq\ in}{3.14}} = \sqrt{16\ sq\ in} = 4\ in$

    b. $R = \sqrt{\dfrac{12.56\ sq\ in}{3.14}} = \sqrt{4\ sq\ in} = 2\ in$

    c. $R = \sqrt{\dfrac{314\ mm^2}{3.14}} = \sqrt{100\ mm^2} = 10\ mm$

    d. $R = \sqrt{\dfrac{28.26\ sq\ in}{3.14}} = \sqrt{9\ sq\ in} = 3\ in$

    e. $R = \sqrt{\dfrac{153.86\ mm^2}{3.14}} = \sqrt{49\ mm^2} = 7\ mm$

13. a. $D = \sqrt[3]{\dfrac{14.1372\ cu\ in}{0.5236}} = \sqrt[3]{27\ cu\ in} = 3\ in$

    b. $D = \sqrt[3]{\dfrac{113.0976\ mm^3}{0.5236}} = \sqrt[3]{216\ mm^3} = 6\ mm$

    c. $D = \sqrt[3]{\dfrac{4.1888\ cu\ in}{0.5236}} = \sqrt[3]{8\ cu\ in} = 2\ in$

    d. $D = \sqrt[3]{\dfrac{0.5236\ cu\ in}{0.5236}} = \sqrt[3]{1\ cu\ in} = 1\ in$

    e. $D = \sqrt[3]{\dfrac{523.6\ mm^3}{0.5236}} = \sqrt[3]{1000\ mm^3} = 10\ mm$

14. 3.953

15. 19.77

16. 0.775

17. 1.871

18. 1.40

19. 4.42

20. 3.847

21. 0.0857

22. a. $R = \sqrt{\dfrac{249.846\ mm^3}{3.14 \times 7\ mm}} = \sqrt{11.36925\ mm^2} = 3.37\ mm$

    b. $R = \sqrt{\dfrac{132.634\ mm^3}{3.14 \times 12\ mm}} = \sqrt{3.52001\ mm^2} = 1.88\ mm$

    c. $R = \sqrt{\dfrac{14\ cu\ in}{3.14 \times 29\ in}} = \sqrt{0.15374\ sq\ in} = 0.39\ in$

    d. $R = \sqrt{\dfrac{10\ cu\ in}{3.14 \times 28\ in}} = \sqrt{0.11374\ sq\ in} = 0.34\ in$

23. a. $D = \sqrt{\dfrac{116.328\ mm^3}{0.262 \times 8\ mm}} = \sqrt{55.5\ mm^2} = 7.45\ mm$

    b. $D = \sqrt{\dfrac{19.388\ cu\ in}{0.262 \times 2\ in}} = \sqrt{37\ sq\ in} = 6.08\ in$

    c. $D = \sqrt{\dfrac{1257.6\ mm^3}{0.262 \times 10\ mm}} = \sqrt{480\ mm^2} = 21.91\ mm$

    d. $D = \sqrt{\dfrac{15\ cu\ in}{0.262 \times 50\ in}} = \sqrt{1.14504\ sq\ in} = 1.07\ in$

24. $3 \times \sqrt{0.825\ in \times 0.007\ in \times 5} = 3 \times \sqrt{0.028875\ sq\ in}$
    $= 0.510\ in$

25. $D = \sqrt{\dfrac{2.70\ in \times 0.25\ in}{0.3}} = \sqrt{2.25\ sq\ in} = 1.5\ in$

UNIT **15**   Table of Decimal Equivalents and Combined Operations of Decimal Fractions

1. 0.78125

2. 0.21875

3. 0.34375

4. 0.8125

5. 0.078125

6. $\dfrac{43}{64}$

7. $\dfrac{5}{16}$

8. $\dfrac{9}{32}$

9. $\dfrac{13}{64}$

10. $\dfrac{35}{64}$

11. $\dfrac{49}{64}$

12. $\dfrac{15}{32}$

13. $\dfrac{1}{2}$

14. $\dfrac{13}{64}$ ~~7/32~~

15. $\dfrac{13}{16}$

16. $0.5231 + 10.375 \div 4.32 \times 0.521 = 0.5231 + 2.4016 \times 0.521 = 0.5231 + 1.2512 = 1.77$

17. $81.07 \div 12.1 + 2 \times 3.7 = 6.7 + 7.4 = 14.1$

18. $\dfrac{56.050}{3.8} \times 0.875 - 3.92 = 14.75 \times 0.875 - 3.92 = 12.9063 - 3.92 = 8.99$

19. $(24.78 - 19.32) \times 4.6 = 5.46 \times 4.6 = 25.12$

20. $(14.6 \div 4 - 1.76)^2 \times 4.5 = (3.65 - 1.76)^2 \times 4.5 = 1.89^2 \times 4.5 = 3.5721 \times 4.5 = 16.07$

21. $27.16 \div \sqrt{1.76 + 12.32} = 27.16 \div \sqrt{14.08} = 27.16 \div 3.7523 = 7.24$

22. $(\sqrt{3.98 + 0.87 \times 3.9})^2 = (\sqrt{3.98 + 3.393})^2 + (\sqrt{7.373})^2 = 7.37$

23. $(3.29 \times 1.7)^2 \div (3.82 - 0.86) = 5.593^2 \div 2.96 = 31.2816 \div 2.96 = 10.57$

24. $0.25 + \left(\dfrac{\sqrt{64} \times 3.87}{8.32 \times 5.13}\right) + 18.3^2 = 0.25 \times \dfrac{30.96}{42.68} + 18.3^2 = 0.25 \times 0.7254 + 334.89 = 1.181 + 334.89 = 335.07$

25. $18.32 - \sqrt{\dfrac{7.86 \times 13.5}{3.5^0 - 0.52}} \times 0.7 - 18.32 - \sqrt{\dfrac{106.11}{11.73}} \times 0.7 = 18.32 - \sqrt{9.0160358} \times 0.7 = 18.32 - 3.00767 \times 0.7$

 $= 18.32 - 2.1054 = 16.21$

26. a. $M = 0.8750'' - (1.5155 \times 0.1250'') + (3 \times 0.0900'') = 0.8750'' - 0.18944'' + 0.27000'' = 0.9556''$

 b. $M = 0.2500'' - (1.5155 \times 0.0500'') + (3 \times 0.0350'') = 0.2500'' - 0.075775'' + 0.10500'' = 0.2792''$

 c. $M = 0.6250'' - (1.5155 \times 0.1000'') + (3 \times 0.0700'') = 0.6250'' - 0.15155'' + 0.21000'' = 0.6835''$

 d. $M = 1.3750'' - (1.5155 \times 0.16667'') + (3 \times 0.1500'') = 1.3750'' - 0.25259'' + 0.45000'' = 1.5724''$

 e. $M = 2.5000'' - (1.5155 \times 0.2500'') + (3 \times 0.1500'') = 2.5000'' - 0.37888'' + 0.45000'' = 2.5711''$

27. $22.225 \text{ mm} - 0.038 \text{ mm} = 22.187 \text{ mm}$

 $22.187 \text{ mm} - 22.103 \text{ mm} = 0.084 \text{ mm}$

28. $A = 1.008'' - 0.400'' - \left(\dfrac{0.244''}{2} + \dfrac{0.390''}{2}\right) = 0.608'' - 0.307'' = 0.301''$

 $B = 0.897'' - 0.400'' + 0.390'' = 0.887''$

 $C = (2 \times 0.625'' - 0.312'') - (0.368'' + 0.180'') = 0.938'' - 0.548'' = 0.390''$

 $D = \left[2 \times 0.625'' - 0.470'' - \left(0.450'' + \dfrac{0.282''}{2}\right)\right] - (0.368'' + 2 \times 0.180'') = (1.720'' - 0.591'') - 0.728''$

 $= 1.129'' - 0.728'' = 0.401''$

 $E = -0.282'' = 1.91667'' - 0.282'' = 1.635''$

 $F = \dfrac{3.090'' - [3 \times (0.470'' + 2 \times 0.180'')]}{2} = \dfrac{3.090'' - 3 \times 0.830''}{2} = 0.300''$

UNIT 15   (continued)

29. a. $C = \dfrac{34.80\,mm}{2} - 0.5 \times \sqrt{4 \times \left(\dfrac{34.80\,mm}{2}\right)^2 - (30.50\,mm)^2}$

   $C = 17.40\ mm - 0.5 \times \sqrt{4 \times 302.76\ mm^2 - 930.25\ mm^2}$

   $C = 17.40\ mm - 0.5 \times \sqrt{280.79\ mm^2}$

   $C = 17.40\ mm - 0.5 \times 16.75679\ mm$

   $C = 17.40\ mm - 8.37839\ mm$

   $C = 9.02\ mm$

   b. $C = \dfrac{55.90\,mm}{2} - 0.5 \times \sqrt{4 \times \left(\dfrac{55.90\,mm}{2}\right)^2 - (40.60\,mm)^2}$

   $C = 27.95\ mm - 0.5 \times \sqrt{4 \times 781.2025\ mm^2 - 1648.36\ mm^2}$

   $C = 27.95\ mm - 0.5 \times \sqrt{1476.45\ mm^2}$

   $C = 27.95\ mm - 0.5 \times 38.424601\ mm$

   $C = 27.95\ mm - 19.2123\ mm$

   $C = 8.74\ mm$

   c. $C = \dfrac{91.40\,mm}{2} - 0.5 \times \sqrt{4 \times \left(\dfrac{91.40\,mm}{2}\right)^2 - (43.40\,mm)^2}$

   $C = 45.70\ mm - 0.5 \times \sqrt{4 \times 2088.49\ mm^2 - 1883.56\ mm^2}$

   $C = 45.70\ mm - 0.5 \times \sqrt{6470.4\ mm^2}$

   $C = 45.70\ mm - 0.5 \times 80.438797\ mm$

   $C = 45.70\ mm - 40.219398\ mm$

   $C = 5.48\ mm$

30. $x = 41.36\ mm \div 2 - (6.30\ mm + 3.15\ mm + 0.40\ mm) = 20.68\ mm - 9.85\ mm = 10.83\ mm$

31. $H = 1.5 \times 0.750'' - 0.866 \times 1.210'' = 1.12500'' - 1.04786'' = 0.077''$

UNIT 16   Computing with a Calculator: Decimals

(All solutions to problems are given within the unit.)

UNIT 17   Introduction to Percents

1. 44%	7. 4%	13. 0.02%	19. 53.125%	25. 0.82	31. 2.249
2. 62.5%	8. 6.2%	14. 300.5%	20. 0.4%	26. 0.19	32. 0.006
3. 25%	9. 0.8%	15. 25%	21. 159%	27. 0.03	33. 0.0473
4. 32.5% 33⅓%	10. 133%	16. 26.25%	22. 228%	28. 0.026	34. 0.125
5. 35%	11. 207.6%	17. 15%	23. 1462.5%	29. 0.2776	35. 0.0075
6. 96%	12. 6.39%	18. 74%	24. 300.5%	30. 1.03	36. 0.001

UNIT **17** *(continued)*

37.	0.02375	41.	$\frac{1}{2}$	44.	$\frac{1}{25}$	47.	$1\frac{9}{10}$	50.	$1\frac{1}{1000}$
38.	0.0005	42.	$\frac{1}{4}$	45.	$\frac{4}{25}$	48.	$\frac{1}{500}$	51.	$\frac{9}{1000}$
39.	0.3725								
40.	2.051	43.	$\frac{5}{8}$	46.	$2\frac{3}{4}$	49.	$\frac{9}{500}$	52.	$\frac{1}{2000}$

UNIT **18** Basic Calculations of Percentages, Percents, and Rates

1.	16	13.	7.14	25.	118.95%	37.	24.49%	49.	4.17	61.	75%
2.	1.72	14.	0.21	26.	37.60%	38.	120.49%	50.	100	62.	16
3.	120	15.	0.13	27.	155.46%	39.	50%	51.	270.57	63.	15.60
4.	22.85	16.	31.88	28.	28.21%	40.	45.65%	52.	200	64.	89.02
5.	78.15	17.	0.99	29.	40%	41.	150	53.	42.93	65.	19.05%
6.	9.82	18.	240.17	30.	250%	42.	31.25	54.	144.44	66.	45.51
7.	101.4	19.	5.38	31.	30.77%	43.	320	55.	0.5	67.	153.99
8.	1.71	20.	0.47	32.	116.98%	44.	3.99	56.	8.33	68.	112.28%
9.	37.47	21.	50%	33.	42.86%	45.	170	57.	3.90	69.	58.05
10.	2.05	22.	27.05%	34.	233.33%	46.	139.64	58.	41.18	70.	132.25%
11.	392	23.	37%	35.	154.55%	47.	184.55	59.	28.87	71.	3.38
12.	22.32	24.	84.07%	36.	13.85%	48.	73.89	60.	0.61	72.	21.72

UNIT **19** Percent Practical Applications

1. $\frac{7.0\,h}{12.5\,h} = 0.56 = 56\%$

2. $\frac{0.188\,cm}{17.875\,cm} = 0.0105 = 1.05\%$

3. $0.80 \times 8.5\ hr = 6.8\ hr$

4. $0.42 \times \$9,255.00 = \$3,887.10$

5. $\frac{120\ units}{0.08} = 1,500\ units$

6. $\frac{4.2\ hp}{0.06} = 70\ hp$

7. $\frac{16\ employees}{130\ employees} = 0.1231 = 12\%$

8. $\frac{\$910,000}{1.40} = \$650,000$

9. $\frac{73.50\ ft}{0.28} = 262.5\ ft$

10. $\frac{955.0\ lb}{0.58} = 1646.55\ lb,\ 1647\ lb$

11. Copper: $0.58 \times 1250\ lb = 725\ lb$
    Tin: $0.40 \times 1250\ lb = 500\ lb$
    Manganese: $0.015 \times 1250\ lb = 19\ lb$
    Other: $0.005 \times 1250\ lb = 6\ lb$

12. Labor: $0.38 \times \$120,000 = \$45,600$
    Materials: $0.45 \times \$120,000 = \$54,000$
    Overhead: $0.17 \times \$120,000 = \$20,400$

13. $\frac{0.125\ in}{12\ in} = 0.01 = 1\%$

14. $0.9862\ in \times 9.25 = 9.12\ in$

UNIT 19 (continued)

15. 9/16 Rework: $\dfrac{44}{1650} = 0.027 = 2.7\%$

    9/16 Scrap: $\dfrac{59}{1650} = 0.036 = 3.6\%$

    9/17 Rework: $\dfrac{29}{1596} = 0.018 = 1.8\%$

    9/17 Scrap: $\dfrac{48}{1596} = 0.030 = 3.0\%$

    9/18 Rework: $\dfrac{52}{1685} = 0.031 = 3.1\%$

    9/18 Scrap: $\dfrac{34}{1685} = 0.020 = 2.0\%$

16. $0.82 \times 8.0\ \text{hp} = 6.6\ \text{hp}$

17. $\dfrac{\$1260}{0.386} = \$3264$

18. $\$745.00 - (0.142 \times \$745 + 0.045 \times \$745 + 0.076 \times \$745) = \$549.07$

19. a. $1470°F - 1300°F = 170°F$

    $\dfrac{170°F}{1300°F} = 0.13 = 13\%$

    b. $2200°F - 1300°F = 900°F$

    $\dfrac{900°F}{1300°F} = 0.69 = 69\%$

    c. $2730°F - 1300°F = 1430°F$

    $\dfrac{1430°F}{1300°F} = 1.1 = 110\%$

20. 2.60 tons = $2.60 \times 2000\ \text{lb} = 5200\ \text{lb}$

    1. $0.0115 \times 5200\ \text{lb} = 60\ \text{lb}$

    2. $0.0075 \times 5200\ \text{lb} = 39\ \text{lb}$

    3. $0.0105 \times 5200\ \text{lb} = 55\ \text{lb}$

    4. $0.0125 \times 5200\ \text{lb} = 65\ \text{lb}$

    5. $0.0095 \times 5200\ \text{lb} = 49\ \text{lb}$

    6. $0.0085 \times 5200\ \text{lb} = 44\ \text{lb}$

21. 2600 castings $- (0.72 \times 2600$ castings$) = 1872$ castings
    1872 castings $- (0.50 \times 1872$ castings$) = 936$ castings

22. $1.20 \times 125\ \text{m} = 150\ \text{m}$

    $175\ \text{m} - 150\ \text{m} = 25\ \text{m}$

    $\dfrac{25\ \text{m}}{150\ \text{m}} = 0.17 = 17\%$

23. $100\% - (85\% + 5\% + 6\%) = 4\%$
    $0.04 \times 450\ \text{lb} = 18\ \text{lb}$

24. $0.94 \times 1638 = 1539.72$, 1539 whole pieces

    $0.955 \times 1454 = 1388.57$, 1388 whole pieces

    1539 pieces $-$ 1388 pieces = 151 pieces

25. 36 pieces + 43 pieces + 52 pieces + 47 pieces
    + 31 pieces = 209 pieces

    735 pieces + 763 pieces + 786 pieces + 733 pieces
    + 748 pieces = 3765 pieces

    $\dfrac{209\ \text{pieces}}{3765\ \text{pieces}} = 0.0555 = 5.6\%$

26. 15,500 pieces $-$ 11,000 pieces = 4500 pieces

    $\dfrac{4500\ \text{pieces}}{11{,}000\ \text{pieces}} = 0.409 = 41\%$

27. $\dfrac{50\ \text{pieces}}{2730\ \text{pieces}} = 0.0183 = 1.83\%$

    $1.83\% - 1.20\% = 0.63\%$

28. $1.5\ \text{lb} + 0.7\ \text{lb} + 0.5\ \text{lb} = 2.7\ \text{lb}$
    $7.8\ \text{lb} - 2.7\ \text{lb} = 5.1\ \text{lb}$

    $\dfrac{5.1\ \text{lb}}{7.8\ \text{lb}} = 0.654 = 65.4\%$

29. $\dfrac{1.3\ \text{hp}}{0.15} = 8.7\ \text{hp}$

30. $0.12 \times \$525.00 = \$63.00$
    $\$525.00 - \$63.00 = \$462.00$
    $0.08 \times \$462.00 = \$36.96$
    $\$462.00 - \$36.96 = \$425.04$

31. $\dfrac{3620\ \text{pieces}}{1.135} = 3189\ \text{pieces}$

32. 0.80×750 pieces = 600 pieces
    0.75×900 pieces = 675 pieces
    600 pieces + 675 pieces = 1275 pieces

    $\dfrac{1275\ \text{pieces}}{8\ \text{hr}} = 159\ \text{pieces per hr}$

33. $\dfrac{1890\ \text{pieces}}{1.08} = 1750\ \text{pieces}$

34. $\$122{,}000 - \$110{,}400 = \$11{,}600$

    $\dfrac{\$11{,}600}{\$122{,}000} = 0.095 = 9.5\%$

35. Job 1: Total Cost $= \$1890 + \$875 + \$1240 = \$4005$

    Labor Cost $= \dfrac{\$1890}{\$4005} = 0.47 = 47\%$

    Material Cost $= \dfrac{\$875}{\$4005} = 0.22 = 22\%$

    Overhead Cost $= \dfrac{\$1240}{\$4005} = 0.31 = 31\%$

35. Job 2: Total Cost $= \$930 + \$1060 + \$880 = \$2870$

    Labor Cost $= \dfrac{\$930}{\$2870} = 0.32 = 32\%$

    Material Cost $= \dfrac{\$1060}{\$2870} = 0.37 = 37\%$

    Overhead Cost $= \dfrac{\$880}{\$2870} = 0.31 = 31\%$

UNIT **19** (*continued*)

35. Job 3: Total Cost = \$2490 + \$1870 + \$1600
 = \$5960

 Labor Cost = $\dfrac{\$2490}{\$5960}$ = 0.42 = 42%

35. Material Cost = $\dfrac{\$1870}{\$5960}$ = 0.31 = 31%

 Overhead Cost = $\dfrac{\$1600}{\$5960}$ = 0.27 = 27%

UNIT **20** Achievement Review—Section One

1. a. $\dfrac{12}{32}$ c. $\dfrac{16}{64}$

 b. $\dfrac{70}{100}$ d. $\dfrac{72}{128}$

2. a. $\dfrac{16}{5}$ d. $\dfrac{107}{8}$

 b. $\dfrac{29}{10}$ e. $\dfrac{201}{32}$

 c. $\dfrac{23}{4}$

3. a. $2\dfrac{1}{2}$ d. $3\dfrac{19}{32}$

 b. $4\dfrac{1}{5}$ e. $5\dfrac{9}{64}$

 c. $18\dfrac{3}{4}$

4. a. $\dfrac{1}{2}$ d. $\dfrac{0}{32}$

 b. $\dfrac{3}{25}$ e. $\dfrac{7}{32}$

 c. $\dfrac{15}{16}$

5. a. $\dfrac{8}{32}, \dfrac{6}{32}, \dfrac{9}{32}$

 b. $\dfrac{28}{64}, \dfrac{10}{64}, \dfrac{9}{64}$

 c. $\dfrac{70}{100}, \dfrac{75}{100}, \dfrac{36}{100}, \dfrac{65}{100}$

6. a. $\dfrac{3}{4}$ e. $\dfrac{55}{64}$

 b. $1\dfrac{3}{8}$ f. $\dfrac{1}{4}$

 c. $1\dfrac{1}{32}$ g. $\dfrac{1}{4}$

 d. $4\dfrac{19}{100}$ h. $\dfrac{25}{64}$

6. i. $5\dfrac{5}{16}$ j. $3\dfrac{29}{32}$

7. a. $\dfrac{5}{16}$ f. $\dfrac{3}{4}$

 b. $\dfrac{2}{5}$ g. $3\dfrac{1}{3}$

 c. $1\dfrac{245}{256}$ h. 48

 d. $25\dfrac{23}{40}$ i. $6\dfrac{3}{4}$

 e. $20\dfrac{5}{8}$ j. $\dfrac{93}{280}$

8. a. $\dfrac{11}{16}$ d. $28\dfrac{3}{8}$

 b. $20\dfrac{59}{64}$ e. $4\dfrac{8}{21}$

 c. $4\dfrac{11}{40}$ f. $1\dfrac{11}{64}$

9. $72'' - \dfrac{3''}{4} = 71\dfrac{1''}{4}$

 $71\dfrac{1''}{4} \quad 1\dfrac{3''}{8} = 51\dfrac{9}{11}$
 = 51 complete pieces

10. $30 \times \left(1\dfrac{3''}{16} + \dfrac{1''}{8}\right) = 39\dfrac{3''}{8}$

11. $\dfrac{50\,\text{in}}{1} \times \dfrac{32\,\text{r}}{1\text{in}} = 1600\,\text{r}$

 $\dfrac{1600\,\text{r}}{2000\,\text{r}/\text{min}} = 8\,\text{min}$

12. $1800 \times \left(1\dfrac{5''}{8} + \dfrac{3''}{16}\right) = 3262\dfrac{1''}{2}$

 $10 \times 12'' = 120''$

 $3262\dfrac{1''}{2} \quad 120'' = 27\dfrac{3}{16}$
 or 28 complete lengths

13. $A = 1\dfrac{3''}{16} + 2\dfrac{1''}{8} = 3\dfrac{5''}{16}$

 $B = 11\dfrac{3''}{4} \div 4 = 2\dfrac{15''}{16}$

 $C = 18\dfrac{19''}{64} - \left(11\dfrac{3''}{4} + 3\dfrac{7''}{16}\right) - 3\dfrac{15''}{64}$

 $D = 5\dfrac{29''}{32} - \left(1\dfrac{1''}{32} + \dfrac{15''}{16}\right) = 3\dfrac{15''}{16}$

 $E = 3 \times 1\dfrac{5''}{32} = 3\dfrac{15''}{32}$

14. a. six tenths

 b. seventy-four hundredths

 c. one hundred forty-seven thousandths

 d. eighty-six ten-thousandths

14. e. four and two hundred eight thousandths

 f. sixteen and four hundred nineteen ten-thousandths

15. a. 0.3   c. 9.026

 b. 0.026   d. 5.0081

16. a. 0.60   c. 0.8073

 b. 5.046   d. 7.001

17. a. 0.75   d. 0.08

 b. 0.875   e. 0.65

 c. 0.667

18. a. $\dfrac{7}{10}$ d. $\dfrac{183}{200}$

 b. $\dfrac{21}{40}$ e. $\dfrac{3}{400}$

 c. $\dfrac{7}{1000}$

19. a. 1.587   d. 9.1053

 b. 6.4274   e. 23.4077

 c. 12.3069   f. 0.356

UNIT 20 (continued)

19. g. 0.1444 i. 0.0022
    h. 0.001 j. 0.002

20. a. 0.5538 f. 2.1795
    b. 8.349 g. 10
    c. 0.3367 h. 133.8667
    d. 0.0009 i. 184.9624
    e. 0.0121 j. 0.0019

21. a. 6.76 d. $\dfrac{9}{25}$
    b. 0.125 e. 32.768
    c. 0.000036

22. a. 7 d. 8
    b. 4 e. 7
    c. $\dfrac{6}{9} = \dfrac{2}{3}$

23. a. 19.47 c. 0.632
    b. 0.935 d. 6.780

24. a. 0.625 d. $\dfrac{21}{32}$
    b. 0.53125 e. $\dfrac{43}{64}$
    c. 0.328125

25. a. $\dfrac{15}{32}$ c. $\dfrac{1}{32}$
    b. $\dfrac{49}{64}$ d. $\dfrac{31}{32}$

26. a. 3.38 c. 28.99
    b. 37.33 d. 21.09

27. A = 0.86603 × 1.5 mm = 1.299 mm
    B = 0.54127 × 1.5 mm = 0.812 mm
    C = 0.21651 × 1.5 mm = 0.325 mm
    D = 0.10825 × 1.5 mm = 0.162 mm
    E = 0.125 × 1.5 mm = 0.188 mm
    F = 0.250 × 1.5 mm = 0.375 mm

28. 0.4573″ − (0.250″ + 0.118″) = 0.0893″

29. (18.10 mm − 17.86 mm) ÷ 2 = 0.12 mm

30. 57.20 mm − 44.10 mm = 13.10 mm
    13.10 mm − 0.30 mm = 12.80 mm
    12.80 mm ÷ 3.20 mm = 4

31. 3.5 min × 120 r/min × 0.030 in/r = 12.6 in

32. a. 72% c. 4%
    b. 203.7% d. 0.03%

33. a. 0.19% c. 0.0075%
    b. 0.007% d. 3.103%

34. a. $\dfrac{3}{10}$ c. $\dfrac{1}{8}$
    b. $1\dfrac{2}{5}$ d. $\dfrac{13}{2000}$

35. a. 9 e. 22.90
    b. 1.27 f. 275.6
    c. 87.36 g. 4
    d. 5.68 h. 1.57

36. a. 20% e. 28.17%
    b. 500% f. 24.49%
    c. 24.69% g. 128.49%
    d. 39.27%

37. a. 33.33 e. 3.90
    b. 16.47 f. 41.18
    c. 223.68 g. 0.61
    d. 59.97

38. a. 75% g. 153.99
    b. 15 h. 112.28%
    c. 15.60 i. 58.05
    d. 89.02 j. 132.25%
    e. 19.05% k. 3.38
    f. 45.51 l. 21.72

39. a. 0.0015 × 250 kg = 0.38 kg
    b. 0.0025 × 250 kg = 0.63 kg

40. 0.145 × $8,792 = $1,275

41. a. 0.04 × 575 kg = 23 kg
    b. 0.015 × 575 kg = 8.6 kg
    c. 0.02 × 575 kg = 11.5 kg

42. 18 × 15.0 ft = 270 ft
    0.70 × 270 ft = 189 ft
    0.75 × 189 ft = 142 ft

43. 100% − (73.6% + 18% + 8% + 0.1%) = 0.3%
    0.003 × 5,800 lb = 17 lb

44. 6.5 × 170 pieces = 1,105 pieces
    2,015 − 1,105 pieces = 910 pieces
    $\dfrac{910 \text{ pieces}}{7}$ = 130 pieces
    $\dfrac{130 \text{ pieces}}{170 \text{ pieces}}$ = 0.7647 = 76%

Section Two
Linear Measurement: Customary (English) and Metric

UNIT 21 Customary (English) and Metric Units of Measure

1. a. $96 \div 12 = 8$ ft

   b. $123 \div 12 = 10.25$ ft

   c. $3\frac{1}{2} \times 12 = 42$ in

   d. $0.1 \times 00 = 144$ in

   e. $1\frac{1}{4} \times 36 = 45$ in

   f. $144 \div 36 = 4$ yd
   yd

   g. $75 \div 12 = 6.25$ ft

   h. $8 \times 3 = 24$ ft

   i. $4.2 \times 3 = 12.6$ ft

   j. $27 \div 3 = 9$ yd

   k. $51 \div 3 = 17$ yd

   l. $\frac{1}{3} \times 36 = 12$ in

   m. $258 \div 12 = 21.5$ ft

   n. $\frac{2}{3} \times 12 = 92$ in

   o. $0.20 \times 36 = 7.2$ in

   p. $140.25 \div 3 = 46.75$

   q. $333 \div 36 = 9.25$ yd

   r. $100 \div 12 = 15.5$ ft

   s. $20\frac{2}{3} \times 3 = 62$ ft

   t. $9.25 \times 12 = 111$ in

2. $120.0 \times 12 = 1440$ inches per minute

3. 230×1.300 in $= 299$ in

   $299 \div 12 = 24.917$ ft

   24.917 ft $\div 6$ ft $= 4.153$ lengths

   $4.153 + 1.5 = 5.653$ lengths or 5 complete lengths

4. $12 \times 8 \times 12 = 1152$ in   *336* *8 BARS 96"/BAR*

   $1152 \div (3.25 + 0.10) = 343.88$ *WRONG*

   or 343 complete pieces

5. a. 29 mm

   b. 157.8 mm

   c. 21.975 cm

   d. 9.783 cm

   e. 97 cm

   f. 170 mm

   g. 0.153 m

   h. 6.73 m

   i. 0.093 cm

   j. 0.8 mm

   k. 8.6 mm

   l. 104.6 cm

   m. 300.3 mm

   n. 87.684 cm

   o. 2.039 m

   p. 0.0347 m

   q. 49 mm

   r. 732.1 cm

   s. 63.77 mm

   t. 934 mm

6. a. 25.73 mm $+ 76$ mm $= 101.73$ mm

   b. 3.7 m $+ 0.98$ m $= 4.68$ m

   c. 59.6 cm $- 6.37$ cm $= 53.23$ cm

   d. 184.8 mm $- 123$ mm $= 61.8$ mm

   e. 106 cm $- 43.7$ cm $= 62.3$ cm

   f. 793 mm $- 523.8$ mm $= 269.2$ mm

   g. 0.214 m $+ 0.876$ m $+ 0.9$ m $= 1.99$ m

   h. 56 mm $+ 49.3$ mm $+ 57.3$ mm $= 162.6$ mm

   i. 54.4 mm $+ 50.5$ mm $+ 204.3$ mm $= 309.2$ mm

   j. 3.927 m $- 0.812$ m $= 3.115$ m

7. 82 mm $- (3 \times 10$ mm$) = 52$ mm

8. a. 1120 mm $\div (34$ mm $+ 3$ mm$) = 30.27$ or 30 complete strips

   b. 1120 mm $- (30 \times 37$ mm$) = 10$ mm

9. a. 37.000×0.03937 in $= 1.457$ in

   b. 126.800×0.03937 in $= 4.992$ in

   c. 17.300×0.3937 in $= 6.811$ in

   d. 0.840×0.3937 in $= 0.331$ in

   e. 2.400×39.37 in $= 94.488$ in

   f. 0.090×39.37 in $= 3.543$ in

   g. 8.000×3.2808 ft $= 26.246$ ft

   h. 10.200×3.2808 ft $= 33.464$ ft

   i. 736.00×0.03937 in $= 28.976$ in

   j. 34.050×0.03937 in $= 1.341$ in

   k. 56.300×0.3937 in $= 22.165$ in

   l. $2.000 \times (3.2808 \div 3)$ yd $= 2.187$ yd

   m. $45.000 \times (0.3937 \div 12)$ ft $= 1.476$ ft

   n. $780.00 \times (0.03937 \div 12)$ ft $= 2.559$ ft

10. a. 4×25.4 mm $= 101.6$ mm

    b. 0.360×25.4 mm $= 9.14$ mm

    c. 34.00×2.54 cm $= 86.36$ cm

    d. 20.85×2.54 cm $= 52.96$ cm

    e. 6.00×0.3048 m $= 1.83$ m

    f. 0.75×0.3048 m $= 0.23$ m

    g. 3.50×0.9144 m $= 3.20$ m

    h. 1.30×0.9144 m $= 1.19$ m

    i. 2.368×25.4 mm $= 60.15$ mm

    j. 0.73×2.54 cm $= 1.85$ cm

    k. $(216.00 \div 12) \times 0.3048$ m $= 5.49$ m

    l. 0.5×25.4 mm $= 12.7$ mm

    m. 3.25×2.54 cm $= 8.26$ cm

    n. $(75.375 \div 12) \times 0.3048$ m $= 1.91$ m

UNIT 21 (*continued*)

11. 34.2 mm = 34.2 × 0.03937 in = 1.34645 in

    35 × (1.34645 in + 0.1875 in) = 53.7 in

12. A = 70.00 × 0.03937 in = 2.756 in

    B = 49.78 × 0.03937 in = 1.960 in

    C = 8.25 × 0.03937 in = 0.325 in

    D = 6.00 × 0.03937 in = 0.236 in

    E = 20.90 × 0.03937 in = 0.823 in

    F = 3.50 × 0.03937 in = 0.138 in

    G = 14.25 × 0.03937 in = 0.561 in

    H = 6.00 × 0.03937 in = 0.236 in

    I = 28.60 × 0.03937 in = 1.126 in

    J = 16.00 × 0.03937 in = 0.630 in

12. K = 5.88 × 0.03937 in = 0.231 in

    L = 9.22 × 0.03937 in = 0.363 in

13. A = 0.620 × 25.4 mm = 15.75 mm

    B = 1.125 × 25.4 mm = 28.58 mm

    C = 12.875 × 25.4 mm = 327.03 mm

    D = 0.988 × 25.4 mm = 25.10 mm

    E = 0.130 × 25.4 mm = 3.30 mm

    F = 0.5 × 25.4 mm = 12.70 mm

    G = 0.984375 × 25.4 mm = 25.00 mm

    H = 0.09375 × 25.4 mm = 2.38 mm

    I = 0.6875 × 25.4 mm = 17.46 mm

    J = 0.375 × 25.4 mm = 9.53 mm

UNIT 22 Degree of Precision, Greatest Possible Error, Absolute Error, and Relative Error

1. a. 0.1″
    b. 4.25″
    c. 4.35″

2. a. 0.01″
    b. 1.615″
    c. 1.625″

3. a. 0.001″
    b. 4.0775″
    c. 4.0785″

4. a. 0.01″
    b. 6.065″
    c. 6.075″

5. a. 0.001″
    b. 15.8845″
    c. 15.8855″

6. a. 0.0001″
    b. 9.18365″
    c. 9.18375″

7. a. 0.001″
    b. 11.0025″
    c. 11.0035″

8. a. 0.1″
    b. 35.95″
    c. 36.05″

9. a. 0.01″
    b. 7.005″
    c. 7.015″

10. a. 0.01″
    b. 22.995″
    c. 23.005″

11. a. 0.1″
    b. 6.05″
    c. 6.15″

12. a. 0.00001″
    b. 14.010695″
    c. 14.010705″

13. a. 0.01 mm
    b. 26.865 mm
    c. 26.875 mm

14. a. 0.1 mm
    b. 15.35 mm
    c. 15.45 mm

15. a. 0.01 mm
    b. 117.055 mm
    c. 117.065 mm

16. a. 0.001 mm
    b. 0.9755 mm
    c. 0.9765 mm

17. a. 0.01 mm
    b. 48.005 mm
    c. 48.015 mm

18. a. 0.001 mm
    b. 104.7985 mm
    c. 104.7995 mm

19. a. 0.01 mm
    b. 6.995 mm
    c. 7.005 mm

20. a. 0.0001 mm
    b. 34.08245 mm
    c. 34.08255 mm

21. a. 0.001 mm
    b. 8.0005 mm
    c. 8.0015 mm

22. a. 0.0001 mm
    b. 13.99995 mm
    c. 14.00005 mm

	GREATEST POSSIBLE ERROR (inches)	ACTUAL LENGTH	
		SMALLEST POSSIBLE (inches)	LARGEST POSSIBLE (inches)
23.	0.025	5.275	5.325
24.	0.01	15.67	15.69
25.	0.0005	0.7525	0.7535
26.	0.0005	0.225	0.2265
27.	0.00005	0.93685	0.93695
28.	$\frac{1}{128}$	$3\frac{79}{128}$	$3\frac{81}{128}$

	GREATEST POSSIBLE ERROR (millimeters)	ACTUAL LENGTH	
		SMALLEST POSSIBLE (millimeters)	LARGEST POSSIBLE (millimeters)
29.	0.5	63.5	64.5
30.	0.25	104.75	105.25
31.	0.25	98.25	98.75
32.	0.011	53.37	53.39
33.	0.005	13.365	13.375
34.	0.001	12.777	12.779

UNIT 22   (continued)

35. Absolute Error = 38.720 in − 38.700 in = 0.020 in

    Relative Error = $\dfrac{0.020\ \text{in}}{38.720\ \text{in}} \times 100 = 0.052\%$

36. Absolute Error = 0.530 mm − 0.520 mm = 0.010 mm

    Relative Error = $\dfrac{0.010\ \text{mm}}{0.530\ \text{mm}} \times 100 = 1.887\%$

37. Absolute Error = 12.900° − 12.700° = 0.200°

    Relative Error = $\dfrac{0.200°}{12.700°} \times 100 = 1.575\%$

38. Absolute Error = 0.485 in − 0.482 in = 0.003 in

    Relative Error = $\dfrac{0.003\ \text{in}}{0.485\ \text{in}} \times 100 = 0.625\%$

39. Absolute Error = 24.000 mm − 23.860 mm = 0.140 mm

    Relative Error = $\dfrac{0.140\ \text{mm}}{23.860\ \text{mm}} \times 100 = 0.587\%$

40. Absolute Error = 6.100° − 6.056° = 0.044°

    Relative Error = $\dfrac{0.044°}{6.056°} \times 100 = 0.727\%$

41. Absolute Error = 1.050 mm − 1.020 mm = 0.030 mm

    Relative Error = $\dfrac{0.030\ \text{mm}}{1.050\ \text{mm}} \times 100 = 2.857\%$

42. Absolute Error = 0.9347 in − 0.9341 in = 0.0006 in

    Relative Error = $\dfrac{0.0006\ \text{in}}{0.9347\ \text{in}} \times 100 = 0.064\%$

43. Absolute Error = 0.015° − 1.005° = 0.010°

    Relative Error = $\dfrac{0.010°}{1.005°} \times 100 = 0.995\%$

44. Absolute Error = 27.200 in − 26.900 in = 0.300 in

    Relative Error = $\dfrac{0.003\ \text{in}}{27.200\ \text{in}} \times 100 = 1.103\%$

45. Absolute Error = 18.302 in − 18.276 in = 0.026 in

    Relative Error = $\dfrac{0.026\ \text{in}}{18.276\ \text{in}} \times 100 = 0.142\%$

46. Absolute Error = 1.000 mm − 0.983 mm = 0.017 mm

    Relative Error = $\dfrac{0.017\ \text{mm}}{1.000\ \text{mm}} \times 100 = 1.700\%$

UNIT 23   Tolerance, Clearance, and Interference

1. a. Tolerance = $5\frac{7''}{10} - 5\frac{13''}{32} = \frac{1''}{32}$

    b. Tolerance = $7'\text{-}9\frac{1''}{16} - 7'\text{-}8\frac{15''}{16} = \frac{1''}{8}$

    c. Min. Limit = 16.76 ″ − 0.03″ = 16.73″

    d. Max. Limit = 0.904″ + 0.007″ = 0.911″

    e. Tolerance = 1.7001″ − 1.6998″ = 0.0003″

    f. Max. Limit = 10.999″ + 0.004″ = 11.003″

2. a. Tolerance = 50.7 mm − 49.9 mm = 0.8 mm

    b. Tolerance = 26.8 cm − 26.6 cm = 0.2 cm

    c. Max. Limit = 258.03 mm + 0.04 mm = 258.07 mm

    d. Min. Limit = 79.65 mm − 0.12 mm = 79.53 mm

    e. Max. Limit = 12.731 cm + 0.006 cm = 12.737 cm

    f. Tolerance = 4.01 mm − 3.98 mm = 0.03 mm

3. a. Max. Limit = 4.640″ + 0.003″ = 4.643″

        Min. Limit = 4.640″

    b. Max. Limit = 5.927″ + 0.005″ = 5.932″

        Min. Limit = 5.927″

    c. Max. Limit = 2.004″

        Min. Limit = 2.004″ − 0.004″ = 2.000″

    d. Max. Limit = 4.6729″

        Min. Limit = 4.6729″ − 0.0012″ = 4.6717″

3. e. Max. Limit = 1.0875″ + 0.0009″ = 1.0884″

        Min. Limit = 1.0875″

    f. Max. Limit = 28.16 mm

        Min. Limit = 28.16 mm − 0.06 mm = 28.10 mm

    g. Max. Limit = 43.94 mm + 0.04 mm = 43.98 mm

        Min. Limit = 43.94 mm

    h. Max. Limit = 118.66 mm + 0.07 mm = 118.73 mm

        Min. Limit = 118.66 mm

    i. Max. Limit = 73.398 mm

        Min. Limit = 73.398 mm − 0.012 mm = 73.386 mm

    j. Max. Limit = 45.106 mm + 0.009 mm = 45.115 mm

        Min. Limit = 45.106 mm

4. a. Max. Limit = 2.812″ + 0.006″ = 2.818″

        Min. Limit = 2.812″ − 0.006″ = 2.806″

    b. Max. Limit = 3.003″ + 0.004″ = 3.007″

        Min. Limit = 3.003″ − 0.004″ = 2.999″

    c. Max. Limit = 3.971″ + 0.010″ = 3.981″

        Min. Limit = 3.971″ − 0.010″ = 3.961″

    d. Max. Limit = 4.0562″ + 0.0012″ = 4.0574″

        Min. Limit = 4.0562″ − 0.0012″ = 4.0550″

    e. Max. Limit = 1.3799″ + 0.0009″ = 1.3808″

        Min. Limit = 1.3799″ − 0.0009″ = 1.3790″

UNIT 23 (*continued*)

4.   f. Max. Limit = 2.0000″ + 0.0007″ = 2.0007″

Min. Limit = 2.0000″ − 0.0007″ = 1.9993″

g. Max. Limit = 43.46 mm + 0.05 mm = 43.51 mm

Min. Limit = 43.46 mm − 0.05 mm = 43.41 mm

h. Max. Limit = 107.07 mm + 0.08 mm = 107.15 mm

Min. Limit = 107.07 mm − 0.08 mm = 106.99 mm

i. Max. Limit = 62.04 mm + 0.10 mm = 62.14 mm

Min. Limit = 62.04 mm − 0.10 mm = 61.94 mm

j. Max. Limit = 10.203 mm + 0.024 mm = 10.227 mm

Min. Limit = 10.203 mm − 0.024 mm = 10.179 mm

k. Max. Limit = 289.005 mm + 0.007 mm = 289.012 mm

Min. Limit = 289.005 mm − 0.007 mm = 288.998 mm

l. Max. Limit = 66.761 mm + 0.015 mm = 66.776 mm

Min. Limit = 66.761 mm − 0.015 mm = 66.746 mm

5.   a. 0.943″ ± 0.005″

b. 1.687″ ± 0.001″

c. 2.998″ ± 0.002″

d. 0.069″ ± 0.004″

e. 4.1880″ ± 0.0007″

f. 0.9984″ ± 0.0037″

g. 0.0006″ ± 0.0004″

h. 8.4660″ ± 0.0011″

i. 44.31 mm ± 0.01 mm

j. 10.02 mm ± 0.04 mm

k. 64.92 mm ± 0.03 mm

l. 38.61 mm ± 0.01 mm

m. 124.9915 mm ± 0.0085 mm

n. 43.078 mm ± 0.013 mm

6. All dimensions are in inches.

		BASIC DIMENSION	MAXIMUM DIAMETER (MAX. LIMIT)	MINIMUM DIAMETER (MIN. LIMIT)	MAXIMUM CLEARANCE	MINIMUM CLEARANCE (ALLOWANCE)
a.	DIA A	1.4580	1.4580	1.4550	0.0090	0.0030
	DIA B	1.4610	1.4640	1.4610		
b.	DIA A	0.6345	0.6345	0.6315	0.0080	0.0020
	DIA B	0.6365	0.6395	0.6365		
c.	DIA A	2.1053	2.1053	2.1023	0.0085	0.0025
	DIA B	2.1078	2.1108	2.1078		

7. All dimensions are in millimeters.

		BASIC DIMENSION	MAXIMUM DIAMETER (MAX. LIMIT)	MINIMUM DIAMETER (MIN. LIMIT)	MAXIMUM INTERFERENCE (ALLOWANCE)	MINIMUM INTERFERENCE
a.	DIA A	20.73	20.75	20.71	0.09	0.01
	DIA B	20.68	20.70	20.66		
b.	DIA A	32.07	32.09	32.05	0.10	0.02
	DIA B	32.01	32.03	31.99		
c.	DIA A	12.72	12.74	12.70	0.11	0.035
	DIA B	12.65	12.67	12.63		

8. All dimensions are in inches.

		BASIC DIMENSION	MAXIMUM DIAMETER (MAX. LIMIT)	MINIMUM DIAMETER (MIN. LIMIT)	MAXIMUM CLEARANCE	MINIMUM CLEARANCE (ALLOWANCE)
a.	DIM A	0.9995	1.0003	0.9987	0.0041	0.0009
	DIM B	1.0020	1.0028	1.0012		
b.	DIM A	2.0334	2.0342	2.0326	0.0042	0.0010
	DIM B	2.0360	2.0368	2.0352		
c.	DIM A	1.4392	1.4400	1.4384	0.0036	0.0004
	DIM B	1.4412	1.4420	1.4404		

UNIT **23** (*continued*)

9. All dimensions are in millimeters.

		BASIC DIMENSION	MAXIMUM DIAMETER (MAX. LIMIT)	MINIMUM DIAMETER (MIN. LIMIT)	MAXIMUM INTERFERENCE (ALLOWANCE)	MINIMUM INTERFERENCE
a.	DIA A	87.58	87.61	87.55	0.14	0.02
	DIA B	87.50	87.53	87.47		
b.	DIA A	9.94	9.97	9.91	0.15	0.03
	DIA B	9.85	9.88	9.82		
c.	DIA A	130.03	130.06	130.00	0.13	0.01
	DIA B	129.96	129.99	129.93		

10. Min. Limit = 0.372″

    Max. Limit = 0.378

    Defective Spacers: 0.379″, 0.370″, 0.380″, 0.371″

11. Max. hole dia = 18.25 mm − 0.03 mm = 18.22 mm

    Min. hole dia = 18.25 mm − 0.07 mm = 18.18 mm

    Mean dia: 18.22 mm − 18.18 mm = 0.04 mm

    0.04 mm ÷ 2 = 0.02 mm

    18.22 mm − 0.02 mm = 18.20 mm

12. $\left(20\dfrac{3''}{8}+\dfrac{1''}{16}\right)-\left[\left(5\dfrac{3''}{16}-\dfrac{1''}{32}\right)+\left(6\dfrac{3''}{4}-\dfrac{1''}{32}\right)\right]=8\dfrac{9''}{16}$

13. Max. thickness = [(26.20 mm + 0.05 mm) − (20.50 mm − 0.01 mm)] ÷ 2 = 2.88 mm

    Min. thickness = [(26.20 mm − 0.05 mm) − (20.50 mm + 0.01 mm)] ÷ 2 = 2.82 mm

14. a. 0.3750″ − 0.0004″ = 0.3746″

     b. 0.3762″ + 0.0004″ = 0.3766″

     c. 2.0000″ + 0.0004″ = 2.0004″

        2.0004″ − (0.3750″ − 0.0008″) = 1.6262″

     d. 2.0000″ − 0.0004″ = 1.9996″

        1.9996″ − 0.3750″ = 1.6246″

     e. 2.0000″ + 0.0004″ = 2.0004″

        2.0004″ − 0.3762″ = 1.6242″

14. f. 2.0000″ − 0.0004″ = 1.9996″

        1.9996″ − (0.3762″ + 0.0008″) = 1.6226″

     g. (2.0000″ − 0.0004″) + (0.3750″ − 0.0008″) = 2.3738″

        (2.0000″ + 0.0004″) + (0.3762″ + 0.0008″) = 2.3774″

        2.3774″ − 2.3738″ = 0.0036″

     h. (2.0000″ + 0.0004″) + 0.3750″ = 2.3754″

        (2.0000″ − 0.0004″) + 0.3762″ = 2.3758″

        2.3758″ − 2.3754″ = 0.0004″

15. Hole 1: Minimum limit = $15\dfrac{7''}{16}-\dfrac{1''}{8}=15\dfrac{5''}{16}$

    Maximum limit = $15\dfrac{7''}{16}+\dfrac{1''}{8}=15\dfrac{9''}{16}$

    Hole 1 location, $15\dfrac{1''}{2}$, is within tolerance.

    Minimum limit between holes = $18\dfrac{7''}{8}-\dfrac{1''}{8}=18\dfrac{3''}{4}$

    Maximum limit between holes = $18\dfrac{7''}{8}+\dfrac{1''}{8}=19''$

    Hole 2: Actual location from Hole 1 = $34\dfrac{3''}{8}-15\dfrac{1''}{2}=18\dfrac{7''}{8}$

    Hole 2 is located within tolerance.

    Hole 3: Actual location from Hole 2 = $53\dfrac{5''}{16}-34\dfrac{3''}{8}=18\dfrac{15''}{16}$

    Hole 3 is located within tolerance.

UNIT 23   *(continued)*

15.   Hole 4:   Actual location from Hole 3 = $72\dfrac{3''}{16} - 53\dfrac{5''}{16} = 18\dfrac{7''}{8}$

Hole 4 is located within tolerance.

Hole 5:   Actual location from Hole 4 = $90\dfrac{3''}{8} - 72\dfrac{3''}{16} = 18\dfrac{3''}{16}$

Hole 5 is drilled out of tolerance.

Hole 6:   Actual location from Hole 5 = $108\dfrac{15''}{16} - 90\dfrac{3''}{8} = 18\dfrac{9''}{16}$

Hole 6 is drilled out of tolerance.

UNIT 24   Customary and Metric Steel Rules

1.
a. $\dfrac{3''}{32}$
b. $\dfrac{5''}{16}$
c. $\dfrac{1''}{2}$
d. $\dfrac{5''}{8}$
e. $\dfrac{3''}{4}$
f. $\dfrac{29''}{32}$
g. $1\dfrac{3''}{32}$
h. $1\dfrac{5''}{16}$
i. $\dfrac{5''}{64}$
j. $\dfrac{7''}{32}$
k. $\dfrac{3''}{8}$
l. $\dfrac{35''}{64}$
m. $\dfrac{51''}{64}$
n. $\dfrac{31''}{32}$
o. $1\dfrac{15''}{64}$
p. $1\dfrac{29''}{64}$

2.
a. $2\dfrac{5''}{16}$
b. $\dfrac{13''}{16}$
c. $1\dfrac{1''}{16}$
d. $\dfrac{5''}{8}$
e. $2\dfrac{9''}{16}$
f. $\dfrac{3''}{8}$
g. $\dfrac{1''}{4}$
h. $3\dfrac{1''}{2}$
i. $\dfrac{11''}{16}$
j. $\dfrac{7''}{8}$

3.
a. $\dfrac{1''}{4}$
b. $\dfrac{9''}{16}$
c. $\dfrac{1''}{2}$
d. $\dfrac{1''}{2}$
e. $\dfrac{11''}{32}$
f. $2\dfrac{7''}{32}$
g. $\dfrac{7''}{32}$
h. $\dfrac{3''}{4}$
i. $\dfrac{23''}{32}$
j. $\dfrac{1''}{2}$
k. $\dfrac{15''}{32}$
l. $\dfrac{3''}{8}$
m. $\dfrac{5''}{32}$
n. $4\dfrac{29''}{32}$

4.
a. $\dfrac{61''}{64}$
b. $2\dfrac{3''}{8}$
c. $1\dfrac{9''}{32}$
d. $3\dfrac{11''}{32}$
e. $\dfrac{7''}{16}$
f. $\dfrac{19''}{64}$
g. $\dfrac{11''}{64}$
h. $1\dfrac{17''}{64}$
i. $2\dfrac{57''}{64}$
j. $\dfrac{33''}{64}$

5.
a. 0.12″
b. 0.22″
c. 0.40″
d. 0.62″
e. 0.80″
f. 1.04″
g. 1.32″
h. 1.42″
i. 0.11″
j. 0.23″
k. 0.38″
l. 0.57″
m. 0.84″
n. 1.07″
o. 1.29″
p. 1.45″

6.
a. 1.76″
b. 2.50″
c. 0.18″
d. 0.46″
e. 2.98″
f. 0.66″
g. 1.36″
h. 0.96″
i. 4.66″
j. 0.58″
k. 1.96″
l. 0.16″
m. 1.86″

7.
A = 0.54″
B = 0.42″
C = 1.38″
D = 1.18″
E = 0.34″
F = 0.28″
G = 1.00″
H = 0.22″
I = 0.10″

8.
a. 5 mm
b. 13 mm
c. 20 mm
d. 26 mm
e. 37 mm
f. 49 mm
g. 61 mm
h. 73 mm
i. 6.5 mm
j. 13 mm
k. 19.5 mm
l. 30.5 mm
m. 44.5 mm
n. 52.5 mm
o. 63.5 mm
p. 71.5 mm

9.
a. 46 mm
b. 70 mm
c. 20 mm
d. 82 mm
e. 10 mm
f. 23 mm
g. 25 mm
h. 121 mm
i. 17 mm
j. 22 mm
k. 36 mm
l. 10 mm
m. 52 mm
n. 6 mm

10.
a. 17 mm
b. 8 mm
c. 15 mm
d. 20 mm
e. 74 mm
f. 8 mm
g. 126 mm
h. 16 mm
i. 42 mm
j. 27 mm
k. 10 mm

UNIT **25** Customary Vernier Calipers and Height Gages

1. a. 2.641″   e. 4.788″
   b. 3.376″   f. 2.991″
   c. 2.021″   g. 1.581″
   d. 0.508″   h. 1.098″

2. a. 1.894″   m. 0.005″
   b. 3.046″   n. 0.842″
   c. 0.056″   o. 3.573″
   d. 5.786″   p. 5.095″
   e. 1.232″   q. 3.340″
   f. 0.091″   r. 2.081″
   g. 3.004″   s. 4.410″
   h. 2.660″   t. 1.000″
   i. 1.013″   u. 0.693″
   j. 5.993″   v. 0.052″
   k. 2.833″   w. 3.021″
   l. 4.951″   x. 2.947″

3.

	A (inches)	B (inches)	C
a.	3.225	3.250	17
b.	2.875	2.900	2
c.	4.825	4.850	14
d.	0.600	0.625	11
e.	4.350	4.375	10
f.	0.075	0.100	9
g.	7.850	7.875	7
h.	1.625	1.650	21
i.	4.025	4.050	9
j.	0.000	0.025	22
k.	3.325	3.350	8
l.	5.975	6.000	24
m.	0.275	0.300	3
n.	0.950	0.975	15

4. a. (1) 4.674″ − 0.232″ = 4.442″
      Setting: 4.425″– 4.450″
      (2) 17
   b. (1) 4.358″ − 0.186″ = 4.172″
      Setting: 4.150″– 4.175″
      (2) 22
   c. (1) $3.664'' - \left(\dfrac{0.123''}{2} + \dfrac{0.137''}{2} \right) = 3.534''$
      Setting: 3.525″– 3.550″
      (2) 9
   d. (1) Max. dim. = $5.345'' - \left(\dfrac{0.746''}{2} + \dfrac{0.476''}{2} \right) = 4.734''$
      Min. dim. = $5.345'' - \left(\dfrac{0.754''}{2} + \dfrac{0.480''}{2} \right) = 4.728''$
      Setting: 4.725″– 4.750″
      (2) Max. dim: 9
          Min. dim: 3
   e. (1) Max. dim. = $3.265'' - \left(\dfrac{0.072''}{2} + \dfrac{0.322''}{2} \right) = 2.918''$
      Min. dim. = $3.529'' - \left(\dfrac{0.378''}{2} + \dfrac{0.332''}{2} \right) = 2.904''$
      Setting: 2.900″– 2.925″
      (2) Max. dim: 18
          Min. dim: 4

5. a. 1.909″   c. 7.969″   e. 2.779″   g. 3.612″
   b. 4.620″   d. 0.439″   f. 6.459″   h. 8.391″

6. Hole 1: $0.640'' - \dfrac{0.376''}{2} = 0.452''$

   Hole 2: $0.640'' + 1.008'' - \dfrac{0.258''}{2} = 1.519''$

   Hole 3: $0.640'' + 1.008'' - 0.514'' - \dfrac{0.188''}{2} = 1.040''$

   Hole 4: $0.640'' + 0.312'' - \dfrac{0.496''}{2} = 0.704''$

   Hole 5: $0.640'' + 0.312'' + 0.810'' - \dfrac{0.127''}{2} = 1.699''$

HOLE NUMBER	HEIGHT GAGE SETTINGS	
	MAIN SCALE SETTING (inches)	VERNIER SCALE SETTING
1	0.450–0.475	2
2	1.500–1.525	19
3	1.025–1.050	15
4	0.700–0.725	4
5	1.675–1.700	24

UNIT 26 Customary Micrometers

1. 0.589″
2. 0.022″
3. 0.736″
4. 0.083″
5. 0.808″
6. 0.388″
7. 0.738″
8. 0.598″
9. 0.157″
10. 0.679″
11. 0.949″
12. 0.520″
13. 0.441″
14. 0.084″
15. 0.153″
16. 0.887″
17. 0.424″
18. 0.023″
19. 0.038″
20. 0.767″
21. 0.983″
22. 0.641″

	BARREL SCALE SETTING (inches)	THIMBLE SCALE SETTING (inches)
23.	0.375–0.400	0.012
24.	0.825–0.850	0.016
25.	0.950–0.975	0.023
26.	0.000–0.025	0.002
27.	0.075–0.100	0.004
28.	0.975–1.000	0.023
29.	0.025–0.050	0.013
30.	0.275–0.300	0.006
31.	0.425–0.450	0.002
32.	0.650–0.675	0.016

33. 0.3637″
34. 0.2336″
35. 0.0982″
36. 0.4980″
37. 0.3105″
38. 0.3283″
39. 0.1448″
40. 0.4333″
41. 0.5157″
42. 0.0674″
43. 0.2749″

44. 0.3116″
45. 0.3928″
46. 0.1333″
47. 0.9717″
48. 0.0865″
49. 0.3004″
50. 0.6462″
51. 0.0009″
52. 0.2957″
53. 0.8594″
54. 0.2398″

	BARREL SCALE SETTING (inches)	THIMBLE SCALE SETTING (inches)	VERNIER SCALE SETTING (inches)
55.	0.775–0.800	0.009–0.010	0.0006
56.	0.100–0.125	0.003–0.004	0.0005
57.	0.000–0.025	0.008–0.009	0.0003
58.	0.975–1.000	0.014–0.015	0.0008
59.	0.300–0.325	0.000–0.001	0.0001
60.	0.000–0.025	0.001–0.002	0.0002
61.	0.800–0.825	0.000–0.001	0.0008
62.	0.300–0.325	0.013–0.014	0.0005
63.	0.975–1.000	0.014–0.015	0.0004
64.	0.025–0.050	0.022–0.023	0.0009

UNIT 27 Customary and Metric Gage Blocks

One combination for each dimension is given. A number of different combinations will produce the given dimensions.

1. 0.1008″, 0.113″, 0.650″, 3.000″
2. 0.1002″, 0.120″, 0.650″, 1.000″
3. 0.1002″, 0.122″, 0.900″, 2.000″
4. 0.1003″, 0.133″, 0.400″
5. 0.1009″, 0.125″, 0.050″
6. 0.1002″, 0.700″, 1.000″, 4.000″
7. 0.123″, 0.850″, 3.000″, 4.000″
8. 0.1009″, 0.149″, 0.750″
9. 0.250″, 1.000″, 2.000″, 3.000″, 4.000″
10. 0.050″, 2.000″, 3.000″, 4.000″
11. 0.1007″, 0.125″, 0.650″, 4.000″
12. 0.1001″, 0.900″

13. 0.1001″, 0.112″, 0.050″
14. 0.1001″, 0.131″, 0.500″, 2.000″
15. 0.140″, 0.950″, 4.000″
16. 0.1007″, 0.130″, 0.850″, 1.000″, 4.000″
17. 0.1009″, 0.128″, 0.750″, 2.000″
18. 0.1004″, 0.125″, 0.450″
19. 0.1007″, 0.127″, 0.550″, 3.000″, 4.000″
20. 0.1001″, 0.110″, 0.800″, 2.000″, 3.000″, 4.000″
21. 0.1006″, 0.134″, 0.200″, 2.000″, 3.000″, 4.000″
22. 0.1008″, 0.120″, 0.600″, 4.000″
23. 0.103″, 0.900″, 1.000″, 4.000″
24. 0.1001″, 0.102″, 0.800″, 2.000″, 3.000″, 4.000″

UNIT **27** *(continued)*

25. 0.1008″, 0.149″, 0.450″

26. 1.005 mm, 1.08 mm, 1.2 mm, 40 mm

27. 1.003 mm, 1.07 mm, 2 mm, 10 mm

28. 1.006 mm, 1.05 mm, 1.3 mm, 1 mm, 30 mm

29. 1.09 mm, 5 mm, 60 mm, 90 mm

30. 1.9 mm, 2 mm, 40 mm, 80 mm, 90 mm

31. 1.007 mm, 1.7 mm, 1 mm, 40 mm

32. 1.009 mm, 1.09 mm, 1.9 mm, 6 mm

33. 1.06 mm, 1.4 mm, 4 mm, 70 mm

34. 1.08 mm, 6 mm, 60 mm, 90 mm

35. 1.06 mm, 1.8 mm, 1 mm, 10 mm

36. 1.007 mm, 1.02 mm, 1.7 mm, 5 mm, 20 mm

37. 1.001 mm, 1.07 mm, 4 mm

38. 1.001 mm, 1.01 mm, 1.1 mm, 2 mm, 80 mm

39. 1.009 mm, 1.09 mm, 7 mm, 30 mm

40. 1.04 mm, 1.4 mm, 2 mm, 40 mm, 90 mm

41. 1.005 mm, 6 mm, 60 mm

42. 1.07 mm, 1.8 mm, 9 mm, 30 mm

43. 1.007 mm, 1 mm

44. 1.03 mm, 1.2 mm, 5 mm, 10 mm, 90 mm

45. 1.03 mm, 2 mm, 20 mm, 80 mm, 90 mm

46. 1.001 mm, 1.06 mm, 1 mm, 70 mm

47. 1.004 mm, 1.8 mm, 9 mm

48. 1.007 mm, 8 mm, 50 mm, 90 mm

49. 1.005 mm, 1.05 mm, 1.5 mm, 2 mm, 50 mm

UNIT **28** Achievement Review—Section Two

1. a. $81 \div 12 = 6.75$; 6.75 ft

   b. $6\frac{1}{4} \times 12 = 75$; 75 in

   c. $9.6 \times 3 = 28.8$; 28.8 ft

   d. 27 mm

   e. 800 mm

   f. 21.8 cm

2. $5\frac{1}{2}$ ft = 66 in; $\left(66\,\text{in} - 2 \times 8\frac{5}{8}\,\text{in}\right) \div 13 = 3\frac{3}{4}$

3. 250×54 mm = 13,500 mm; 13.500 m

   13.500 m ÷ 3 m = 4.5 lengths

   4.5 lengths + 0.5 length = 5 complete lengths

4. a. 47×0.03937 in = 1.850 in

   b. 5.5×3.2808 ft = 18.044 ft

   c. 16.8×0.3937 in = 6.614 in

   d. 4.75×25.4 mm = 120.65 mm

   e. 31×2.54 cm = 78.74 cm

   f. 4.5×0.3048 m = 1.372 m

5.

	GREATEST POSSIBLE ERROR	ACTUAL LENGTH	
		SMALLEST POSSIBLE	LARGEST POSSIBLE
a.	0.01″	4.27″	4.29″
b.	0.00005″	0.83665″	0.83675″
c.	0.01 mm	46.15 mm	46.17 mm
d.	0.005 mm	16.445 mm	16.455 mm

6. a. Absolute Error = 5.963 in − 5.960 in = 0.003 in

   Relative Error = $\frac{0.003\,\text{In}}{5.963\,\text{in}} \times 100 = 0.050\%$

   b. Absolute Error = 0.392 mm − 0.388 mm = 0.004 mm

   Relative Error = $\frac{0.004\,\text{mm}}{0.392\,\text{mm}} \times 100 = 1.020\%$

   c. Absolute Error = 7.200° − 7.123° = 0.077°

   Relative Error = $\frac{0.077°}{7.123°} \times 100 = 1.081\%$

   d. Absolute Error = 0.1070 in − 0.0990 in = 0.008 in

   Relative Error = $\frac{0.008\,\text{in}}{0.1070\,\text{in}} \times 100 = 7.477\%$

   e. Absolute Error = 0.8639 in − 0.8634 in = 0.0005 in

   Relative Error = $\frac{0.0005\,\text{in}}{0.8639\,\text{in}} \times 100 = 0.058\%$

   f. Absolute Error = 0.713° − 0.706° = 0.007°

   Relative Error = $\frac{0.007°}{0.713°} \times 100 = 0.982\%$

7. a. Max. limit = 1.714″ + 0.005″ = 1.719″

   Min. limit = 1.714″ − 0.005″ = 1.709″

   b. Max. limit = 4.0688″ + 0.0000″ = 4.0688″

   Min. limit = 4.0688″ − 0.0012″ = 4.0676″

   c. Max. limit = 5.9047″ + 0.0008″ = 5.9055″

   Min. limit = 5.9047″ − 0.0000″ = 5.9047″

   d. Max. limit = 64.91 mm + 0.08 mm = 64.99 mm

   Min. limit = 64.91 mm − 0.08 mm = 64.83 mm

UNIT 28   (*continued*)

7. e. Max. limit = 173.003 + 0.000 mm = 173.003 mm

    Min. limit = 173.003 mm − 0.013 mm = 172.990 mm

8. a. 0.876″ + 0.003 ″ = 0.879″; 0.879″ ± 0.003″

    b. 5.2619″ − 0.0006″ = 5.2613″; 5.2613″ ± 0.0006″

    c. 37.53 mm − 0.015 mm = 37.515 mm; 37.515 mm ± 0.015 mm

    d. 78.909 mm + 0.0045 mm = 78.9135 mm; 78.9135 mm ± 0.0045 mm

9. a. 0.9980″ − 0.0007″ = 0.9973″

    1.0006″ + 0.0007″ = 1.0013″

    1.0013″ − 0.9973″ = 0.0040″

    b. 0.9980″ + 0.0007″ = 0.9987″

    1.0006″ − 0.0007″ = 0.9999″

    0.9999″ − 0.9987″ = 0.0012″

    c. 1.3004″ − 0.0007″ = 1.2997″

    1.3010″ + 0.0007″ = 1.3017″

    1.3017″ − 1.2997″ = 0.0020″

    d. 1.3010″ − 1.3004″ = 0.0006″

    e. 1.6250″ + 0.0005″ = 1.6255″

    1.6232″ − 0.0005″ = 1.6227″

    1.6255″ − 1.6227″ = 0.0028″

    f. 1.6250″ − 1.6232″ = 0.0018″

    g. 0.5967″ + 0.0003″ = 0.5970″

    0.5952″ − 0.0003″ = 0.5949″

    0.5970″ − 0.5949″ = 0.0021″

    h. 0.5967″ − 0.0003″ = 0.5964″

    0.5952″ + 0.0003″ = 0.5955″

    0.5964″ − 0.5955″ = 0.0009″

10. 38.54 mm − 0.04 mm = 38.50 mm

    10.38 mm + 0.02 mm = 10.40 mm

    11.52 mm + 0.02 mm = 11.54 mm

    38.50 mm − (10.40 mm + 11.54 mm) = 16.56 mm

11. a. $\dfrac{3″}{32}$ i. $\dfrac{3″}{64}$

    b. $\dfrac{11″}{32}$ j. $\dfrac{13″}{64}$

    c. $\dfrac{9″}{16}$ k. $\dfrac{23″}{64}$

    d. $\dfrac{25″}{32}$ l. $\dfrac{17″}{32}$

    e. $\dfrac{29″}{32}$ m. $\dfrac{49″}{64}$

    f. $1\dfrac{3″}{32}$ n. $\dfrac{61″}{64}$

    g. $1\dfrac{7″}{32}$ o. $1\dfrac{7″}{32}$

    h. $1\dfrac{11″}{32}$ p. $1\dfrac{25″}{64}$

12. a. 0.08″   g. 1.32″   l. 0.51″

    b. 0.3″   h. 1.44″   m. 0.71″

    c. 0.56″   i. 0.05″   n. 1.05″

    d. 0.76″   j. 0.19″   o. 1.23″

    e. 0.96″   k. 0.32″   p. 1.49″

    f. 1.14″

13. a. 6 mm   g. 66 mm   l. 28.5 mm

    b. 19 mm   h. 74 mm   m. 45.5 mm

    c. 29 mm   i. 4.5 mm   n. 54 mm

    d. 43 mm   j. 11 mm   o. 65.5 mm

    e. 49 mm   k. 21.5 mm   p. 72.5 mm

    f. 57 mm

14. a. 3.781″   b. 7.721″   c. 2.888″

15. a. (1) 0.558″   (3) 0.679″

        (2) 0.089″   (4) 0.638″

    b. (1) 0.3023″   (3) 0.0732″

        (2) 0.2855″   (4) 0.4180″

16. a. 0.1004″, 0.128″, 0.150″

    b. 0.1006″, 0.148″, 0.300″, 2.000″

    c. 0.1002″, 0.106″, 0.500″, 1.000″

    d. 0.1007″, 0.146″, 0.400″, 5.000″

    e. 0.1001″, 0.140″, 0.850″, 2.000″

    f. 0.1009″, 0.100″

    g. 0.1005″, 0.139″, 0.650″, 3.000″, 4.000″

    h. 0.1004″, 0.101″, 0.800″, 3.000″, 4.000″

17. a. 1.03 mm, 1.5 mm, 5 mm, 60 mm

    b. 1.02 mm, 1.2 mm, 3 mm, 30 mm, 90 mm

    c. 1.002 mm, 1.09 mm, 3 mm, 80 mm

    d. 1.004 mm, 1.07 mm, 1.2 mm, 10 mm

    e. 1.006 mm, 1.06 mm, 4 mm, 60 mm

    f. 1.004 mm, 1.3 mm, 1 mm, 40 mm

    g. 1.008 mm, 1.09 mm, 1.9 mm, 6 mm, 90 mm

    h. 1.001 mm, 1.07 mm, 5 mm, 10 mm, 90 mm

Section Three
Fundamentals of Algebra

<hr>

UNIT 29 Symbolism

1. $6x + y$

2. $a + 12$

3. $21 - b$

4. $b - 21$

5. $\dfrac{r}{s}$

6. $2L - \dfrac{1}{2}P$

7. $\dfrac{xy}{m^2}$

8. a. $3'' + x + 4'' + x + y + 5'' = 12'' + 2x + y$

   b. $x + 4'' + x = 2x + 4$

9. a. $R + 1\dfrac{1}{2}R = 2\dfrac{1}{2}R$

   b. $R + R + \dfrac{3}{4}R = 2\dfrac{3}{4}R$

   c. $1\dfrac{1}{2}R + \dfrac{3}{4}R = 2\dfrac{1}{4}R$

   d.
   $R + R + 1\dfrac{1}{2}R + 1\dfrac{1}{2}R + \dfrac{5}{8}R + \dfrac{5}{8}R = 6\dfrac{1}{4}R$

10. a. $12.5\,\text{mm} \quad h$

    b. $L - I$

    c. $12.5\,\text{mm} - H$

11. $n - p - t$

12. a. $r = 0.866s$

    b. $R = 1.155r$

    c. $A = 2.598R^2$

13. a. $5(5) + 3(3)^2 = 25 + 27 = 52$

    b. $5(3) + 5 = 15 + 5 = 20$

    c. $\dfrac{10(3)}{5} = \dfrac{30}{5} = 6$

    d. $\dfrac{5 + 3}{5 - 3} = \dfrac{8}{2} = 4$

    e. $\dfrac{5 + 5(3)}{5(3) - 5} = \dfrac{20}{20} = 1$

14. a. $\dfrac{8}{4} + 2 - 3 = 2 + 2 - 3 = 1$

    b. $8(4) + [3 + 4(4) - 8] = 32(3 + 16 - 8)$
       $= 32(11) = 352$

    c. $5(8) - [8(4) + 3] = 40 - (32 + 3)$
       $= 40 - 35 = 5$

    d. $3(2)(8-2) - 4\dfrac{8}{2} = 6(6) - 4(4) = 36 - 16 = 20$

    e. $\dfrac{12(4)}{2} - [3(8) - (4 + 2) + 4] = 24 - [24 - 6 + 4]$
       $= 24 - 22 = 2$

15. a. $2(12)(6) + 7 = 144 + 7 = 151$

    b. $3(12) - 2(6) + (12)6 = 36 - 12 + 72 = 96$

    c. $\dfrac{5(12)(6) - 2(6)}{8(12) - 12(6)} = \dfrac{360 - 12}{96 - 72} = \dfrac{348}{24} = 14.5$

    d. $\dfrac{4(12) - 4(6)}{3} - \dfrac{48 - 24}{3} - 8$

    e. $6(12) - 3(6) + (12)(6) = 72 - 18 + 72 = 126$

16. a. $5 + 5(4^2) - 3^0 = 5 + 5(16) - 27 = 5 + 80 - 27 = 58$

    b. $(4 + 2)^2 (5 - 3)^2 = (6^2)(2^2) = (36)(4) = 144$

    c. $\dfrac{[4(3)]^2}{2} - 4(3) + 5^3 = \dfrac{12^2}{2} + 125$
       $= 72 - 12 + 125 = 185$

    d. $\dfrac{4^3 + 3(4) - 12}{5^2 + 15} = \dfrac{64 + 12 - 12}{25 + 15} = \dfrac{64}{40} = 1\dfrac{3}{5}$

    e. $\dfrac{3^3}{3(4) - 9} + 5^2[5(4) - 6(3)]^2 = \dfrac{27}{3} + 25(20 - 18)^2$
       $= 9 + 25(4) = 109$

17. a. $\dfrac{1}{2}(15.00\,\text{in})^2 = \dfrac{1}{2}(225.00\,\text{sq in}) = 112.5\,\text{sq in}$

    b. $0.7071(15.00\,\text{in}) = 10.6065\,\text{in}, 10.6\,\text{in}$

18. a. $[\pi(60.120\,\text{mm})(122.25°)] \div 180° = 128.2759\,\text{mm}, 128.3\,\text{mm}$

    b. $\dfrac{1}{2}(60.120\,\text{mm})(128.2759\,\text{mm}) = 3855.973\,\text{mm}^2, 3856.0\,\text{mm}$

19. a. $\dfrac{1}{2}(7.930\,\text{in} + 9.032\,\text{in} + 12.360\,\text{in}) = 14.661\,\text{in}, 14.7\,\text{in}$

    b. $\sqrt{14.661\,\text{in}(14.661\,\text{in} - 7.930\,\text{in})(14.661\,\text{in} - 9.032\,\text{in})(14.661\,\text{in} - 12.360\,\text{in})} =$

    $\sqrt{14.661\,\text{in}(6.731\,\text{in})(5.629\,\text{in})(2.301\,\text{in})} = \sqrt{1278.177\,\text{in}^4} = 35.752\,\text{in}^2, 35.8\,\text{sq in}$

UNIT 29 *(continued)*

20. a. $[(120.06 \text{ mm})^2 + 4(30.85 \text{ mm})^2] \div 8(30.85 \text{ mm}) = 18{,}221.2936 \text{ mm}^2 \div 246.8 \text{ mm} = 73.8302 \text{ mm}, 73.8 \text{ mm}$

   b. $0.0175 (73.8302 \text{ mm})(106.80) = 137.9886 \text{ mm}, 138.0 \text{ mm}$

21. $[(6.000 \text{ in} + 4.076 \text{ in})5.122 \text{ in} + 1.008 \text{ in}(4.076 \text{ in}) + 1.500 \text{ in}(6.000 \text{ in})] \div 2 = [51.6093 \text{ sq in} + 4.1086 \text{ sq in} + 9.0000 \text{ sq in}] \div 2 = 32.359 \text{ sq in}, 32.4 \text{ sq in}$

22. $2(14.50 \text{ in}) + [11(12.25 \text{ in}) + 11(8.00 \text{ in})] \div 7 + (12.25 \text{ in} - 8.00 \text{ in})^2 \div 4(14.50 \text{ in}) = 29.00 \text{ in} + 31.82 \text{ in} + 0.31 \text{ in} = 61.13 \text{ in}, 61.1 \text{ in}$

23. $6.18 \text{ mm}(3.26 \text{ mm}) + 2(2.25 \text{ mm})(0.50 \text{ mm} + 1.06 \text{ mm}) = 20.147 \text{ mm}^2 + 7.020 \text{ mm}^2 = 27.167 \text{ mm}^2, 27.2 \text{ mm}^2$

24. $\pi[5.00 \text{ in}(3.00 \text{ in}) - 4.00 \text{ in}(2.00 \text{ in})] = \pi(15.00 \text{ sq in} - 8.00 \text{ sq in}) = 21.99 \text{ sq in} = 22.0 \text{ sq in}$

25. $\pi[(8.103 \text{ in})^2 - (5.076 \text{ in})^2] \div 2 = \pi(39.8928 \text{ sq in}) \div 2 = 62.664 \text{ sq in}, 62.7 \text{ sq in}$

26. $2.00 \text{ cm}[15.15 \text{ cm} + 2(5.12 \text{ cm} - 2.00 \text{ cm})] = 2.00 \text{ cm}(21.39 \text{ cm}) = 42.78 \text{ cm}^2 = 42.8 \text{ cm}^2$

27. a. $\sqrt{(5.500 \text{ in} - 2.512 \text{ in})^2 + (4.074)^2} = \sqrt{8.9281 \text{ sq in} + 16.5975 \text{ sq in}} = \sqrt{25.5256 \text{ sq in}} = 5.0523 \text{ in}, 5.1 \text{ in}$

   b. $1.05(4.074 \text{ in})[(5.500 \text{ in})^2 + (5.500 \text{ in})(2.512 \text{ in}) + (2.512 \text{ in})^2] = 4.2777 \text{ in}(30.25 \text{ sq in} + 13.816 \text{ sq in} + 6.310 \text{ sq in}) = 4.2777 \text{ in}(50.376 \text{ sq in}) = 215.49 \text{ cu in}, 215.5 \text{ cu in}$

28. $[2(10.235 \text{ in}) + 12.043 \text{ in}](7.126 \text{ in})(8.000 \text{ in}) \div 6 = (32.513 \text{ in})(7.126 \text{ in})(8.000 \text{ in}) \div 6 = 1853.501 \text{ cu in} \div 6 = 308.917 \text{ cu in}, 308.9 \text{ cu in}$

UNIT 30 Signed Numbers

1. a. (+)9
   b. (+)5
   c. (+)6
   d. (−)6
   e. (−)10
   f. (+)7
   g. (−)20
   h. (−)10
   i. (+)3
   j. (−)8
   k. (−)11
   l. (−)6
   m. (+)17.5
   n. (−)17.5
   o. (+)6.5
   p. (+)1.5
   q. $(-)5\frac{1}{4}$
   r. $(-)5\frac{3}{4}$

2. a. +5; 19
   b. +7; 10

2. c. −1; 7
   d. +13; 5
   e. +20; 42
   f. −4; 12
   g. +23; 8.7
   h. +1.8; 3.6
   i. +17.6; 39.5

3. a. −25, −18, −1, 0, +2, +4, +17
   b. −21, −19, −5, −2, 0, +5, +13, +27
   c. −25, −10, −7, 0, +7, +10, +14, +25
   d. −14.9, −3.6, −2.5, 0, +0.3, +15, +17
   e. $-16, -13\frac{7}{8}, -3\frac{5}{8}, +6, +14\frac{1}{8}$

4. a. 23, 14; 9
   b. 17, 9; 8
   c. 6, 6; 0
   d. 25, 13; 12
   e. 16, 16; 0
   f. 33.7, 29.7; 4

5. a. 23
   b. 30

5. c. 25
   d. −23
   e. −33
   f. 7
   g. −8
   h. −1
   i. −6
   j. −22
   k. −13
   l. $-3\frac{1}{8}$
   m. $-13\frac{5}{16}$
   n. −14.47
   o. 0.43
   p. 1
   q. −39.62
   r. 31.25
   s. −28.9
   t. −14.06

6. a. −6
   b. 18
   c. −8
   d. 11
   e. 0
   f. 0
   g. −80
   h. 12
   i. −44
   j. 2.2
   k. −4.1
   l. −101.2
   m. 101.2
   n. −0.03
   o. $-3\frac{1}{4}$
   p. 10
   q. 14
   r. −1
   s. 11.15
   t. −27.62

UNIT **30** *(continued)*

7. a. −24
   b. 24
   c. −30
   d. 30
   e. −35
   f. 28
   g. 0
   h. −32.5
   i. 0.32
   j. 0.036
   k. $-1\dfrac{1}{8}$
   l. 0
   m. −8
   n. −8
   o. 0
   p. 7350.48
   q. 10.6
   r. −0.221
   s. 0.384
   t. −0.3

8. a. 2
   b. −4
   c. 2
   d. −7
   e. 5
   f. −8
   g. −5
   h. 4
   i. 0
   j. 6
   k. 1

8. l. 112
   m. $-3\dfrac{1}{2}$
   n. −5.463
   o. −0.685
   p. −5.6
   q. −5.5
   r. −5.3
   s. −38.119
   t. 5.727

9. a. 4
   b. 8
   c. −8
   d. −64
   e. 16
   f. 32
   g. 30
   h. −125
   i. 64
   j. 2.56
   k. −0.064
   l. 0.647
   m. 2.496
   n. −0.614
   o. 0.389
   p. $-\dfrac{8}{27}$
   q. −0.830
   r. 0.003
   s. −1.749
   t. 0.001

10. a. 4
   b. −4
   c. −3
   d. −10
   e. 10
   f. −2
   g. 5
   h. 2
   i. 1
   j. −1
   k. −1
   l. 0
   m. $\dfrac{1}{2}$
   n. $\dfrac{2}{-3}$
   o. $\dfrac{1}{2}$
   p. $\dfrac{3}{-5}$
   q. −6.184
   r. −2.437
   s. −0.923
   t. −0.258

11. a. 3
   b. 9
   c. 2
   d. 4
   e. −2
   f. 2
   g. −5
   h. 5
   i. 42.103

11. j. 0.155
   k. 4.002
   l. 0.060

12. $19 + 6 + 25 = 50$

13. $4 - 5(-2) = 4 + 10 = 14$

14. $-2(6) + 3(-2) = -12 + (-6) = -18$

15. $5 - 3(2) - (-5) = 5 - 6 + 5 = 4$

16. $\dfrac{6 - 30}{21 - 9} = \dfrac{-24}{12} = -2$

17. $-27 + 27 - (-18) - (-3) = 21$

18. $25 + (-2) + 0 = 23$

19. $(16 - 30)^2 + 2(-27) = (-14)^2 - 54 = 196 - 54 = 142$

20. $-8 + 4 - 120 = -124$

21. $\dfrac{50}{10} - \dfrac{-64}{16} = 9$

22. $-23.0399 + 3.9912 + 3277.3711 = 3257.722$

23. $3.4831 - (-6.1893) = 9.672$

24. $-14.8869 + 3\sqrt{46.3812} = -14.8869 + 3.5929 = -11.295$

25. $0.0086 + 0.00002 = 0.009$

26. $6(-2)(7) + 15 - (-2)(7) = -84 + 15 + 14 = -55$

27. $\dfrac{-3(-3)(10) - 2(10)(-4)}{(-3)(10)(-4) - 35} = \dfrac{90 + 80}{120 - 35} = \dfrac{170}{85} = 2$

28. $[-5 - (-7)]\,[3(-5) - 2(-7)] = 2(-15 + 14) = 2(-1) = -2$

29. $\dfrac{(-2)^3 + 4(-4) - (-4)(4)}{4^2 - [2 + (-2)]} = \dfrac{-8 - 16 + 16}{16 - 0} = \dfrac{-8}{16} = -0.5$

30. $\dfrac{(-5)^2}{5} - \dfrac{21 + (-1)^3}{(-5)(-1)} = \dfrac{25}{5} - \dfrac{20}{5} = 5 - 4 = 1$

31. $\sqrt{6[-6(-2) - 6]} - (-2)^3 = \sqrt{6(6)} - (-8) = 6 + 8 = 14$

32. $\dfrac{(-5.67)^2}{5.31} - \dfrac{21 + (-1.87)^3}{(-5.67)(-1.87)} = 6.0544 - 1.3639 = 4.691$

33. $\sqrt{6[(-6.07)(-2.91) - 6]} - (1.56)^3 = 8.3655 - 3.7964 = 4.569$

34. $5\sqrt[3]{8.26} + [(8.26)(-7.09) - (-10.55)] - (-10.55)^3 = 10.1072 + (-48.0134) - (-1174.2414) = 1136.335$

35. $\dfrac{\sqrt[4]{(-2.93)(-5.86) + (-2.93)(-5.86) + 19}}{(-5.86)^2 + 2(-2.93) - 7} = \dfrac{\sqrt[4]{70.5094}}{21.4796} = \dfrac{2.8978}{21.4796} = 0.135$

UNIT 31   Algebraic Operations of Addition, Subtraction, and Multiplication

1. $19y$

2. $22xy$

3. $-22xy$

4. $21m^2$

5. 0

6. $4c^3$

7. $-10pt$

8. $-0.4x$

9. $15.2a^2b$

10. $0.03y$

11. $1\frac{1}{4}xy$

12. $-\frac{3}{8}c^2d$

13. $2.91gh^3$

14. $-0.1abc$

15. $11P$

16. $-3dt^2$

17. $-1\frac{7}{8}xy$

18. $-0.61D$

19. $6.666M$

20. $12.8xy^2$

21. a. $2.3x$ e. $7.2x$
    b. $3.8x$ f. $3.1x$
    c. $6.1x$ g. $1.1x$
    d. $4.0x$

22. $-14x - 5xy + 5y$

23. $2a - 11m$

24. $-19ab + 2a^2b^2 - 16a^3b$

25. $3xy^2 + 3x^2y$

26. $9a - 11b$

27. $-2x^3 - 7x^2 + 4x + 12$

28. $b^4 + 8b^3c - 2b^2c - 7bc$

29. 0

30. $13.3M - 2.1N$

31. $-0.4c + 3.6cd + 3.7d$

32. $25xy^2$

33. $2xy$

34. $-4xy$

35. $-2xy$

36. $18ab$

37. $-10a^2$

38. $-1.6a^2b^2$

39. $12mn^3$

40. $-8mn^3$

41. $1\frac{1}{4}x^2$

42. $13a - 9a^2$

43. $-13a + 7a^2$

44. $0.2xy - 0.9xy^2$

45. $-2ax^2$

46. $\frac{7}{8}dt$

47. d^2t^2

48. $21 - 3x$

49. $3x - 21$

50. $-9.6d$

51. 0

52. $-5a^2 + 7a$

53. $x^2 + 3xy$

54. 2

55. 0

56. $xy^2 - x^2y^2 + x^3y^2$

57. $3a^3 - 1.3a^2 + a$

58. $5x + 3xy - 7y - 3y^2 + x^2y$

59. $-d^2 - 2dt + dt^2 + 4$

60. $27L - 18H + 4$

61. $8.08e + 15.76f + 10.03$

62. $-15b^5c$

63. x^3

64. $15a^6$

65. $56a^4b^3c^3$

66. $-5a^3bx^3y^3$

67. 0

68. $21a^5b^5$

69. $3d^8r^4$

70. $-3d^8r^4$

71. $0.21x^7y^4$

72. $\frac{3}{32}a^5$

73. 0

74. m^2st^3

75. $-3.36bc$

76. abc^6d

77. $-2x^8y^6$

78. $-\frac{2}{3}mt^5$

79. $-49a^4b^4$

80. $1.2a^3b^5$

81. $-x^4y^2$

82. d^4m^5

83. $-10x^2y^3 + 15x^5y$

84. $-3a^4 + 3a^5b$

85. $-8a^4b^5 + 2a^3b^4 + 4a^3b^2$

86. $x^3y^2 + xy^5 + x^2y^3$

87. $-4dt - 4t^2 + 4$

88. $-m^6t^3s^6 + m^3t^3s^4 - m^2t^3s^9$

89. $3x^3 + 27x + 7x^2 + 63$

90. $-14x^5 + 7x^2y^2 + 2x^3y^3 - y^5$

91. $10a^3x^6 + 5ab^2x^4 + 2a^2bx^4 + b^3x^2$

92. $-12a^4b^6 + 15a^2b^3xy + 20a^2b^3xy^2 - 25x^2y^3$

UNIT 32   Algebraic Operations of Division, Powers, and Roots

1. $2x$

2. $-4a^3b^2$

3. -1

4. 1

5. 0

6. $7a^3$

7. $-6H$

8. $-DM^2$

9. 3.7

10. $-4PV$

11. $5cd$

12. $-3y^3$

13. $8g^2h$

14. $48y$

15. xz^2

16. $-18bc^2y$

17. $4P^2V$

18. $-4x$

19. $\frac{1}{4}FS^2$

20. $8xyz$

21. $8x^2 + 12x$

22. $3x^2y^2 - 2xy$

23. $-3x^5y + 2xy^3$

24. $0.5x - y$

25. $-15a - 25a^4$

26. $3b^2 \ominus 2a^3$ SHOULD BE +

27. $-2cd + 5c^2d + 1$

28. $0.4x^3y^2 + 0.1x^2y^3$

29. $3a^2x + ax^2 - 2$

30. $1 - 5x - 2y^2$

31. $4a - 6a^2c - 8c^2$

32. $-5e^2 - ef + 2e^2f$

33. $9a^2b^2$

34. $-64x^3y^3$

35. $8x^6y^3$

36. $16a^8b^6$

37. $-27c^9d^6e^{12}$

38. $4M^2S^4$

39. $49x^8y^{10}$

40. $81N^8P^8T^{12}$

41. $a^9b^3c^6$

42. $-8a^6b^3c^9$

43. $-x^{12}y^{15}z^3$

44. $64C^6F^2H^4$

45. $0.064x^9y^3$

46. $-0.125c^6d^9e^3$

47. $18.49M^4N^4P^2$

48. $\frac{27}{64}a^3b^3c^9$

49. $-512a^{12}b^{18}c^3$

50. $-27x^6y^{12}z^9$

51. $0.36d^6e^6f^{12}$

52. $64x^{18}y^{18}$

53. $9x^4 - 30x^2y^3 + 25y^6$

54. $a^8 + 2a^4b^9 + b^9$

55. $25t^4 - 60t^2x + 36x^2$

56. $a^4b^6 + 2a^3b^6 + a^2b^6$

57. $0.16d^4t^6 - 0.16d^2t^4 + 0.04t^2$

58. $0.04x^4y^2 + 0.4x^2y^5 + y^8$

59. $\frac{4}{9}c^4d^2 + c^3d^3 + \frac{9}{16}c^2d^4$

60. $x^{12} - 2x^6y^6 + y^{12}$

61. $a^{16}b^4 + 2a^8b^2x^6y^3 + x^{12}y^6$

62. $4cd^3$

63. m^3n^2s

64. $4xy^3$

65. $9x^4y^3$

66. p^3t^2w

67. $-3x^2y^4$

68. $0.5h^2y$

69. $0.4a^4cf^3$

70. $\frac{2}{3}ab^2c^3$

71. $\frac{1}{4}xy$

72. $\frac{2}{3}m^2n$

73. $-4d^2t^3$

74. $2xy^2$

75. $2h^2$

76. $5b\sqrt{a}$

77. $4a\sqrt[3]{c}$

78. $-\frac{1}{4}xy^2\sqrt[3]{z^2}$

79. $\frac{3}{4}ac\sqrt{b}$

80. $3de^2\sqrt[3]{f^2}$

81. $-2a\sqrt[5]{b^3}$

82. $9a - 2a^2 + a^3$

83. $9b - 15b^2 + c - d$

84. $5 + x^2$

85. $-ab - a^2b + a$

86. $-2c^3 + d - 12$

87. $-16 - xy$

88. $-23a^2b + a - b^2$

89. $1 - r$

90. 0

91. $-2x + 24$

92. $34 - c^2d$

93. $6 + c^2d$

94. $7 - 17x^2y^2$

95. $6a^2 - 6b$

96. $4 - c^4 + 2c$

97. $3b$

98. $2 - 4x + 11x^2$

99. $7y^6 + 15$

100. $-3x^2y^3 + 10$

101. $2\frac{2}{3}d$

102. $3x^4$

103. $100a - 5a^4b^6$

UNIT 32   (*continued*)

104. $-80a + 5a^4b^6$

105. $5f^4 + 6f^2h$

106. 6.25×10^2

107. 8×10^4

108. 1.32×10^6

109. 9.76×10^5

110. 7.3×10^{-3}

111. 1.5×10^{-2}

112. 4×10^{-5}

113. 2×10^{-1}

114. 3.9×10^1

115. 3.9×10^{-4}

116. 1.75×10^5

117. 1.75×10^{-3}

118. 3000

119. 160,000

120. 850

121. 5,090,000

122. 0.47

123. 0.0000632

124. 0.00105

125. 0.000003123

126. 73,120

127. 0.0007321

128. 2,090,000

129. 0.0209

130. $(2.50 \times 5.10) \times 10^{3+5} = 12.8 \times 10^8 = 1.28 \times 10^9$

131. $(3.10 \times 5.20) \times 10^{-3+(-4)} = 16.1 \times 10^{-7} = 1.61 \times 10^{-6}$

132. $(-7.60 \times 1.90) \times 10^{4+5} = -14.4 \times 10^9 = -1.44 \times 10^{10}$

133. $(2.43 \div 7.60) \times 10^{-6-3} = 0.3197 \times 10^{-9} = 3.20 \times 10^{-10}$

134. $(8.51 \div 6.30) \times 10^{7-(-5)} = 1.35 \times 10^{7+5} = 1.35 \times 10^{12}$

135. $(1.25 \times 6.30 \div 7.83) \times 10^{4+5-3} = 1.01 \times 10^6$

136. $(8.76 \times 1.05 \div 6.37) \times 10^{-5+9-3} = 1.44 \times 10^1$

137. $(5.50 \times (-6.00) \div 6.92) \times 10^{4+6-(-3)} = -4.77 \times 10^{13}$

138. $[8.46 \div (3.90 \times 6.77)] \times 10^{-5-7-(-3)} = 0.320 \times 10^{-9} = 3.20 \times 10^{-10}$

139. $(1.510 \times 10^3) \times (3.05 \times 10^4) = (1.51 \times 3.05) \times 10^{3+4} = 4.61 \times 10^7$

140. $(3.00 \times 10^{-4}) \times (2.10 \times 10^{-3}) = (3.00 \times 2.10) \times 10^{-4+(-3)} = 6.30 \times 10^{-7}$

141. $(-5.61 \times 10^4) \times (7.81 \times 10^5) = (-5.61 \times 7.81) \times 10^{4+5} = -43.8 \times 10^9 = -4.38 \times 10^{10}$

142. $(6.177 \times 10^4) \times (5.31 \times 10^4) = (6.177 \times 5.31) \times 10^{4+4} = 32.8 \times 10^8 = 3.28 \times 10^9$

143. $(8.21 \times 10^{-5}) \div (-3.15 \times 10^2) = (8.21 \div (-3.15) \times 10^{-5-2}) = -2.61 \times 10^{-7}$

144. $(-6.23 \times 10^{-3}) \times (7.42 \times 10^5) \div 6.51 \times 10^5 = (-6.23 \times 7.42 \div 6.51) \times 10^{-3+5-5} = -7.10 \times 10^{-3}$

145. $(6.53 \times 10^4) \times (5.17 \times 10^5) \div (7.86 \times 10^{-3}) = (6.53 \times 5.17 \div 7.86) \times 10^{4+5-(-3)} = 4.30 \times 10^{12}$

146. $(-8.29 \times 10^{-4}) \div [(4.05 \times 10^5) \times (3.12 \times 10^{-3})] = [-8.29 \div (4.05 \times 3.12)] \times 10^{-4-5-(-3)} = -0.656 \times 10^{-6} = -6.56 \times 10^{-7}$

147. $(5.18 \times 10^5) \times (6.12 \times 10^{-3}) \div [(3.74 \times 10^4) \times (8.30 \times 10^{-5}) = (5.18 \times 6.12) \div (3.74 \times 8.30)] \times 10^{5+(-3)-4-(-5)} = 1.02 \times 10^3$

148. a. Expansion $= 6.7520\,\text{in} \times \left(\dfrac{1.244 \times 10^{-5}\,\text{in}/\text{in}}{1^\circ\text{F}} \right) \times (255.0^\circ\text{F} - 68.0^\circ\text{F}) = 0.013\,\text{in}$

    b. Expansion $= 35.750\,\text{ft} \times \left(\dfrac{9.000 \times 10^{-6}\,\text{ft}/\text{ft}}{1^\circ\text{F}} \right) \times (97.0^\circ\text{F} - 35.0^\circ\text{F}) = 0.020\,\text{ft}$

    c. Expansion $= 3.0950\,\text{in} \times \left(\dfrac{6.330 \times 10^{-6}\,\text{in}/\text{in}}{1^\circ\text{F}} \right) \times (743.0^\circ\text{F} - 84.0^\circ\text{F}) = 0.013\,\text{in}$

UNIT 33 Introduction to Equations

1. $x + 20 = 32$
   $x = 12$

2. $x - 7 = 15$
   $x = 22$

3. $5x = 55$
   $x = 11$

4. $\dfrac{x}{4} = 9$
   $x = 36$

5. $\dfrac{32}{x} = 8$
   $x = 4$

6. $x + 2x = 36$
   $3x = 36$
   $x = 12$

7. $5x - x = 48$
   $4x = 48$
   $x = 12$

8. $7x + 8x = 60$
   $15x = 60$
   $x = 4$

9. $\dfrac{60}{3x} = 4$
   $x = 5$

10. $x + 3x = 32''$
    $4x = 32''$
    $x = 8''$
    $3x = 24''$

11. Let x = thickness of third block.
    $x + 2x + 3(2x) = 4.5''$
    $9x = 4.5''$
    $x = 0.5''$
    $2x = 1''$
    $3(2x) = 3''$

12. Let x = number of degrees between hole 1 and hole 2.
    a. $x + 2x + 4x + 8x = 300°$
    $15x = 300°$
    $x = 20°$
    b. $2(20°) = 40°$
    c. $2(40°) = 80°$
    d. $2(80°) = 160°$

13. Let x = depth of finish cut.
    $x + (x + 6.35\,\text{mm}) = 8.58\,\text{mm}$
    $2x + 6.35\,\text{mm} = 8.58\,\text{mm}$
    $x = 1.115\,\text{mm}$

14. $x + 2'' = 6\dfrac{1''}{4}$
    $x = 4\dfrac{1''}{4}$

15. $x + 2x = 150\,\text{mm}$
    $3x = 150\,\text{mm}$
    $x = 50\,\text{mm}$

16. $x + 2x + 3x = 18''$
    $6x = 18''$
    $x = 3''$

17. $x + 4x + 20° = 80°$
    $5x + 20° = 80°$
    $x = 12°$

18. $3x + 2'' + 4x = 23''$
    $7x + 2'' = 23''$
    $x = 3''$

19. $2x + 1.5x + 0.5x + x = 180°$
    $5x = 180°$
    $x = 36°$

20. $40\,\text{mm} + 4x + 2x + 30\,\text{mm} = 250\,\text{mm}$
    $6x + 70\,\text{mm} = 250\,\text{mm}$
    $x = 30\,\text{mm}$

21. $x + 4x + x + 6x + x + 8x + x = 11''$
    $22x = 11''$
    $x = \dfrac{1''}{2}$

22. $2L + L + 3L + 2L + L = 180\,\text{mm}$
    $9L = 20\,\text{mm}$
    a. $2(20\,\text{mm}) = 40\,\text{mm}$
    b. $20\,\text{mm}$
    c. $3(20\,\text{mm}) = 60\,\text{mm}$
    d. $2(20\,\text{mm}) = 40\,\text{mm}$
    e. $20\,\text{mm}$
    f. $20\,\text{mm} + 3(20\,\text{mm}) = 80\,\text{mm}$
    g. $3(20\,\text{mm}) + 2(20\,\text{mm}) + 20\,\text{mm} = 120\,\text{mm}$

23. $\left(h + \dfrac{1''}{4}\right) + h + \left(2h + \dfrac{3''}{4}\right) = 3''$
    $4h + 1'' = 3''$
    $h = \dfrac{1''}{2}$

UNIT **33** (*continued*)

23. a. $\dfrac{1'}{2} + \dfrac{1'}{4} = \dfrac{3''}{4}$

    b. $\dfrac{1'}{2}$

    c. $2\left(\dfrac{1''}{2}\right) + \dfrac{3''}{4} = 1\dfrac{3''}{4}$

24. $y + 2y + (3y - 20°) + (4y - 40°) = 180°$

    $\qquad\qquad 10y - 60° = 180°$

    $\qquad\qquad\qquad y = 24°$

    a. 24°

    b. 2(24°) = 48°

    c. 3(24°) − 20° = 52°

    d. 4(24°) − 40° = 56°

25. $10x = 30$

    $\quad x = 3$

26. $x = 9$

27. $10y = 70y = 7$

    $\quad y = 7$

28. $y = 15$

29. $a = 6$

30. $b = 93$

31. $6b = 96$

    $\quad b = 16$

32. $15a = 90$

    $\quad a = 6$

33. $x = 84$

34. $x = 60$

35. $x = 3$

36. $d = 30$

37. $0.25x = 12$

    $\quad x = 48$

38. $20x = 80$

    $\quad x = 4$

39. $\dfrac{12y}{3} = 80$

    $\quad 4y = 80$

    $\quad y = 20$

40. $9 = b + 3$

    $\quad b = 6$

UNIT **34** Solution of Equations by the Subtraction, Addition, and Division Principles of Equality

1. 7

2. 9

3. 19

4. 34

5. 4

6. 35

7. 43

8. −1

9. −22

10. −19

11. −53

12. −46

13. 43

14. 3

15. −50

16. 7.1

17. 18.8

18. −42.4

19. 16.14

20. 0.999

21. 0

22. $3\dfrac{1}{4}$

23. $-1\dfrac{5}{8}$

24. $3\dfrac{1}{16}$

25. $-1\dfrac{1}{4}$

26. $\dfrac{7}{8}$

27. $-23\dfrac{1}{8}$

28. −0.986

29. −17.101

30. −5.079

31. $x + 9'' = 27''$

    $\quad x = 18''$

32. $y + 38.50\,\text{mm} = 97.23\,\text{mm}$

    $\quad y = 58.73\,\text{mm}$

33. $r + \dfrac{5''}{8} = 1\dfrac{7''}{16}$

    $\quad r = \dfrac{13''}{16}$

34. $T + 2.125'' = 2.563''$

    $\quad T = 0.438''$

35. $x + 90.65\,\text{mm} = 128.26\,\text{mm}$

    $\quad x = 37.61\,\text{mm}$

36. $H + 0.387'' = 1.015''$

    $\quad H = 0.628''$

37. $x + 0.750'' = 0.8508''$

    $\quad x = 0.1008''$

38. $x + 193.75\,\text{mm} = 278.12\,\text{mm}$

    $\quad x = 84.37\,\text{mm}$

39. $x + \dfrac{9''}{32} = 7\dfrac{5''}{8}$

    $\quad x = 7\dfrac{11''}{32}$

40. $x + 0.0008'' = 0.3968''$

    $\quad x = 0.3960''$

41. $4.7144'' = D + 2(0.1429'')$

    $4.7144'' = D + 0.2858''$

    $\quad D = 4.4286''$

42. $52\,\text{mm} = d + 2(9.40\,\text{mm})$

    $52\,\text{mm} = d + 18.80\,\text{mm}$

    $\quad d = 33.20\,\text{mm}$

43. $0.3082'' = 0.1429'' + d$

    $\quad d = 0.1653''$

44. 46

45. −10

46. 13

47. 135

48. 3

49. 28

50. −19

51. 83

52. 20

53. 14

54. 9

55. 78

56. 51

57. 9.3

58. 1.1

59. −3.69

60. 8.14

61. −0.005

62. 105.70

63. 0.09

64. 108.748

65. −4.89

UNIT **34**   (*continued*)

66. 1

67. $\dfrac{1}{2}$

68. $18\dfrac{1}{2}$

69. $-16\dfrac{5}{32}$

70. 0

71. 18.052

72. $-\dfrac{1}{32}$

73. 48.1995

74. $x - 14.29\,\text{mm} = 44.45\,\text{mm}$
    $x = 58.74\,\text{mm}$

75. $x - 3\dfrac{3''}{8} = 1\dfrac{1''}{8}$
    $x - 4\dfrac{1''}{2}$

76. $x - 1.650'' = 0.250''$
    $x = 1.900''$

77. $22.5\,\text{mm} = D - 30.8\,\text{mm}$
    $D = 53.3\,\text{mm}$

78. $3.0118'' = D - 2(0.1608'')$
    $3.0118'' = D - 0.3216''$
    $D = 3.3334''$

79. $382\,\text{mm} = L.S. - 4(112\,\text{mm})$
    $382\,\text{mm} = L.S. - 448\,\text{mm}$
    $L.S. = 830\,\text{mm}$

80. 8

81. −3

82. 5

83. 6

84. −9

85. 9

86. 0.08

87. 2.5

88. −4.5

89. −19

90. 0

91. 0

92. 3

93. 20

94. −8.8

95. −1.8

96. 0

97. 19.75

98. 12

99. 11

100. −7.2

101. 32

102. 64

103. −72

104. 6

105. $-4\dfrac{1}{2}$

106. 1

107. 0.2

108. −823

109. $\dfrac{9}{17}$

110. $3x = 63.09$
     $x = 21.03$

111. $4x = 87°$
     $x = 21.75°$

112. $500x = 3.300''$
     $x = 0.0066''$

113. $392.50\,\text{mm} = 3.1416d$
     $d = 124.94\,\text{mm}$

114. $0.125'' = 0.866p$
     $p = 0.144''$

115. $9.50'' = (3\,\text{min})(0.050''/\text{r})N$
     $9.50'' = (0.150\,\text{min}/\text{r})N$
     $N = 63.33\,\text{r}/\text{min}$

UNIT **35**   Solution of Equations by the Multiplication, Root, and Power Principles of Equality

1. 30

2. 60

3. 63

4. 24

5. 27

6. −24

7. 0

8. −90

9. 36

10. −52

11. 21.5

12. −12

13. 23.4

14. −4.8

15. −6

16. −4.32

17. 0

18. −114

19. 0.001

20. 0.0252

21. 0.0624

22. 3.5

23. $3\dfrac{3}{4}$

24. $-\dfrac{3}{32}$

25. 2

26. $-3\dfrac{1}{2}$

27. $\dfrac{3}{4}$

28. $-15\dfrac{1}{8}$

29. 0.9

30. −1.276

31. $\dfrac{x}{4} = 108.78\,\text{mm}$
    $x = 435.12\,\text{mm}$

32. $\dfrac{x}{5} = 30°$
    $x = 150°$

33. $\dfrac{x}{10} = 0.70711''$
    $x = 7.0711''$

34. $\dfrac{Area}{5\dfrac{1}{2}\,\text{ft}} = 3\dfrac{1}{4}\,\text{ft}$
    $Area = 17\dfrac{7}{8}\,\text{sq ft}$

35. $\dfrac{x}{0.6495} = 0.050''$
    $x = 0.032''$

UNIT 35 *(continued)*

36. $150 \text{ lb} = \dfrac{W}{7.5 \text{ ft}}$

$W = 1125 \text{ ft-lb}$

37. $52.14 \text{ mm} = \dfrac{C}{3.1416}$

$C = 163.8 \text{ mm}$

38. $5 \text{ teeth/in} = \dfrac{N}{5.6000 \text{ in}}$

$N = 28 \text{ teeth}$

39. 4
40. 9
41. 9
42. 7
43. 4
44. −4
45. 12
46. −4
47. −5
48. 0
49. 100
50. −5
51. $\dfrac{3}{5}$
52. $\dfrac{1}{4}$
53. $\dfrac{3}{5}$
54. $\dfrac{1}{4}$
55. $-\dfrac{1}{2}$
56. $1\dfrac{1}{3}$
57. $\dfrac{4}{5}$

58. $-\dfrac{4}{5}$
59. 0.2
60. 0.8
61. 1.659
62. 0.041
63. 0.497
64. −0.497
65. 1.673
66. 2.656
67. 0.340
68. −1.163

69. a. $s^2 = 36 \text{ sq in}$

$s = 6 \text{ in}$

b. $s^2 = \dfrac{25}{64} \text{ sq ft}$

$s = \dfrac{5}{8} \text{ ft}$

c. $s^2 = 1.44 \text{ m}^2$

$s = 1.2 \text{ m}$

d. $s^2 = 64.700 \text{ m}^2$

$s = 8.044 \text{ m}$

e. $s^2 = 0.049 \text{ sq ft}$

$s = 0.221 \text{ ft}$

70. a. $s^3 = 125 \text{ cu in}$

$s = 5 \text{ in}$

b. $s^3 = \dfrac{27}{216} \text{ cu ft}$

$s = \dfrac{3}{6} \text{ ft} = \dfrac{1}{2} \text{ ft}$

c. $s^3 = 0.642 \text{ m}^3$

$s = 0.863 \text{ m}$

70. d. $s^3 = 92.76 \text{ mm}$

$s = 4.527 \text{ mm}$

e. $s^3 = 0.026 \text{ cu ft}$

$s = 0.296 \text{ ft}$

71. 36
72. 144
73. 1.44
74. 0.64
75. 0.6724
76. 27
77. 4.913
78. −64
79. −0.001
80. 81
81. 0
82. 1
83. −32
84. 0.0081
85. −0.216
86. 0.0001
87. 0.001
88. $\dfrac{1}{16}$
89. $\dfrac{9}{64}$
90. $\dfrac{8}{27}$
91. $\dfrac{1}{256}$
92. $\dfrac{-27}{125}$

93. $\dfrac{25}{64}$
94. 1.578
95. 23.591
96. −1.017
97. 0.480
98. 0.048
99. −26.016
100. 0.322

101. a. $\sqrt{A} = 3.4 \text{ in}$

$A = 11.56 \text{ sq in}$

b. $\sqrt{A} = 0.75 \text{ ft}$

$A = 0.563 \text{ sq ft}$

c. $\sqrt{A} = 0.652 \text{ m}$

$A = 0.425 \text{ m}^2$

d. $\sqrt{A} = 2.162 \text{ mm}$

$A = 4.674 \text{ mm}^2$

e. $\sqrt{A} = 1.290 \text{ in}$

$A = 1.664 \text{ sq in}$

102. a. $\sqrt[3]{V} = 3.300 \text{ in}$

$V = 35.94 \text{ cu in}$

b. $\sqrt[3]{V} = 0.900 \text{ ft}$

$V = 0.73 \text{ cu ft}$

c. $\sqrt[3]{V} = 0.62 \text{ m}$

$V = 0.238 \text{ m}^3$

d. $\sqrt[3]{V} = 4.073 \text{ mm}$

$V = 67.57 \text{ mm}^3$

e. $\sqrt[3]{V} = 1.281 \text{ in}$

$V = 2.10 \text{ cu in}$

UNIT 36 Solution of Equations Consisting of Combined Operations and Rearrangement of Formulas

1. $5x = 45$

$x = 9$

2. $14M + 5 = 89$

$14M = 84$

$M = 6$

3. $6E = 42$

$E = 7$

4. $3B = 28$

$B = 9\dfrac{1}{3}$

5. $7T = 14$

$T = 2$

6. $5N = 80$

$N = 16$

7. $2.5A + 8 = 10.5$

$2.5A = 2.5$

$A = 1$

8. $12 + x - 8 = 18$

$x + 4 = 18$

$x = 14$

9. $3H + 2 - H = 20$

$2H + 2 = 20$

$2H = 18$

$H = 9$

10. $12 = -2 - C - 4 - 2C$

$12 = -6 - 3C$

$18 = -3C$

$C = -6$

UNIT **36** (*continued*)

11. $-5R - 30 = 10R - 20$

$-10 = 15R$

$R = -0.67$

12. $0.30E = 9.39$

$E = 31.3$

13. $7.2F + 5F - 40.5 = 0.6F + 15.18$

$12.2F - 40.5 = 0.6F + 15.18$

$11.6F = 55.68$

$F = 4.8$

14. $\dfrac{P}{7} = -1.7$

$P = 11.9$

15. $\dfrac{1}{4}W + W - 8 = \dfrac{3}{4}$

$1\dfrac{1}{4}W = 8\dfrac{3}{4}$

$W = 7$

16. $\dfrac{1}{8}D - 3D + 21 = 5\dfrac{1}{8}D - 3$

$-2\dfrac{7}{8}D + 21 = 5\dfrac{1}{8}D - 3$

$24 = 8D$

$D = 3$

17. $0.58y = 18.3 - 0.02y$

$0.60y = 18.3$

$y = 30.5$

18. $2H^2 - 20 = H^2 - 4H + 4H - 16$

$2H^2 - 20 = H^2 - 16$

$H^2 = 4$

$H = 2$

19. $36 = 4A^2$

$9 = A^2$

$A = 3$

20. $4x + x^2 + 20 = x^2 - x + 5$

$5x = -15$

$x = -3$

21. $\dfrac{b^3}{8} + 34 = 42$

$\dfrac{b^3}{8} = 8$

$b^3 = 64$

$b = 4$

22. $3F^3 + F^2 + 8F = 8F = F^2 + 81$

$3F^3 = 81$

$F^3 = 27$

$F = 3$

23. $9 + y^2 = y^2 - y - 4y + 4$

$9 = -5y + 4$

$5 = -5y$

$y = -1$

24. $\dfrac{1}{2}B - 3 + B^2 = \dfrac{1}{2}B + 22$

$B^2 = 25$

$B = 5$

25. $-4y + 6 = 2\sqrt{y} - 4y$

$6 = 2\sqrt{y}$

$3 = \sqrt{y}$

$y = 9$

26. $14\sqrt{x} = 6\sqrt{x} + 48 + 16$

$8\sqrt{x} = 64$

$\sqrt{x} = 8$

$x = 64$

27. $8.12P^2 + 6.83P + 5.05 = 16.7P^2 + 6.83P$

$5.05 = 8.85P^2$

$P^2 = 0.58857$

$P = 0.76719, 0.77$

28. $7.3\sqrt{x} = 3(\sqrt{x} + 8.06) - 4.59$

$4.3\sqrt{x} = 19.59$

$\sqrt{x} = 4.55581$

$x = 20.7554, 20.76$

29. $\sqrt{B^2} - 2.53B = -2.53(B - 3.95)$

$\sqrt{B^2} = 9.9935$

$B = 9.9935, 9.99$ *SHOULD BE NEG.*

30. $(2y)^3 - 2.80(5.89 + 3y) = 23.87 - 8.40y$

$8y^3 = 40.362$

$y^3 = 5.04525$

$y = 1.715119, 1.72$

31. $2.125 = 2.380P + 0.250$

$2.125 = 2.380P$

$P = 0.893$

32. $0.1760 = 3H \div 8$

$1.408 = 3H$

$H = 0.469$

UNIT 36 *(continued)*

33. $22 = 0.000016M(50.8)$

    $22 = 0.0008128M$

    $M = 27,066.929$

34. $24 = 0.707D(8)$

    $24 = 5.656D$

    $D = 4.243$

35. $0.4134 = T - \dfrac{1.732}{20}$

    $0.4134 = T - 0.0866$

    $T = 0.5$

36. $0.250 = \dfrac{D_2 - 0.875}{2}$

    $0.500 = D_2 - 0.875$

    $D_2 = 1.375$

37. $1000 = \dfrac{0.290W}{0.750^2}$

    $1000 = \dfrac{0.290W}{0.5625}$

    $562.5 = 0.290W$

    $W = 1939.655$

38. $1150 = St\,[0.55(0.750^2) - 0.25(0.750)]$

    $1150 = St\,(0.309375 - 0.1875)$

    $1150 = St\,(0.121875)$

    $St = 9435.897$

39. $3.3700 = 3.2000 - 0.866(0.125) + 3W$

    $3.3700 = 3.2000 - 0.10825 + 3W$

    $3.3700 = 3.09175 + 3W$

    $0.27825 = 3W$

    $W = 0.093$

40. $\dfrac{1}{4} = \dfrac{16}{4}\left[\dfrac{1}{2}\left(D_1 - 2\dfrac{1}{2}\right)\right]$

    $\dfrac{1}{4} = 4\left(\dfrac{1}{2}D - 1\dfrac{1}{4}\right)$

    $\dfrac{1}{4} = 2D_1 - 5$

    $5\dfrac{1}{4} = 2D_1$

    $D_1 = 2\dfrac{5}{8}$

41. $210 = \dfrac{3.1416(6)N}{12}$

    $210 = 1.5708N$

    $N = 133.690$

42. $4.3750 = \dfrac{0.3927(N + 2)}{3.1416}$

    $13.7445 = 0.3927(N + 2)$

    $13.7445 = 0.3927N + 0.7854$

    $12.9591 = 0.3927N$

    $N = 33$

43. $12.700 = \sqrt{\dfrac{6^2}{4} + h^2}$

    $12.700 = \sqrt{9 + h^2}$

    $161.29 = 9 + h^2$

    $152.29 = h^2$

    $h = 12.341$

44. $7.600 = 2\sqrt{3.750(2r - 3.750)}$

    $7.600 = 2\sqrt{7.5r - 14.0625}$

    $3.800 = \sqrt{7.5r - 14.0625}$

    $14.440 = 7.5r - 14.0625$

    $28.5025 = 7.5r$

    $r = 3.800$

45. a. $a = \dfrac{A}{b}$

    b. $b = \dfrac{A}{a}$

    c. $d = \sqrt{a^2 + b^2}$

    $d^2 = a^2 + b^2$

    $a^2 = d^2 - b^2$

    $a = \sqrt{d^2 - b^2}$

    d. $b = \sqrt{d^2 - a^2}$

46. a. $r = \dfrac{R}{1.155}$

    b. $R^2 = \dfrac{A}{2.598}$

    $R = \sqrt{\dfrac{A}{2.598}}$

47. a. $FW = \sqrt{D_o^2 - D^2}$

    $FW^2 = \left(\sqrt{D_o^2 - D^2}\right)^2$

    $FW^2 = D_o^2 - D^2$

    $FW^2 + D^2 = D_o^2$

    $D_o = \sqrt{FW^2 + D^2}$

    b. $FW^2 = D_o^2 - D^2$

    $FW^2 - D_o^2 = -D^2$

    $D^2 = D_o^2 - FW^2$

    $D = \sqrt{D_o^2 - FW^2}$

47. c. $D_o = 2C - d + 2a$

    $D_o - 2C - 2a = -d$

    $d = 2a + 2C - D_o$

    d. $a = (D_o - 2C + d)2$

48. a. $A = \pi R^2 - \pi r^2$

    $\pi R^2 = A + \pi r^2$

    $R^2 = \dfrac{A + \pi r^2}{\pi}$

    $R = \sqrt{\dfrac{A + \pi r^2}{\pi}}$

    b. $A = \pi R^2 - \pi r^2$

    $\pi r^2 = \pi R^2 - A$

    $r^2 = \dfrac{\pi R^2 - A}{\pi}$

    $r = \sqrt{\dfrac{\pi R^2 - A}{\pi}}$

49. a. $D = M + 1.5155P - 3W$

    b. $1.5155P = D + 3W - M$

    $P = \dfrac{D + 3W - M}{1.5155}$

    c. $3W = M - D + 1.5155P$

    $W = \dfrac{M - D + 1.5155P}{3}$

50. a. $\angle A = 180° - \angle B - \angle C$

    b. $\angle B = 180° - \angle A - \angle C$

    c. $\angle C = 180° - \angle A - \angle B$

51. a. $L = 1.57D + 1.57d - 2x$

    $1.57D = L - 1.57d - 2x$

    $D = \dfrac{L - 1.57d - 2x}{1.57}$

    b. $d = \dfrac{L - 1.57D - 2x}{1.57}$

    c. $x = \dfrac{L - 1.57D - 1.57d}{2}$

52. a. $x = \dfrac{By(F - 1)}{C}$

    b. $B = \dfrac{Cx}{y(F - 1)}$

    c. $C = \dfrac{By(F - 1)}{x}$

53. a. $S = \dfrac{Ca}{C - F}$

    b. $SC = Ca + SF$

    $C = \dfrac{Ca + SF}{S}$

UNIT **36**   *(continued)*

54. $1.50 = \dfrac{6.2832T(2250)}{33.000}$

$150(33,000) = 14,137.2T$

$\dfrac{1.50(33,000)}{14,137.2} = T$

$T = 3.50, \ 3.50 \text{ lb ft}$

55.   a. $69.5 \text{ cm}^3 = 1.05\,[(2.38 \text{ cm})^2 + (2.38 \text{ cm})(1.46 \text{ cm}) + (1.46 \text{ cm})^2]\,h$

$h = \dfrac{69.5 \text{ cm}^3}{1.05(11.2708 \text{ cm}^2)}$

$h = 5.87 \text{ cm}$

b. $0.875 \text{ in} = \sqrt{(0.420 \text{ in} - 0.200 \text{ in})^2 + h^2}$

$0.765625 \text{ in}^2 \quad 0.0484 \text{ in}^2 \quad + \ h^2$

$0.717225 \text{ in}^2 = h^2$

$h = 0.847 \text{ in}$

UNIT **37**   Ratio and Proportion

1. $\dfrac{2}{7}$

2. $\dfrac{7}{2}$

3. $\dfrac{2}{11}$

4. $\dfrac{1}{3}$

5. $\dfrac{6}{23}$

6. $\dfrac{1}{7}$

7. $\dfrac{13}{9}$

8. $\dfrac{39}{50}$

9. $\dfrac{a}{3}$

10. $\dfrac{1}{x}$

11. $\dfrac{4}{3}$

12. $\dfrac{3}{4}$

13. $\dfrac{3}{(2.5)(12)} = \dfrac{1}{10}$

14.

	$\dfrac{E}{F}$	$\dfrac{G}{F}$	$\dfrac{E}{H}$	$\dfrac{F}{G}$	$\dfrac{F}{H}$	$\dfrac{G}{H}$	$\dfrac{G}{E}$	$\dfrac{H}{F}$
a.	$\dfrac{4}{3}$	$\dfrac{2}{1}$	$\dfrac{8}{3}$	$\dfrac{3}{2}$	$\dfrac{2}{1}$	$\dfrac{4}{3}$	$\dfrac{1}{2}$	$\dfrac{1}{2}$
b.	$\dfrac{5}{4}$	$\dfrac{2}{1}$	$\dfrac{5}{2}$	$\dfrac{8}{5}$	$\dfrac{2}{1}$	$\dfrac{5}{4}$	$\dfrac{1}{2}$	$\dfrac{1}{2}$
c.	$\dfrac{4}{3}$	$\dfrac{2}{1}$	$\dfrac{4}{1}$	$\dfrac{3}{2}$	$\dfrac{3}{1}$	$\dfrac{2}{1}$	$\dfrac{1}{2}$	$\dfrac{1}{3}$
d.	$\dfrac{5}{4}$	$\dfrac{3}{2}$	$\dfrac{5}{2}$	$\dfrac{6}{5}$	$\dfrac{2}{1}$	$\dfrac{5}{3}$	$\dfrac{2}{3}$	$\dfrac{1}{2}$

15.   a. $\dfrac{2}{1}$ e. $\dfrac{2}{7}$ h. $\dfrac{5}{2}$

b. $\dfrac{2}{3}$ f. $\dfrac{7}{1}$ i. $\dfrac{2}{1}$

c. $\dfrac{3}{2}$ g. $\dfrac{7}{3}$ j. $\dfrac{3}{7}$

d. $\dfrac{3}{5}$

16. $\dfrac{120}{18(60)} = \dfrac{1}{9}$

17. $24x = 12$

$x = 0.5$

18. $15A = 90$

$A = 6$

19. $9E = 315$

$E = 35$

20. $3y = 312$

$y = 104$

21. $5c = 60$

$c = 12$

22. $3P = 27$

$P = 9$

23. $6F = 105$

$F = 17.5$

24. $4H = 300$

$H = 75$

25. $22.0T = 49.5$

$T = 2.25$

26. $3M = 1.92$

$M = 0.64$

27. $4L = 32.8$

$L = 8.2$

28. $y = -30.6$

29. $A^2 = 16$

$A = 4$

30. $\dfrac{1}{2}N = 1\dfrac{1}{2}$

$N = 3$

31. $3F = 1\dfrac{1}{4}$

$F = \dfrac{5}{12}$

32. $\dfrac{3}{8}G = \dfrac{7}{32}$

$G = \dfrac{7}{12}$

33. $-\dfrac{1}{8}x = 3\dfrac{15}{16}$

$x = -31\dfrac{1}{2}$

34. $2R^2 = 50$

$R^2 = 25$

$R = 5$

35. $8E + 24 = 132$

$8E = 108$

$E = 13.5$

36. $9M - 45 = 180$

$9M = 225$

$M = 25$

37. $(3H^2 - 12)(5.87) = 76.1824$

$17.61H^2 - 70.44 = 76.1824$

$17.61H^2 = 146.6224$

$H^2 = 8.3261$

$H = 2.885$

UNIT **37**   (*continued*)

38. $1.86(E - 15) = 0.36(E + 7.53)$

$1.86E - 27.9 = 0.36E + 2.7108$

$1.5E = 30.6108$

$E = 20.407$

39. $0.86(8.62M + 23.30) = 12.36(7.62M + 0.05)$

$7.4132M + 20.038 = 94.1832M + 0.618$

$19.42 = 86.77M$

$M = 0.224$

40. $3.04(P^2 - 186.73) = 5.65P(-23.30P)$

$3.04P^2 - 567.6592 = -131.645P^2$

$134.685P^2 = 567.6592$

$P^2 = 4.2147$

$P = 2.053$

41. a. $\dfrac{18\ in}{4.5\ in} = \dfrac{C}{3\ in}$

$C = \dfrac{3\ in\,(18\ in)}{4.5\ in}$

$C = 12\ in$

b. $\dfrac{6\frac{1}{2}\ in}{1\frac{5}{8}\ in} = \dfrac{4\frac{1}{2}\ in}{D}$

$D = \dfrac{(1\frac{5}{8}\ in)(4\frac{1}{2}\ in)}{6\frac{1}{2}\ in}$

$D = 1\frac{1}{8}\ in$

c. $\dfrac{87.5\ mm}{B} = \dfrac{75\ mm}{62.5\ mm}$

$B = \dfrac{87.5\ mm(62.5\ mm)}{75\ mm}$

$B = 72.9\ mm$

d. $\dfrac{A}{25.8\ mm} = \dfrac{20.6\ mm}{16.4\ mm}$

$A = \dfrac{25.8\ mm\,(20.6\ mm)}{16.4\ mm}$

$A = 32.4\ mm$

42. a. $\dfrac{1.250}{1} = \dfrac{L}{7.94\ mm}$

$L = 1.250(7.94\ mm)$

$L = 9.925\ mm$

42. b. $\dfrac{1\frac{1}{4}}{1} = \dfrac{L}{\frac{1}{2}\ in}$

$L = (1\frac{1}{4})(\frac{1}{2}\ in)$

$L = \dfrac{5}{8}\ in$

c. $\dfrac{1\frac{1}{2}}{1} = \dfrac{\frac{3}{4}\ in}{D}$

$D = \dfrac{\frac{3}{4}\ in}{1\frac{1}{2}}$

$D = \dfrac{1}{2}\ in$

d. $\dfrac{1.375}{1} = \dfrac{8.73\ mm}{D}$

$D = \dfrac{8.73\ mm}{1.375}$

$D = 6.349\ mm$

e. $\dfrac{1.250}{1} = \dfrac{L}{16.12\ mm}$

$L = 1.250(16.12\ mm)$

$L = 20.15\ mm$

f. $\dfrac{1.375}{1} = \dfrac{1.032\ in}{D}$

$D = \dfrac{1.032\ in}{1.375}$

$D = 0.751\ in$

g. $\dfrac{1.250}{1} = \dfrac{L}{0.875\ in}$

$L = 1.250(0.875\ in)$

$L = 1.094\ in$

h. $\dfrac{1.500}{1} = \dfrac{L}{3.68\ mm}$

$L = 1.500(3.68\ mm)$

$L = 5.52\ mm$

i. $\dfrac{1.125}{1} = \dfrac{0.281\ in}{D}$

$D = \dfrac{0.281\ in}{1.125}$

$D = 0.250\ in$

j. $\dfrac{1.000}{1} = \dfrac{L}{7.50\ mm}$

$L = 7.50\ mm$

43. a. $\dfrac{1}{2} = \dfrac{B}{16.062\ in}$

$B = \dfrac{16.062\ in}{2}$

$B = 8.031\ in$

b. $\dfrac{4}{1} = \dfrac{G}{0.281\ in}$

$G = 4(0.281\ in)$

$G = 1.124\ in$

c. $\dfrac{1}{4} = \dfrac{B}{16.062\ in}$

$B = \dfrac{16.062\ in}{4}$

$B = 4.016\ in$

d. $\dfrac{2}{1} = \dfrac{C}{1.360\ in}$

$C = 2(1.360\ in)$

$C = 2.720\ in$

e. $\dfrac{1\frac{1}{2}}{1} = \dfrac{A}{1.872\ in}$

$A = 1.5(1.872\ in)$

$A = 2.808\ in$

f. $\dfrac{3}{4} = \dfrac{E}{10.600\ in}$

$E = \dfrac{3(10.600\ in)}{4}$

$E = 7.950\ in$

g. $\dfrac{3}{1} = \dfrac{H}{0.375\ in}$

$H = 3(0.375\ in)$

$H = 1.125\ in$

h. $\dfrac{1}{8} = \dfrac{F}{12.600\ in}$

$F = \dfrac{12.600\ in}{8}$

$F = 1.575\ in$

i. $\dfrac{1}{2} = \dfrac{E}{10.600\ in}$

$E = \dfrac{10.600\ in}{2}$

$E = 5.300\ in$

j. $\dfrac{6}{1} = \dfrac{G}{0.281\ in}$

$G = 6(0.281\ in)$

$G = 1.686\ in$

UNIT **37**   (*continued*)

43. k. $\dfrac{3}{4} = \dfrac{F}{12.600 \text{ in}}$

$F = \dfrac{3(12.600 \text{ in})}{4}$

$F = 9.450 \text{ in}$

l. $\dfrac{1\frac{1}{2}}{1} = \dfrac{C}{1.360 \text{ in}}$

$C = 1.5(1.360 \text{ in})$

$C = 2.040 \text{ in}$

m. $\dfrac{1}{2} = \dfrac{F}{12.600 \text{ in}}$

$F = \dfrac{12.600 \text{ in}}{2}$

$F = 6.300 \text{ in}$

n. $\dfrac{3}{1} = \dfrac{G}{0.281 \text{ in}}$

$G = 3(0.281 \text{ in})$

$G = 0.843 \text{ in}$

o. $\dfrac{1}{4} = \dfrac{B}{16.062 \text{ in}}$

$B = \dfrac{16.062 \text{ in}}{4}$

$B = 4.016 \text{ in}$

43. p. $\dfrac{2}{1} = \dfrac{A}{1.872 \text{ in}}$

$A = 2(1.872 \text{ in})$

$A = 3.744 \text{ in}$

44. a. $\dfrac{1}{2} = \dfrac{32}{T_L}$

$T_L = 2(32)$

$T_L = 64 \text{ teeth}$

b. $\dfrac{7}{15} = \dfrac{35}{T_L}$

$T_L = \dfrac{15(35)}{7}$

$T_L = 75 \text{ teeth}$

c. $\dfrac{3}{5} = \dfrac{T_S}{40}$

$T_S = \dfrac{3(40)}{5}$

$T_S = 24 \text{ teeth}$

d. $\dfrac{8}{N_C} = \dfrac{28}{42}$

$N_C = \dfrac{8(42)}{28}$

$N_C = 12 \text{ threads per inch}$

45. a. $\dfrac{A}{0.50 \text{ in}} = \dfrac{3.06 \text{ in}}{1.80 \text{ in}}$

$A = \dfrac{(0.50 \text{ in})(3.06 \text{ in})}{1.80 \text{ in}}$

$A = 0.85 \text{ in}$

b. $\dfrac{B}{0.60 \text{ in}} = \dfrac{3.06 \text{ in}}{1.80 \text{ in}}$

$B = \dfrac{(0.60 \text{ in})(3.06 \text{ in})}{1.80 \text{ in}}$

$B = 1.02 \text{ in}$

c. $\dfrac{C}{0.80 \text{ in}} = \dfrac{3.06 \text{ in}}{1.80 \text{ in}}$

$C = \dfrac{(0.80 \text{ in})(3.06 \text{ in})}{1.80 \text{ in}}$

$C = 1.36 \text{ in}$

d. $\dfrac{D}{0.90 \text{ in}} = \dfrac{3.06 \text{ in}}{1.80 \text{ in}}$

$D = \dfrac{(0.90 \text{ in})(3.06 \text{ in})}{1.00 \text{ in}}$

$D = 1.53 \text{ in}$

UNIT **38**   Direct and Inverse Proportions

1. a. $\dfrac{38 \text{ mm}}{18.40 \text{ mm}} = \dfrac{3.10 \text{ mm}}{x}$

$x = \dfrac{18.40(3.10 \text{ mm})}{38}$

$x = 1.50 \text{ mm}$

b. $\dfrac{38 \text{ mm}}{31.75 \text{ mm}} = \dfrac{3.10 \text{ mm}}{x}$

$x = \dfrac{31.75(3.10 \text{ mm})}{38}$

$x = 2.59 \text{ mm}$

c. $\dfrac{38 \text{ mm}}{14.28 \text{ mm}} = \dfrac{3.10 \text{ mm}}{x}$

$x = 14.28 \dfrac{(3.10 \text{ mm})}{38}$

$x = 1.16 \text{ mm}$

1. d. $\dfrac{38 \text{ mm}}{28.58 \text{ mm}} = \dfrac{3.10 \text{ mm}}{x}$

$x = 28.58 \dfrac{(3.10 \text{ mm})}{38}$

$x = 2.33 \text{ mm}$

e. $\dfrac{38 \text{ mm}}{28.60 \text{ mm}} = \dfrac{3.10 \text{ mm}}{x}$

$x = 28.60 \dfrac{(3.10 \text{ mm})}{38}$

$x = 2.33 \text{ mm}$

2. a. $\dfrac{4.250 \text{ in}}{x} = \dfrac{0.130 \text{ in}}{0.030 \text{ in}}$

$x = \dfrac{4.250 \text{ in}(0.030)}{0.130}$

$x = 0.981 \text{ in}$

2. b. $\dfrac{4.250 \text{ in}}{x} = \dfrac{0.130 \text{ in}}{0.108 \text{ in}}$

$x = \dfrac{4.250 \text{ in}(0.108)}{0.130}$

$x = 3.531 \text{ in}$

c. $\dfrac{4.250 \text{ in}}{x} = \dfrac{0.130 \text{ in}}{0.068 \text{ in}}$

$x = \dfrac{4.250 \text{ in}(0.068)}{0.130}$

$x = 2.223 \text{ in}$

d. $\dfrac{4.250 \text{ in}}{x} = \dfrac{0.130 \text{ in}}{0.008 \text{ in}}$

$x = \dfrac{4.250 \text{ in}(0.008)}{0.130}$

$x = 0.262 \text{ in}$

UNIT 38   (continued)

2. e. $\dfrac{4.250 \text{ in}}{x} = \dfrac{0.130 \text{ in}}{0.093 \text{ in}}$

$x = \dfrac{4.250 \text{ in}(0.093)}{0.130}$

$x = 3.040 \text{ in}$

3. a. $1.500 \text{ in} - 0.700 \text{ in} = 0.800 \text{ in}$

$\dfrac{10.200 \text{ in}}{6.500 \text{ in}} = \dfrac{0.800 \text{ in}}{x}$

$x = \dfrac{0.800 \text{ in}(6.500)}{10.200}$

$x = 0.510 \text{ in}$

DIA C = 1.500 in − 0.510 in = 0.990 in

b. $1.250 \text{ in} - 0.375 \text{ in} = 0.875 \text{ in}$

$\dfrac{8.750 \text{ in}}{4.875 \text{ in}} = \dfrac{0.875 \text{ in}}{x}$

$x = \dfrac{4.875 \text{ in}(0.875)}{8.750}$

$x = 0.4875 \text{ in}$

DIA C = 1.250 in − 0.4875 in = 0.763 in

c. $106.250 \text{ mm} - 62.500 \text{ mm} = 43.750 \text{ mm}$

$\dfrac{550.000 \text{ mm}}{337.500 \text{ mm}} = \dfrac{43.750 \text{ mm}}{x}$

$x = \dfrac{337.500 \text{ mm}(43.750)}{550.000}$

$x = 26.8466 \text{ mm}$

DIA C = 106.250 mm − 26.847 mm = 79.403 mm

d. $22.500 \text{ mm} - 10.000 \text{ mm} = 12.500 \text{ mm}$

$\dfrac{147.500 \text{ mm}}{112.500 \text{ mm}} = \dfrac{12.500 \text{ mm}}{x}$

$x = \dfrac{112.500 \text{ mm}(12.500)}{147.500}$

$x = 9.5339 \text{ mm}$

DIA C = 22.500 mm − 9.534 mm = 12.966 mm

e. $1.325 \text{ in} - 0.410 \text{ in} = 0.915 \text{ in}$

$\dfrac{8.800 \text{ in}}{8.620 \text{ in}} = \dfrac{0.915 \text{ in}}{x}$

$x = \dfrac{0.915 \text{ in}(8.620)}{8.800}$

$x = 0.896 \text{ in}$

DIA C = 1.325 in − 0.896 in = 0.429 in

4. $\dfrac{8.25 \text{ ft}}{2.50 \text{ ft}} = \dfrac{325 \text{ lb}}{x}$

$x = \dfrac{325 \text{ lb}(2.50)}{8.25}$

$x = 98 \text{ lb}$

5. $\dfrac{1350 \text{ parts}}{x} = \dfrac{6.75 \text{ h}}{8.25 \text{ h}}$

$x = \dfrac{1350 \text{ parts}(8.25)}{6.75}$

$x = 1650 \text{ parts}$

6. $\dfrac{3 \text{ machines}}{2 \text{ machines}} = \dfrac{x}{1.6 \text{ h}}$

$x = \dfrac{1.6 \text{ h}(3)}{2}$

$x = 2.4 \text{ h}$

7. $\dfrac{76 \text{ kg}}{96 \text{ kg}} = \dfrac{0.38 \text{ kg}}{x}$

$x = \dfrac{96(0.38 \text{ kg})}{76}$

$x = 0.48 \text{ kg}$

8. Let x = revolutions per minute of the 6.5-inch pulley.
    Let y = revolutions per minute of the 3.5-inch pulley.

$\dfrac{10 \text{ in}}{6.5 \text{ in}} = \dfrac{x}{160 \text{ rpm}}$

$x = \dfrac{10(160 \text{ rpm})}{6.5}$

$x = 246.15 \text{ rpm}$

$\dfrac{8 \text{ in}}{3.5 \text{ in}} = \dfrac{y}{246.15 \text{ rpm}}$

$y = \dfrac{8(246.15 \text{ rpm})}{3.5}$

$y = 562.6 \text{ rpm}$

9. a. $\dfrac{48 \text{ teeth}}{20 \text{ teeth}} = \dfrac{x}{100 \text{ rpm}}$

$x = \dfrac{48(100 \text{ rpm})}{20}$

$x = 240 \text{ rpm}$

b. $\dfrac{32 \text{ teeth}}{24 \text{ teeth}} = \dfrac{210 \text{ rpm}}{x}$

$x = \dfrac{24(210 \text{ rpm})}{32}$

$x = 157.5 \text{ rpm}$

c. $\dfrac{35 \text{ teeth}}{x} = \dfrac{200 \text{ rpm}}{160 \text{ rpm}}$

$x = \dfrac{35 \text{ teeth}(160)}{200}$

$x = 28 \text{ teeth}$

d. $\dfrac{x}{15 \text{ teeth}} = \dfrac{250 \text{ rpm}}{150 \text{ rpm}}$

$x = \dfrac{15 \text{ teeth}(250)}{150}$

$x = 25 \text{ teeth}$

UNIT **38**   (*continued*)

9. e. $\dfrac{54 \text{ teeth}}{26 \text{ teeth}} = \dfrac{x}{80 \text{ rpm}}$

$x = \dfrac{54(80 \text{ rpm})}{26}$

$x = 166.2 \text{ rpm}$

10. a. $\dfrac{80 \text{ teeth}}{30 \text{ teeth}} = \dfrac{x}{120 \text{ rpm}}$

$x = \dfrac{8(120 \text{ rpm})}{3}$

$x = 320 \text{ rpm}$

$y = x = 320 \text{ rpm}$

$\dfrac{50 \text{ teeth}}{20 \text{ teeth}} = \dfrac{z}{320 \text{ rpm}}$

$z = \dfrac{5(320 \text{ rpm})}{2}$

$z = 800 \text{ rpm}$

10. b. $\dfrac{60 \text{ teeth}}{x} = \dfrac{300 \text{ rpm}}{100 \text{ rpm}}$

$x = \dfrac{60 \text{ teeth}}{3}$

$x = 20 \text{ teeth}$

$z = 300 \text{ rpm}$

$\dfrac{45 \text{ teeth}}{y} = \dfrac{450 \text{ rpm}}{300 \text{ rpm}}$

$y = \dfrac{45 \text{ teeth}(300)}{450}$

$y = 30 \text{ teeth}$

c. $\dfrac{60 \text{ teeth}}{36 \text{ teeth}} = \dfrac{280 \text{ rpm}}{z}$

$z = \dfrac{3(280 \text{ rpm})}{5}$

$z = 168 \text{ rpm}$

$y = z = 168 \text{ rpm}$

$\dfrac{x}{24 \text{ teeth}} = \dfrac{168 \text{ rpm}}{144 \text{ rpm}}$

$x = \dfrac{24 \text{ teeth}(168)}{144}$

$x = 28 \text{ teeth}$

10. d. $z = 175 \text{ rpm}$

$\dfrac{55 \text{ teeth}}{25 \text{ teeth}} = \dfrac{175 \text{ rpm}}{y}$

$y = \dfrac{25(175 \text{ rpm})}{55}$

$y = 79.5 \text{ rpm}$

$\dfrac{x}{15 \text{ teeth}} = \dfrac{350 \text{ rpm}}{175 \text{ rpm}}$

$x = \dfrac{15 \text{ teeth}(350)}{175}$

$x = 30 \text{ teeth}$

UNIT **39** Applications of Formulas to Cutting Speed, Revolutions Per Minute, and Cutting Time

1. $C = \dfrac{3.1416(0.475)(460)}{12} = 57 \text{ fpm}$

2. $C = \dfrac{3.1416(2.750)(50)}{12} = 36 \text{ fpm}$

3. $C = \dfrac{3.1416(4.000)(86)}{12} = 90 \text{ fpm}$

4. $C = \dfrac{3.1416(0.850)(175)}{12} = 39 \text{ fpm}$

5. $C = \dfrac{3.1416(1.750)(218)}{12} = 100 \text{ fpm}$

6. $C = \dfrac{3.1416(196.00)(59)}{1000} = 36 \text{ m / min}$

7. $C = \dfrac{3.1416(53.98)(764)}{1000} = 130 \text{ m / min}$

8. $C = \dfrac{3.1416(3.25)(1525)}{1000} = 16 \text{ m / min}$

9. $C = \dfrac{3.1416(133.35)(254)}{1000} = 106 \text{ m / min}$

10. $C = \dfrac{3.1416(6.35)(4584)}{1000} = 91 \text{ m / min}$

11. $N = \dfrac{12(70)}{3.1416(2.400)} = 111 \text{ rpm}$

12. $N = \dfrac{12(120)}{3.1416(0.750)} = 611 \text{ rpm}$

13. $N = \dfrac{12(90)}{3.1416(8.000)} = 43 \text{ rpm}$

14. $N = \dfrac{12(180)}{3.1416(8.000)} = 86 \text{ rpm}$

15. $N = \dfrac{12(200)}{3.1416(0.375)} = 2037 \text{ rpm}$

16. $N = \dfrac{1000(130)}{3.1416(25.50)} = 1623 \text{ r / min}$

17. $N = \dfrac{1000(100)}{3.1416(66.70)} = 477 \text{ r / min}$

18. $N = \dfrac{1000(30)}{3.1416(6.35)} = 1504 \text{ r / min}$

UNIT **39** (*continued*)

19. $N = \dfrac{1000(180)}{3.1416(15.80)} = 3626 \text{ r / min}$

20. $N = \dfrac{1000(150)}{3.1416(114.30)} = 418 \text{ r / min}$

21. $T = \dfrac{20}{0.002(2100)} = 4.8 \text{ min}$

22. $T = \dfrac{925}{0.12(610)} = 12.6 \text{ min}$

23. $T = \dfrac{8}{0.008(350)} = 2.985 \text{ min}$

    $4T = 4(2.985 \text{ min}) = 11.9 \text{ min}$

24. $C = \dfrac{3.1416(3.5)(55)}{12} = 50 \text{ fpm}$

25. $C = \dfrac{3.1416(50)(286)}{1000} = 45 \text{ m / min}$

26. $C = \dfrac{3.1416(16)(1194)}{12} = 5001 \text{ fpm}$

27. $C = \dfrac{3.1416(2.125)(275)}{12} = 153 \text{ fpm}$

28. $C = \dfrac{3.1416(100)(86)}{1000} = 27 \text{ m / min}$

29. $N = \dfrac{12(180)}{3.1416(3.750)} = 183 \text{ rpm}$

30. $N = \dfrac{1000(20)}{3.1416(22)} = 289 \text{ r / min}$

31. $N = \dfrac{1000(1800)}{3.1416(150)} = 3820 \text{ r / min}$

32. $N = \dfrac{12(550)}{3.1416(1.250)} = 1681 \text{ rpm}$

33. $N = \dfrac{12(40)}{3.1416(1.750)} = 87 \text{ rpm}$

34. $T = \dfrac{27}{0.015(270)} = 6.667 \text{ min}$

    $5T = 5(6.667) = 33.3 \text{ min}$

35. $T = \dfrac{812.000}{0.80(640)} = 1.6 \text{ min}$

36. $T = \dfrac{57.15}{0.05(9200)} = 0.1242 \text{ min}$

    $15T = 15(0.1242 \text{ min}) = 1.9 \text{ min}$

37. $T = \dfrac{14.5}{0.020(250)} = 2.9 \text{ min}$

    $30(2)(2.9 \text{ min}) + 30(3 \text{ min}) = 264 \text{ min}$

38. $T = \dfrac{21}{0.02(525)} = 2 \text{ min}$

    $9'' \quad 2\dfrac{1''}{4} = 4 \text{ cuts per piece}$

    $7(4)(2 \text{ min}) = 56 \text{ min}$

39. $N = \dfrac{12(300)}{3.1416(3)} = 381.971 \text{ rpm}$

    $1.02 = \dfrac{11.3}{F(381.971)}$

    $389.61042F = 11.3$

    $F = 0.029 \text{ inch per revolution}$

40. $T = \dfrac{6.5(60)}{2300} = 0.1696 \text{ min}$

    $0.1696 = \dfrac{1.75}{F(1600)}$

    $271.36F = 1.75$

    $F = 0.006 \text{ inch per revolution}$

41. $N = \dfrac{12(200)}{3.1416(1.25)} = 611.15355$

    $T = \dfrac{16.5}{0.015(611.15355)} = 1.80 \text{ min}$

    $\dfrac{1500(1.80)}{60} = 45 \text{ h}$

42. $\quad 1.195 = \dfrac{560}{0.25N}$

    $2.9875N = 560$

    $N = 187.4477 \text{ r / min}$

    $60 = \dfrac{3.1416D\,(187.4477)}{1000}$

    $60000 = 588.88569D$

    $D = 101.89 \text{ mm}$

43. $N = \dfrac{12(300)}{3.1416(0.250)} = 4583.65 \text{ rpm}$

    $T = \dfrac{1.625}{0.004(4583.65)} = 0.0886 \text{ min}$

    $850(6)(0.0886) + 850(0.5 \text{ min}) = 876.86 \text{ min}$

    $\dfrac{876.86}{60} = 14.61 \text{ h}$

44. $C = \dfrac{500 + 800}{2} = 650 \text{ fpm}$

    $N = \dfrac{4(650)}{3.500} = 743 \text{ rpm}$

45. $C = 200 \text{ fpm}$

    $N = \dfrac{4(200)}{5.200} = 154 \text{ rpm}$

UNIT **39** (*continued*)

46. $C = 40$ fpm

$N = \dfrac{4(40)}{0.480} = 333$ rpm

47. $C = 140$ fpm

$N = \dfrac{4(140)}{0.375} = 1493$ rpm

48. $C = \dfrac{250 + 450}{2} = 350$ fpm

$N = \dfrac{4(350)}{4.000} = 350$ rpm

49. $C = 350$ fpm

$N = \dfrac{4(350)}{6.100} = 230$ rpm

50. $C = 60$ fpm

$N = \dfrac{4(60)}{1.100} = 218$ rpm

51. $C = \dfrac{400 + 800}{2} = 600$ fpm

$N = \dfrac{4(600)}{3.00} = 800$ rpm

52. $C = \dfrac{225 + 450}{2} = 337.5$ fpm

$N = \dfrac{4(337.5)}{2.500} = 540$ rpm

53. $C = 600$ fpm

$N = \dfrac{4(600)}{5.800} = 414$ rpm

54. $C = \dfrac{200 + 400}{2} = 300$ fpm

$N = \dfrac{4(300)}{4.500} = 267$ rpm

55. $C = 300$ fpm

$N = \dfrac{4(300)}{2.750} = 436$ rpm

56. $C = 100$ fpm

$N = \dfrac{4(100)}{0.620} = 645$ rpm

57. $C = 600$ fpm

$N = \dfrac{4(600)}{7.000} = 343$ rpm

58. $C = 70$ fpm

$N = \dfrac{4(70)}{0.375} = 747$ rpm

UNIT **40** Applications of Formulas to Spur Gears

1. $P = \dfrac{3.1416}{P_c} = \dfrac{3.1416}{1.5708} = 2$

2. $P_c = \dfrac{3.1416}{P} = \dfrac{3.1416}{10} = 0.3142$ inch

3. $P_c = \dfrac{3.1416D}{N} = \dfrac{3.1416(5.2000)}{26} = \dfrac{16.3363}{26}$

$= 0.6283$ inch

4. $P = \dfrac{N}{D} = \dfrac{44}{12.5714} = 3.5$

5. $D = \dfrac{N}{P} = \dfrac{26}{7} = 3.7143$ inches

6. $D = \dfrac{NP_c}{3.1416} = \dfrac{12(0.3142)}{3.1416} = 1.2002$ inches

7. $P_c = \dfrac{3.1416}{P} = \dfrac{3.1416}{18} = 0.1745$ inch

8. $P = \dfrac{N}{D} = \dfrac{16}{0.7273} = 22$

9. $N = PD = 12(1.1667) = 14$ teeth

10. $N = \dfrac{3.1416D}{P_c} = \dfrac{3.1416(8.4000)}{0.6283} = 42$ teeth

11. $D_o = \dfrac{N + 2}{P} = \dfrac{56 + 2}{8} = \dfrac{58}{8} = 7.25$ inches

12. $a = \dfrac{1}{P} = \dfrac{1}{14} = 0.0714$ inch

13. $D_R = D - 2d = 1.3333 - 2(0.0643) = 1.2047$ inches

14. $WD = \dfrac{2.157}{P} = \dfrac{2.157}{3.4} = 0.6344$ inch

15. $W_D = 0.6366P_c = 0.6366(0.2856) - 0.1818$ inch

16. $C = 0.050P_c = 0.050(1.4650) = 0.0733$ inch

17. $T = \dfrac{1.5708}{P} = \dfrac{1.5708}{20} = 0.0785$ inch

18. $D_o = D + 2a = 3.5000 + 2(0.1818)$

$= 3.5000 + 0.3636 = 3.8636$ inches

19. $d = 0.3683p_c = 0.3683(0.0954) = 0.0351$ inch

UNIT 40   (continued)

20. $a = 0.3183P_C = 0.3183(0.8976) = 0.2857$ inch

21. $WD = a + d = 0.1429 + 0.1653 = 0.3082$ inch

22. $d = \dfrac{1.157}{P} = \dfrac{1.157}{4} = 0.2893$ inch

23. $WD = 0.6866P_C = 0.6866(0.3076) = 0.2122$ inch

24. $C = \dfrac{0.157}{P} = \dfrac{0.157}{17} = 0.0092$ inch

25. $W_D = \dfrac{2.000}{P} = \dfrac{2.000}{9} = 0.2222$ inch

26. $$a = 0.3183P_C$$
$$\frac{a}{0.3183} = P_C$$
$$\frac{0.0857}{0.3183} = P_C$$
$$0.2692 \text{ inch} = P_C$$

27. $a = \dfrac{1}{P}$
$aP = 1$
$P = \dfrac{1}{a}$
$P = \dfrac{1}{0.0666}$
$P = 15$

28. $$D_O = D + 2a$$
$$D_O - 2a = D$$
$$4.8 - 2(0.2) = D$$
$$4.8 - 0.4 = D$$
$$4.4 \text{ inches} = D$$

29. $D_O = \dfrac{N + 2}{P}$
$D_O P = N + 2$
$P = \dfrac{N + 2}{D_O}$
$P = \dfrac{17 + 2}{2.7144}$
$P = 7$

30. $$D_O = \frac{P_C(N + 2)}{3.1416}$$
$$3.1416D_O = P_C N + 2P_C$$
$$3.1416D_O - 2P_C = P_C N$$
$$\frac{3.1416D_O - 2P_C}{P_C} = N$$
$$N = \frac{3.1416(4.3750) - 2(0.3927)}{0.3927}$$
$$N = 33 \text{ teeth}$$

31. $W_D = \dfrac{2.000}{P}$
$W_D P = 2.000$
$P = \dfrac{2.000}{W_D}$
$P = \dfrac{2.000}{0.0769}$
$P = 26$

32. $$W_D = 0.6366P_C$$
$$\frac{W_D}{0.6366} = P_C$$
$$\frac{0.4500}{0.6366} = P_C$$
$$0.7069 \text{ inch} = P_C$$

33. $$D_O = D + 2a$$
$$D_O - D = 2a$$
$$\frac{D_O - D}{2} = a$$
$$\frac{4.7144 - 4.4286}{2} = a$$
$$0.1429 \text{ inch} = a$$

> **Note:**   Other combinations of formulas can be used for solving some problems.

34. $P = \dfrac{N}{D} = \dfrac{72}{6.0000} = 12$

$a = \dfrac{1}{P} = \dfrac{1}{12} = 0.0833$ inch

35. $P = \dfrac{N}{D} = \dfrac{44}{3.6667} = 12$

$d = \dfrac{1.157}{P} = \dfrac{1.157}{12} = 0.0964$ inch

36. $P_C = \dfrac{3.1416D}{N} = \dfrac{3.1416(2.5000)}{10} = 0.7854$ inch

$WD = 0.6866P_C = 0.6866(0.7854) = 0.5393$ inch

37. $P = \dfrac{N}{D} = \dfrac{90}{12.8571} = 7$

$W_D = \dfrac{2.000}{P} = \dfrac{2.000}{7} = 0.2857$ inch

UNIT **40** (*continued*)

38. $N = PD = 16(1.0625) = 17$

$D_O = \dfrac{N + 2}{P} = \dfrac{17 + 2}{16} = 1.1875$ inches

39. $d = \dfrac{1.157}{p} = \dfrac{1.157}{12} = 0.0964$ inch

$D_R = D - 2d = 2.9167 - 2(0.0964) = 2.7239$ inches

40. $P = \dfrac{N}{D} = \dfrac{29}{2.0714} = 14$

$d = \dfrac{1.157}{P} = \dfrac{1.157}{14} = 0.0826$ inch

$D_R = D - 2d = 2.0714 - 2(0.0826) = 1.9062$ inches

41. $P = \dfrac{N}{D} = \dfrac{75}{6.8182} = 11$

$C = \dfrac{0.157}{P} = \dfrac{0.157}{11} = 0.0143$ inch

42. $a = \dfrac{1}{P}$

$aP = 1$

$P = \dfrac{1}{a}$

$P = \dfrac{1}{0.1429}$

$P = 7$

$T = \dfrac{1.5708}{P} = \dfrac{1.5708}{7} = 0.2244$ inch

43. $a = \dfrac{1}{P}$

$aP = 1$

$P = \dfrac{1}{a}$

$P = \dfrac{1}{0.0455}$

$P = 22$

$N = PD = (22)(1.0455) = 23$ teeth

44. Average backlash $= \dfrac{0.030}{P} = \dfrac{0.030}{7} = 0.0043$ inch

45. Average backlash $= \dfrac{0.030}{P} = \dfrac{0.030}{20} = 0.0015$ inch

46. Average backlash $= \dfrac{0.030}{P} = \dfrac{0.030}{3.5} = 0.0086$ inch

47. $WD = \dfrac{2.157}{P}$

$P = \dfrac{2.157}{WD}$

$P = \dfrac{2.157}{0.2696}$

$P = 8$

Average backlash $= \dfrac{0.030}{P} = \dfrac{0.030}{8} = 0.0038$ inch

48. $W_D = \dfrac{2.000}{P}$

$P = \dfrac{2.000}{W_D}$

$P = \dfrac{2.000}{0.1176}$

$P = 17$

Average backlash $= \dfrac{0.030}{P} = \dfrac{0.030}{17} = 0.0018$ inch

49. $P = \dfrac{N}{D} = \dfrac{24}{4.800} = 5$

Average backlash $= \dfrac{0.030}{P} = \dfrac{0.030}{5} = 0.0060$ inch

50. Center Distance $= \dfrac{4.1667 + 2.8300}{2} = 3.4984$ inches

51. Center Distance $= \dfrac{8.6752 + 4.8889}{2} = 6.7821$ inches

52. Pinion: $D = \dfrac{N}{P} = \dfrac{23}{9} = 2.5556$ inches

Gear: $D = \dfrac{N}{P} = \dfrac{38}{9} = 4.2222$ inches

Center Distance $= \dfrac{4.2222 + 2.5556}{2} = 3.3889$ inches

53. Pinion: $D = \dfrac{N}{P} = \dfrac{18}{16} = 1.1250$ inches

Gear: $D = \dfrac{N}{P} = \dfrac{44}{16} = 2.7500$ inches

Center Distance $= \dfrac{2.7500 + 1.1250}{2} = 1.9375$ inches

54. Pinion: $D = \dfrac{NP_C}{3.1416} = \dfrac{(37)(0.1745)}{3.1416} = 2.0551$ inches

Gear: $D = \dfrac{NP_C}{3.1416} = \dfrac{(55)(0.1745)}{3.1416} = 3.0550$ inches

Center Distance $= \dfrac{3.0550 + 2.0551}{2} = 2.5551$ inches

55. a. $D = mN = 6.5\,mm(18) = 117\,mm$

b. $P_C = \dfrac{m}{0.3183} = 6.5\,mm \div 0.3183 = 20.421\,mm$

c. $D_O = m(N + 2) = (6.5\,mm)(18 + 2) = 130\,mm$

d. $a = m = 6.5\,mm$

e. $W_D = 2m = 2(6.5\,mm) = 13\,mm$

f. $T = 1.5708m = 1.5708(6.5\,mm) = 10.210\,mm$

56. a. $D = mN = 9\,mm(24) = 216\,mm$

b. $P_C = \dfrac{m}{0.3183} = 9\,mm \div 0.3183 = 28.275\,mm$

c. $D_O = m(N + 2) = (9\,mm)(24 + 2) = 234\,mm$

UNIT **40** *(continued)*

56. d. $a = m = 9\,mm$

 e. $W_D = 2m = 2(9\,mm) = 18\,mm$

 f. $T = 1.5708m = 1.5708(9\,mm) = 14.137\,mm$

57. a. $D = mN = 2.5\,mm(10) = 25\,mm$

 b. $P_c = \dfrac{m}{0.3183} = 2.5\,mm \div 0.3183 = 7.854\,mm$

 c. $D_O = m(N + 2) = (2.5\,mm)(10 + 2) = 30\,mm$

 d. $a = m = 2.5\,mm$

 e. $W_D = 2m = 2(2.5\,mm) = 5\,mm$

 f. $T = 1.5708m = 1.5708(2.5\,mm) = 3.927\,mm$

58. a. $D = mN = 3.75\,mm(16) = 60\,mm$

 b. $P_c = \dfrac{m}{0.3183} = 3.75\,mm \div 0.3183 = 11.781\,mm$

 c. $D_O = m(N + 2) = (3.75\,mm)(16 + 2) = 67.5\,mm$

 d. $a = m = 3.75\,mm$

 e. $W_D = 2m = 2(3.75\,mm) = 7.5\,mm$

 f. $T = 1.5708m = 1.5708(3.75\,mm) = 5.8905\,mm$

59. a. $D = mN = 10\,mm(26) = 260\,mm$

 b. $P_c = \dfrac{m}{0.3183} = 10\,mm \div 0.3183 = 31.417\,mm$

59. c. $D_O = m(N + 2) = (10\,mm)(26 + 2) = 280\,mm$

 d. $a = m = 10\,mm$

 e. $W_D = 2m = 2(10\,mm) = 20\,mm$

 f. $T = 1.5708m = 1.5708(10\,mm) = 15.708\,mm$

60. $WD = 2.157m = 2.157(5\,mm) = 10.785\,mm$

61. $D = mN$

 $120\,mm = (4\,mm)N$

 $30 \text{ teeth} = N$

62. $W_D = 2m$

 $13\,mm = 2m$

 $6.5\,mm = m$

63. $d = 1.167m = 1.167(7\,mm) = 8.169\,mm$

64. $D_O = m(N + 2)$

 $220\,mm = m(38 + 2)$

 $5.5\,mm = m$

UNIT **41** Achievement Review—Section Three

1. a. $x + y - c$ b. $ab \div d$ c. $2M - P^2$

2. a. $[5(4) + 6(5)] \div 4(5) = (20 + 30) \div 20 = 50 \div 20 = 2.5$

 b. $3(6)(3) - [2(6) + 3] = 54 - (12 + 3) = 54 - 15 = 39$

 c. $5.125^2 + (2(3.062))^2 - \left(\dfrac{6.127}{3.062}\right)^2 = 26.22656 + 37.5034 - 4.0039 = 59.765$

 d. $\sqrt{(10.26)(6.59 + 8.00)}\left(\dfrac{5(10.26)}{8.00} + 10.26\right) = 10.3737(16.6725) = 172.955$

3. a. -37 e. 0.78 i. -125

 b. 16 f. -6 j. -3

 c. -14.4 g. 32 k. $\dfrac{1}{16}$

 d. -72 h. 36 l. 1.448

 m. $16.1604 + 2.0770 - (-21.8476) = 40.085$

 n. $-15.7768 \div 30.95 = -0.510$

4. a. $13P$

 b. $-1.18H^2$

 c. $5d + 22d^2$

 d. $5a - 2a^2 - 6a + 4a^2 = -a + 2a^2$

4. e. $-90x^3y$

 f. $5.9e^2f^4$

 g. $32x - 8x^2$

 h. $3fg^3 - 5g - 10f$

 i. $-18x^5 + 6x^2y^2 + 3x^3y^3 - y^5$

 j. $-64a^9b^3c^6$

 k. $[(xy^2)^3 - (x^2y^2)][(xy^2)^3 - (x^2y^2)] =$
 $(x^3y^6 - x^2y^2)(x^3y^6 - x^2y^2) =$
 $x^6y^{12} - x^5y^8 - x^5y^8 + x^4y^4 =$
 $x^6y^{12} - 2x^5y^8 + x^4y^4$

 l. $-3a^2bc^3$

UNIT **41**   (*continued*)

4. m. $\dfrac{5}{8}e^2gd^{\frac{1}{2}}$ or $\dfrac{5}{8}e^2g\sqrt{d}$

n. $-6x^2 - 6y + 12x$

o. $36 - m^3 - m + m^3 - 12 = 24 - m$

p. $-3a(4a^2) + 6a^2 = -12a^3 + 6a^2$

q. $9y + 8x - x^3y^2 + xy + 12x = 9y + 20x + xy - x^3y^2$

r. $b(b + 7m)(b + 7m) - b(b - 7m)(b - 7m) =$
    $b(b^2 + 14bm + 49m^2) - b(b^2 - 14bm + 49m^2) =$
    $b^3 + 14b^2m + 49bm^2 - b^3 + 14b^2m - 49bm^2 = 28b^2m$

5. a. 21
    b. 38
    c. 14
    d. 32.2
    e. -39.3
    f. -1.4
    g. -12
    h. 5.8
    i. 74.052

    j. -6.784
    k. -0.333
    l. 3
    m. 9
    n. $\dfrac{-2}{3}$
    o. 166.204
    p. 202.572
    q. -0.305
    r. 0.887

6. a. $32 + P - 18 - 45$
        $P + 14 = 45$
        $P = 31$

    b. $10M - 40 = -5M + 20$
        $15M = 60$
        $M = 4$

    c. $7.1E + 3E - 18 = 0.5E + 22.8$
        $9.6E = 40.8$
        $E = 4.25$

    d. $\dfrac{H}{4} = 5.8$
        $H = 23.2$

    e. $\dfrac{1}{4}F + 6F - 3 = 15\dfrac{3}{4}$
        $6\dfrac{1}{4}F = 18\dfrac{3}{4}$
        $F = 3$

    f. $12x^2 - 53 = x^2 - 9$
        $11x^2 = 44$
        $x^2 = 4$
        $x = 2$

    g. $-8.53G + 31.3051 = -104.652$
        $G = \dfrac{-135.957}{-8.53}$
        $G = 15.939$

6. h. $T^2 - 8T - 7.8T + 62.4 = T^2 + 0.3$
        $-15.8T = -62.1$
        $T = 3.930$

    i. $59.66\sqrt{x} = 8.71(1.07\sqrt{x} + 55.32)$
        $59.66\sqrt{x} = 9.3197\sqrt{x} + 481.8372$
        $50.3403\sqrt{x} = 481.8372$
        $\sqrt{x} = \dfrac{481.8372}{50.3403}$
        $x = 91.616$

    j. $14.8\sqrt{H} = 0$
        $H = 0$

7. a. $36 = 0.707D(12)$
        $36 = 8.484D$
        $D = 4.243$

    b. $0.3 = \dfrac{5E}{6 + 5(4)}$
        $0.3 = \dfrac{5E}{26}$
        $7.8 = 5E$
        $E = 1.56$

    c. $600 = \dfrac{0.290W}{0.375^2}$
        $600 = \dfrac{0.290W}{0.140625}$
        $84.375 = 0.290W$
        $W = 290.948$

    d. $10.096 = \sqrt{8.053^2 + b^2}$
        $101.9292 = 64.8508 + b^2$
        $b^2 = 37.0784$
        $b = 6.089$

    e. $105.823 = 1.570(5.897)(R^2 + 2.023^2)$
        $105.823 = 9.25829R^2 + 37.8898$
        $\dfrac{67.9332}{9.25829} = R^2$
        $R = 2.709$

8. a. $E = IR + Ir$
        $E - IR = Ir$
        $r = \dfrac{E - IR}{I}$

    b. $D_o - 2C + d = 2a$
        $a = \dfrac{D_o - 2C + d}{2}$

    c. $M - D + 1.5155P = 3W$
        $W = \dfrac{M - D + 1.5155P}{3}$

UNIT **41** (*continued*)

8. d. $r^2 = x^2 + y^2$
$r^2 - x^2 = y^2$
$y = \sqrt{r^2 - x^2}$

e. $L - 3.14(0.5D + 0.5d) = 2x$
$$x = \frac{L - 3.14(0.5D + 0.5d)}{2}$$

f. $2.5HP = D^2N$
$$\frac{2.5HP}{N} = D^2$$
$$D = \sqrt{\frac{2.5HP}{N}}$$

9. a. $2P = 38.4$
$P = 19.2$

b. $0.9E = 9.72$
$E = 10.8$

c. $\frac{3}{8}H = \frac{1}{8}$
$H = \frac{1}{3}$

d. $84 = 6C + 42$
$42 = 6C$
$C = 7$

e. $8.2M = 266.5$
$M = 32.5$

f. $22.517x = 17.5134$
$$x = \frac{17.5134}{22.517}$$
$x = 0.778$

g. $10.9225T = 90.4549$
$$T = \frac{90.4549}{10.9225}$$
$T = 8.282$

9. h. $10.360N - 26.0554 = 15.89835$
$$N = \frac{41.95375}{10.360}$$
$N = 4.050$

10. a. $\frac{3.2625}{2.1250} = \frac{0.0975}{x}$
$3.2625x = 0.2071875$
$x = 0.064$ in

b. $\frac{2550}{x} = \frac{8.5}{10}$
$8.5x = 25500$
$x = 3000$ parts

c. $\frac{12}{16} = \frac{x}{420}$
$16x = 5040$
$x = 315$ rpm

11. a. $C = \frac{3.1416(2.300)(250)}{12} = 150$ fpm

b. $N = \frac{1000(160)}{3.1416(40.00)} = 1273$ r / min

c. $T = \frac{58.00}{0.05(6500)} = 0.17846$ min
$20(0.17846) = 3.57$ min

d. $P = \frac{44}{12.5714} = 3.5$

e. $P = \frac{20}{5.0000} = 4$
$WD = \frac{2.157}{4} = 0.5393$ in

12. a. $(3.76 \times 2.87) \times 10^{4+3} = 10.79 \times 10^7 = 1.08 \times 10^8$

b. $(8.63 \div 5.77) \times 10^{7-(-5)} = 1.50 \times 10^{12}$

c. $(9.76 \times 1.77 \div 5.87) \times 10^{-5+9-3} = 2.94 \times 10^1$

d. $(9.09 \div (4.72 \times 6.15)) \times 10^{-5-6-(-3)} = 0.313 \times 10^{-8} = 3.13 \times 10^{-9}$

13. a. $(2.1 \times 10^{-4}) \times (3.9 \times 10^{-4}) = (2.1 \times 3.9) \times 10^{-4+(-4)} = 8.19 \times 10^{-8}$

b. $(1.476 \times 10^6) \times (-3.73 \times 10^{-5}) = (1.476 \times (-3.73)) \times 10^{6+(-5)} = -5.51 \times 10^1$

c. $(2.87 \times 10^{-5}) \times (2.16 \times 10^8)(9.81 \times 10^{-3}) = (2.87 \times 2.16 \, 9.81) \times 10^{5+8-(-3)} = 0.632 \times 10^6$
$= 6.32 \times 10^{-5}$

d. $((5.03 \times 10^{-3}) \times (4.06 \times 10^{-4})) \div ((4.16 \times 10^5) \times (3.92 \times 10^{-3})) = (5.03 \times 4.06) \div (4.16 \times 3.92)$
$\times 10^{-3+(-4)-5-(-3)} = 1.25 \times 10^{-9}$

Section Four
Fundamentals of Plane Geometry

UNIT 42 Lines and Angular Measure

1. a. parallel
   b. perpendicular
   c. oblique

2. a. 360°
   b. 60′
   c. 60″
   d. 60(60) = 3600″
   e. 60(360) = 21,600′

3. a. ∥   d. ′
   b. ⊥   e. ″
   c. °

4. $0.50° = 0.50(60′) = 30′$
   $13.50° = 13°30′$

5. $0.85° = 0.85(60′) = 51′$
   $67.85° = 67°51′$

6. $0.10° = 0.10(60′) = 6′$
   $48.10° = 48°06′$

7. $0.70° = 0.70(60′) = 42′$
   $117.70° = 117°42′$

8. $0.60° = 0.60(60′) = 36′$
   $18.60° = 18°36′$

9. $0.15° = 0.15(60′) = 9′$
   $93.15° = 93°09′$

10. $0.08° = 0.08(60′) = 5′$
    $81.08° = 81°05′$

11. $0.47° = 0.47(60′) = 28′$
    $6.47° = 6°28′$

12. $0.91° = 0.91(60′) = 55′$
    $125.91° = 125°55′$

13. $0.67° = 0.67(60′) = 40′$
    $77.67° = 77°40′$

14. $0.1380° = 0.1380(60′) = 8.28′$
    $0.28′ = 0.28(60″) = 17″$
    $52.1380° = 52°08′17″$

15. $0.0710° = 0.0710(60′) = 4.26′$
    $0.26′ = 0.26(60″) = 16″$
    $212.0710° = 212°04′16″$

16. $0.9250° = 0.9250(60′) = 55.5′$
    $0.5′ = 0.5(60″) = 30$
    $7.9250° = 7°55′30″$

17. $0.4440° = 0.4440(60′) = 26.64′$
    $0.64′ = 0.64(60″) = 38″$
    $44.4440° = 44°26′38″$

18. $0.9330° = 0.9330(60′) = 55.98′$
    $0.98′ = 0.98(60″) = 59″$
    $73.9330° = 73°55′59″$

19. $0.0090° = 0.0090(60′) = 0.54′$
    $0.54′ = 0.54(60″) = 32″$
    $103.0090° = 103°0′32″$

20. $0.9365° = 0.9365(60′) = 56.19′$
    $0.19′ = 0.19(60″) = 11″$
    $37.9365° = 37°56′11″$

21. $0.9056° = 0.9056(60′) = 54.336′$
    $0.336′ = 0.336(60″) = 20″$
    $89.9056° = 89°54′20″$

22. $0.0692° = 0.0692(60′) = 4.152′$
    $0.152′ = 0.152(60″) = 09″$
    $182.0692° = 182°04′09″$

23. $0.8973° = 0.8973(60′) = 53.838′$
    $0.838′ = 0.838(60″) = 50″$
    $19.8973° = 19°53′50″$

24. $40′ = 40 ÷ 60 = 0.67°$
    $22°40′ = 22.67°$

25. $45′ = 45 ÷ 60 = 0.75°$
    $107°45′ = 107.75°$

26. $10′ = 10 ÷ 60 = 0.17°$
    $6°10′ = 6.17°$

27. $16′ = 16 ÷ 60 = 0.27°$
    $87°16′ = 87.27°$

28. $7′ = 7 ÷ 60 = 0.12°$
    $122°07′ = 122.12°$

29. $48′ = 48 ÷ 60 = 0.80°$
    $56°48′ = 56.80°$

30. $37′ = 37 ÷ 60 = 0.62°$
    $87°37′ = 87.62°$

31. $19′ = 19 ÷ 60 = 0.32°$
    $2°19′ = 2.32°$

32. $8′ = 8 ÷ 60 = 0.13°$
    $32°08′ = 32.13°$

33. $59′ = 59 ÷ 60 = 0.98°$
    $79°59′ = 79.98°$

34. $30″ = 30 ÷ 60 = 0.5′$
    $18.5′ = 18.5 ÷ 60 = 0.3083°$
    $28°18′30″ = 28.3083°$

35. $45″ = 45 ÷ 60 = 0.75′$
    $8.75′ = 8.75 ÷ 60 = 0.1458°$
    $57°08′45″ = 57.1458°$

36. $10″ = 10 ÷ 60 = 0.16667′$
    $50.16667′ = 50.16667 ÷ 60 = 0.8361°$
    $130°50′10″ = 130.8361°$

37. $25″ = 25 ÷ 60 = 0.41667′$
    $20.41667′ = 20.41667 ÷ 60 = 0.3403°$
    $98°20′25″ = 98.3403°$

38. $18″ = 18 ÷ 60 = 0.3′$
    $27.3′ = 27.3 ÷ 60 = 0.4550°$
    $176°27′18″ = 176.4550°$

39. $13″ = 13 ÷ 60 = 0.21667′$
    $7.21667′ = 7.21667 ÷ 60 = 0.1203°$
    $2°07′13″ = 2.1203°$

40. $59″ = 59 ÷ 60 = 0.98333′$
    $49.98333′ = 49.98333 ÷ 60 = 0.8331°$
    $19°49′59″ = 19.8331°$

UNIT 42   (continued)

41. 6″ = 6 ÷ 60 = 0.1′
    12.1′ = 12.1 ÷ 60 = 0.2017°
    61°12′6″ = 61.2017°

42. ∠1 = 68° + 31° + 29° = 128°

43. ∠2 = 17°34′ + 59°18′ = 76°52′

44. ∠3 = 25°02′ + 71°12′ + 19°33′ = 115°47′

45. ∠1 + ∠2 + ∠3 = 81°51′ + 73°47′ + 88°30′ = 242°128′ = 244°08′

46. ∠5 = 15°18′27″ + 43°32′06″ = 58°50′33″

47. ∠6 = 9°29′53″ + 37°12′19″ = 46°41′72″ = 46°42′12″

48. ∠7 + ∠8 + ∠9 = 23°32′11″+ 30°15′41″ + 55°50′47″ = 108°97′99″ = 108°98′39″ = 109°38′39″

49. ∠1 + ∠2 + ∠3 + ∠4 + ∠5 = 90° + 88°13′48″ + 51°37″ + 222°19′54″ + 87°49′18″ = 538°118′120″ = 538°120′ = 540°

50. 25°

51. 16°09′

52. 62°83′ − 32°58′ = 30°25′

53. 109°21′09″

54. 49°33′72″ − 19°13′42″ = 30°20′30″

55. ∠1 = 121° − 77° = 44°

56. ∠3 − ∠2 = 84°12′ − 51°17′ = 32°55′

57. ∠2 = 48°13′42″ − 26°14′07″ = 21°59′35″

58. ∠1 − ∠2 = 37°56′11″ − 14°55′47″ = 23°0′24″

59. ∠1 + ∠2 + ∠3 + ∠4 + ∠5 = 90° + 90° + 118°17′35″ + 241°42′26″ + 82°56′ = 621°115′61″ = 621°116′01″ = 622°56′01″
    ∠6 = 719°59′60″ − 622°56′01″ = 97°03′59″

60. 7(15°) = 105°

61. 3(29°19′) = 87°57′

62. 2(43°43′) = 86°86′ = 87°26′

63. 5(22°10′13″) = 110°50′65″ = 110°51′05″

64. 8(43°23′28″) = 344°184′224″ = 344°187′44″ = 347°07′44″

65. ∠3 = 2(42°) = 84°

66. ∠4 = 3(39°14′) = 117°42′

67. ∠6 = 5(54°03′) = 265°205′ = 270°15′

68. 94° ÷ 2 = 47°

69. 87° ÷ 2 = 43°30′

70. 105°20′ ÷ 4 = 26°20′

71. ∠1 = 137° ÷ 2 = 68°30′

72. x = 109° ÷ 4 = 27°15′

73. y = 360° ÷ 7 = 51°25′43″ (rounded)

74. ∠1 + ∠2 + ∠3 + ∠4 = 360° − 49° = 311°
    ∠1 = 311° ÷ 4 = 77°45′

75. $\angle 1 = \dfrac{1440° - 4(118°14′23″)}{6} = \dfrac{1440° - 472°57′32″}{6} = \dfrac{967°02′28″}{6} = 161°10′25″$ (rounded)

UNIT 43   Protractors—Simple Semicircular and Vernier

1. ∠A = 25°
   ∠B = 42°
   ∠C = 57°
   ∠D = 77°
   ∠E = 93°
   ∠F = 11°
   ∠G = 27°
   ∠H = 46°
   ∠ I = 76°
   ∠ J = 87°

2. a.
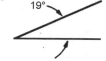

   b.
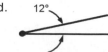

2. c.

   d.

2. e.
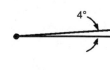

   f.
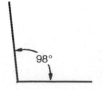

UNIT **43**   *(continued)*

2. g.

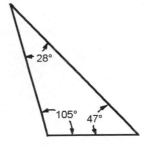

97°

h.

123°

i.

150°

j.

166°

3.

28°

105°   47°

The third angle measures
28°.

4

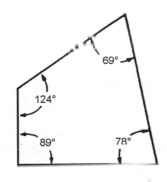

69°

124°

89°   78°

The fourth angle measures
78°.

5. ∠ 1 = 29°
    ∠ 2 = 133°
    ∠ 3 = 29°
    ∠ 4 = 58°
    ∠ 5 = 39°
    ∠ 6 = 27°
    ∠ 7 = 122°
    ∠ 8 = 31°
    ∠ 9 = 72°
    ∠10 = 103°
    ∠11 = 64°
    ∠12 = 118°
    ∠13 = 150°
    ∠14 = 19°

6. 10°30′
7. 19°45′
8. 29°25′
9. 50°15′
10. 59°25′
11. 20°15′

12. 10°20′
13. 20°30′
14. 50°15′
15. a. 47°
    b. 14°
    c. 73°
    d. 85°
    e. 22°11′
    f. 44°41′
    g. 68°17′
    h. 11°40′33″
    i. 30°50′1″

16. a. 167°
    b. 115°
    c. 89°
    d. 0°1′
    e. 179°11′
    f. 90°1′
    g. 177°16′40″
    h. 111°38′31″
    i. 46°27′52″

UNIT **44**   Types of Angles and Angular Geometric Principles

1. a. ∠A, ∠BAF, ∠FAB
    b. ∠B, ∠ABC, ∠CBA
    c. ∠3, ∠BCD, ∠DCB
    d. ∠4, ∠CDE, ∠EDC
    e. ∠5, ∠DEF, ∠FED
    f. ∠6, ∠AFE, ∠EFA

2. a. ∠DCE, ∠ECD
    b. ∠FBC, ∠6
    c. ∠DCB, ∠BCD
    d. ∠BCE, ∠2
    e. ∠ABF, ∠FBA
    f. ∠DCB, ∠3

3. a. acute   g. straight
    b. right   h. acute
    c. right   i. right
    d. acute   j. reflex
    e. acute   k. straight
    f. obtuse

4. ∠1 and ∠11, ∠5 and ∠6, ∠9 and ∠10

5. a. ∠3 and ∠6, ∠4 and ∠5
    b. ∠1 and ∠6, ∠2 and ∠5, ∠3 and ∠8, ∠4 and ∠7

6. ∠1 = 38°, ∠2 = 63°14′, ∠3 = 78°46′, ∠4 = 97°, ∠5 = 161°46′

7. a. ∠2 = 148°, ∠3 = 32°, ∠4 = 148°
    b. ∠2 = 144°41′, ∠3 = 35°19′, ∠4 = 144°41′

8. a. ∠2 = 112°, ∠3 = 68°, ∠4 = 112°, ∠5 = 68°, ∠6 = 112°, ∠7 = 68°, ∠8 = 112°
    b. ∠2 = 127°05′, ∠3 = 52°55′, ∠4 = 127°05′, ∠5 = 52°55′,
       ∠6 = 127°05′, ∠7 = 52°55′, ∠8 = 127°05′

9. a. ∠1, ∠2, ∠5, ∠7, ∠9, ∠11, ∠13, ∠15 = 109°
       ∠3, ∠4, ∠6, ∠8, ∠10, ∠12, ∠14 = 71°
    b. ∠1, ∠2, ∠5, ∠7, ∠9, ∠11, ∠13, ∠15 = 93°08′
       ∠3, ∠4, ∠6, ∠8, ∠10, ∠12, ∠14 = 86°52′

10. a. ∠1, ∠2, ∠6, ∠8, ∠10, ∠12, ∠13 = 97°
       ∠3, ∠4, ∠5, ∠7, ∠9, ∠11, ∠15, ∠16 = 83°
       ∠14, ∠17, ∠20 = 49°
       ∠18 = 53°
       ∠19, ∠21, ∠22 = 78°

UNIT **44**   (*continued*)

10. b. ∠1, ∠2, ∠6, ∠8, ∠10, ∠12, ∠13 = 112°23′

∠3, ∠4, ∠5, ∠7, ∠9, ∠11, ∠15, ∠16 = 67°37′

∠14, ∠17, ∠20 = 39°44′

∠18 = 55°34′

∠19, ∠21, ∠22 = 84°42′

11. a. ∠2 = ∠1 = 67°, ∠3 = 180° − 67° = 113°

b. ∠2 = ∠1 = 74°12′, ∠3 = 180° − 74°12′ = 105°48′

12. a. ∠1 = 180° − 116° = 64°, ∠2 = ∠3 = ∠4 = 116°

b. ∠1 = 180° − 107°43′ = 72°17′, ∠2 = ∠3 = ∠4 = 107°43′

UNIT **45**   Introduction to Triangles

1. isosceles

2. scalene

3. scalene

4. isosceles

5. right

6. right and isosceles

7. equilateral

8. equilateral

9. 180°

10. a. ∠3 = 180° − (56° + 86°) = 38°

b. ∠1 = 180° − (80° + 46°) = 53°

11. a. ∠6 = 180° − (32°43′ + 119°17′) = 28°

b. ∠4 = 180° − (123°17′13″ + 27°) = 29°42′47″

12. a. ∠B = 180° − (90° + 19°43′) = 70°17′

b. ∠A = 180° − (90° + 67°58′) = 22°02′

13. △ ABC is equilateral

a. AB = 17.3″

b. AC = 17.3″

14. △ EFG is isosceles

a. ∠G = ∠E = 81°

b. ∠F = 180° − 2(83°27′) = 13°06′

15. The △ is isosceles

a. ∠1 = (180° − 17°) ÷ 2 = 81°30′

b. ∠2 = (180° − 25°19′) ÷ 2 = 77°20′30″

16. The △ is an isosceles right △

a. ∠3 = (180° − 90°) ÷ 2 = 45°

b. ∠4 = ∠3 = 45°

17. a. ∠A = 180° − (26° + 33°) = 121°

∠2 = 180° − (121° + 48°) = 11°

b. ∠A = 180° − (28° + 33°) = 119°

∠3 = 180° − (119° + 15°) = 46°

18. a. ∠BAD = ∠ADC = 23°30′

∠2 = 180° − (23°30′ + 86°32′) = 69°58′

b. ∠1 = 180° − (23°30′ + 67°47′) = 88°43′

19. a. ∠DCE = ∠BCA = 35°

∠CDE = ∠FDG = 97°

∠3 = 180° − (35° + 97°) = 48°

b. ∠AEB = 59° − 48° = 11°

∠4 = 180° − (11° + 190°) = 79°

20. a. ∠BCF = ∠E = 66°43′

∠A = 180° − (90° + 66°43′) = 23°17′

b. ∠BCF = 180° − (19°07′ + 90°) = 70°53′

∠E = ∠BCF = 70°53′

21. a. ∠A   b. ∠C   c. ∠B

22. a. FG   b. EG   c. EF

23. a. ∠D   b. ∠E   c. ∠2

24. a. ∠K   b. ∠J   c. ∠L

UNIT 46 Geometric Principles for Triangles and Other Common Polygons

1. Pairs A, B, D, and F

2. a. $\dfrac{\overset{3}{\cancel{15}}}{\underset{2}{10}} = \dfrac{AC}{6}$

    $2AC = 18$
    $AC = 9\ in$

   b. $\dfrac{\overset{3}{\cancel{15}}}{\underset{2}{10}} = \dfrac{12}{DE}$

    $3DE = 24$
    $DE = 8\ in$

3. a. $\dfrac{70.82}{121.55} = \dfrac{HK}{95.87}$

    $121.55HK = 6789.5134$
    $HK = 55.86\ mm$

   b. $\dfrac{70.82}{121.55} = \dfrac{54.68}{LM}$

    $70.82LM = 6646.354$
    $LM = 90.05\ mm$

4. a. $56°$ b. $23°$

   c. $180° - (56° + 23°) = 180° - 79° = 101°$
   d. $101°$

5. a. $180° - (90° + 37°18') = 52°42'$
   b. $37°18'$

6. a. $180° - (76°10' + 25°27') = 180° - 101°37'$
      $= 78°23'$
   b. $180° - 25°27' = 154°33'$

7. a. $79°$
   b. $180° - (90° + 79°) = 180° - 169° = 11°$
   c. $11°$

8. a. $\dfrac{A}{260.0} = \dfrac{300.0}{425.0}$

    $A = \dfrac{(300.00)(260.0)}{425.0}$

    $A = 183.5\ mm$

   b. $B = \dfrac{(300.0)(498.2)}{425.0}$

    $B = 351.7\ mm$

9. a. $\dfrac{2.200}{4.000} = \dfrac{2.700}{x}$

    $2.200x = 10.800$
    $x = 4.909\ in$

   b. $\dfrac{2.200}{4.000} = \dfrac{y}{4.800}$

    $4.000y = 10.560$
    $y = 2.640\ in$

10. The triangle is isosceles.

    a. $x = \dfrac{18.4\,in}{2} = 9.2\,in$

    b. $\angle 1 = 38°40'$

11. The triangle is isosceles.

    a. $x = 72.5\ mm$
    b. $y = 2(56.8\,mm) = 113.6\ mm$

12. The triangle is isosceles.

    a. $\angle 1 = \dfrac{64°58'}{2} = 32°29'$

    b. $\angle 2 = 180° - (90° + 32°29') = 180° - 122°29' = 57°31'$

13. $\triangle ABC$ is equilateral

    a. $x = 118.30\ mm$
    b. $y = 118.30\ mm$

14. $\triangle EFG$ is equilateral and each angle is $60°$.

    a. $\angle 1 = 30°$

    b. $x = \dfrac{7.85\,in}{2} = 3.93\,in$

15. a. $x^2 = d^2 + e^2$

      $x^2 = (9\,in)^2 + (12\,in)^2$
      $x^2 = 81\,sq\,in + 144\,sq\,in$
      $x^2 = 225\,sq\,in$
      $x = 15\,in$

    b. $x^2 = (3\,in)^2 + (4\,in)^2$
      $x^2 = 9\,sq\,in + 16\,sq\,in$
      $x^2 = 25\,sq\,in$
      $x = 5\,in$

16. a. $m^2 = y^2 + g^2$
       $(123\,mm)^2 = y^2 + (108\,mm)^2$
          $y^2 = 15{,}129\,mm^2 - 11{,}664\,mm^2$
          $y^2 = 3465\,mm^2$
          $y = 59\,mm$

    b. $m^2 = y^2 + g^2$
       $(170\,mm)^2 = y^2 + (153.70\,mm)^2$
          $y^2 = 5276.31\,mm^2$
          $y = 73\,mm^2$

17. a. $PS = Radius\ A = 360\ mm$
       $TS^2 = x^2 + PS^2$
       $TS^2 = (480\,mm)^2 + (360\,mm)^2$
       $TS^2 = 230{,}400\,mm^2 + 129{,}600\,mm^2$
       $TS^2 = 360{,}000\,mm^2$
       $TS = 600\ mm$
       $SM = Radius\ A = 360\ mm$
       $y = TS + SM = 600\ mm + 360\ mm = 960\ mm$

UNIT **46**   *(continued)*

17. b. $TS^2 = x^2 + PS^2$

$TS^2 = (288 \text{ mm})^2 + (216 \text{ mm})^2$

$TS^2 = 82{,}944 \text{ mm}^2 + 46{,}656 \text{ mm}^2$

$TS^2 = 129{,}600 \text{ mm}^2$

$TS = 360 \text{ mm}$

$y = TS + SM = 360 \text{ mm} + 216 \text{ mm} = 576 \text{ mm}$

18. a. $CD = 30.263 \text{ in} \div 2 = 15.1315 \text{ in}$

$A = 7.000 \text{ in} + 15.1315 \text{ in}$

$A = 22.132 \text{ in}$

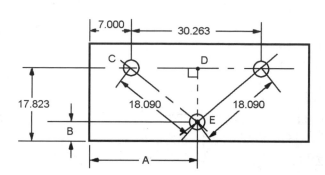

b. $CE^2 = CD^2 + DE^2$

$(18.090 \text{ in})^2 = (15.1315 \text{ in})^2 + DE^2$

$327.2481 \text{ sq in} = 228.9623 \text{ sq in} + DE^2$

$98.2858 \text{ sq in} = DE^2$

$9.9139 = DE$

$B = 17.823 \text{ in} - 9.9139 \text{ in}$

$B = 7.909 \text{ in}$

19. a. $(1.700 \text{ in})^2 = (0.800 \text{ in})^2 + AB^2$

$AB^2 = (1.700 \text{ in})^2 - (0.800 \text{ in})^2$

$AB^2 = 2.890 \text{ sq in} - 0.640 \text{ sq in}$

$AB^2 = 2.250 \text{ sq in}$

$AB = 1.500 \text{ in}$

$ED = 1.850 \text{ in} + 0.800 \text{ in} = 2.650 \text{ in}$

$y^2 = ED^2 + CD^2$

$CD^2 = (2.800 \text{ in})^2 - (2.650 \text{ in})^2$

$CD^2 = 7.840 \text{ sq in} - 7.0225 \text{ sq in}$

$CD^2 = 0.8175 \text{ sq in}$

$CD = 0.904 \text{ in}$

$x = AB + 1.375 \text{ in} + CD$

$x = 1.500 \text{in} + 1.375 \text{ in} + 0.904 \text{ in}$

$x = 3.779 \text{ in}$

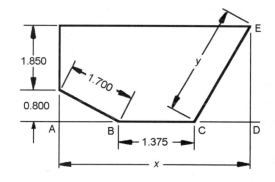

b. $y^2 = ED^2 + CD^2$

$CD^2 = (3.000 \text{ in})^2 - (2.650 \text{ in})^2$

$CD^2 = 9.000 \text{ sq in} - 7.0225 \text{ sq in}$

$CD^2 = 1.9775 \text{ sq in}$

$CD = 1.406 \text{ in}$

$x = AB + 1.375 \text{ in} + CD$

$x = 1.500 \text{ in} + 1.375 \text{ in} + 1.406 \text{ in}$

$x = 4.281 \text{in}$

UNIT **46**   *(continued)*

20. a. AB = 1.100 in

BC = y − (1.100 in + 0.685 in)

= 2.145 in − 1.785 in = 0.360 in

AB² = AC² + BC²

AC² = (1.100 in)² − (0.360 in)²

AC² = 1.210 sq in − 0.1296 sq in

AC² = 1.0804 sq in

AC = 1.039 in

DC = 5.820 in − 2.100 in = 3.720 in

x = DC − AC = 3.720 in − 1.039 in

 = ⌐ 001 in

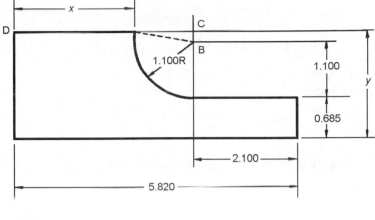

b. BC = y − 1.785 in = 2.265 in − 1.785 in = 0.480 in

AC² = (1.100 in)² − (0.480 in)²

AC² = 1.210 sq in − 0.2304 sq in

AC² = 0.9796 sq in

AC = 0.990 in

x = DC − AC = 3.720 in − 0.990 in = 2.730 in

21. x: AB² = (60 mm)² + (124 mm)² y: CE = 90 mm − 50 mm

AB² = 3600 mm² + 15,376 mm²   CE = 40 mm

AB² = 18,976 mm y² = (40 mm)² + (187.75 mm)²

AB = 137.75 mm y² = 1600 mm² + 35,250.063 mm²

x = 50 mm + 137.75 mm y² = 36,850.063 mm²

x = 187.75 mm y = 191.96 mm

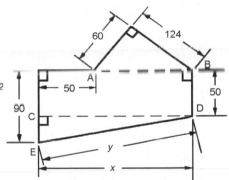

22. Sum of all ∠s = (N − 2)180° = (4 − 2)180 = 2(180) = 360°

a. ∠1 = 360° − (109.62° + 87.0° + 62.05°) = 101.33°

b. ∠2 = 360° − (109.62° + 114.0° + 62.05°) = 74.33°

23. Sum of all ∠s = (N − 2)180° = (8 − 2)180 = 6(180) = 1080°

a. ∠2 = 1080° − [90° + 114° + (360° − 96°) + 83° + 78° = (360° − 64°) + 90°] = 1080° − 1015° = 65°

b. ∠1 = 1800° − [(360° − 96°) + 83° + 78° + (360° − 64°) + 83° + 90° + 90°] = 1080° = 984° = 96°

24. a. ∠BFE = ∠1 = 37°

∠ABF = 180° − (90° + 52°) = 38°

∠CBF = 180° − 38° = 142°

∠BCD = 180° − 84° = 96°

α = 360° − 151° = 209°

The sum of all ∠s in BC DEF = (5 − 2)180° = 540°

∠2 = 540° − (37° + 142° + 96° + 209°) = 56°

b. ∠2 = 540° − (29° + 142° + 96° + 209°) = 64°

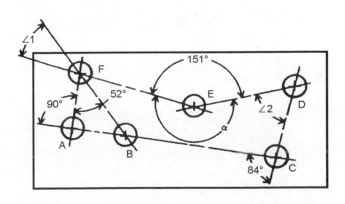

UNIT 47 Introduction to Circles

1. a. Chord
    b. Diameter or Chord
    c. Radius
    d. Center

2. a. Arc
    b. Secant
    c. Tangent
    d. Chord
    e. Tangent Point

3. a. Sector
    b. Segment
    c. Radius
    d. Radius
    e. Chord
    f. Arc

4. a. Central Angle
    b. Inscribed Angle
    c. Radius
    d. Chord
    e. Chord
    f. Arc

5. a. $C = 3.1416(6.500 \text{ in}) = 20.420 \text{ in}$
    b. $C = 3.1416(30.000 \text{ mm}) = 94.248 \text{ mm}$
    c. $C = 2(3.1416)(18.600 \text{ mm}) = 116.868 \text{ mm}$ *116.867*
    d. $C = 2(3.1416)(2.930 \text{ in}) = 18.410 \text{ in}$
    e. $35.000 \text{ in} = 3.1416d$
    $\qquad d = 11.141 \text{ in}$
    f. $218.000 \text{ mm} = 3.1416d$
    $\qquad d = 69.391 \text{ mm}$ *69.392 mm*
    g. $327.000 \text{ mm} = 2(3.1416)(r)$
    $\qquad r = 52.044 \text{ mm}$
    h. $7.680 \text{ in} = 2(3.1416)(r)$
    $\qquad r = 1.222 \text{ in}$

6. $C = 3.1416(30 \text{ in}) = 94.248 \text{ in}$
    $60(94.248 \text{ in}) = 5654.88 \text{ in}$
    $5654.88 \div 12 = 471 \text{ ft}$

7. Inside diameter $= 79.20 \text{ mm} - 2(6.00 \text{ mm}) = 67.20 \text{ mm}$
    $C = 3.1416(67.20 \text{ mm}) = 211.12 \text{ mm}$

8. $C = 3.1416(0.80 \text{ m}) = 2.51328 \text{ m}$
    $5(240)(2.51328 \text{ m}) = 3016 \text{ m}$

9. $C = 3.1416(14 \text{ in})$
    $C = 43.98 \text{ in}$
    Length $= 43.98 \text{ in} + 2(62.00 \text{ in})$
    Length $= 167.98 \text{ in}$

10. Apply Principle 11.
    a. 2.67″   b. 2.67″

11. Apply Principle 12.
    a. 4.090″   b. 3.980″

12. Apply Principle 13.
    a. $\dfrac{80°}{140°} = \dfrac{160 \text{ mm}}{\overset{\frown}{HP}}$
    $\overset{\frown}{HP} = 280 \text{ mm}$
    b. $\dfrac{80°}{140°} = \dfrac{\overset{\frown}{EF}}{284 \text{ mm}}$
    $\overset{\frown}{EF} = 162 \text{ mm}$

13. Apply Principle 13.
    a. $\dfrac{4.800″}{5.760″} = \dfrac{\angle 1}{120°}$
    $\angle 1 = 100°$
    b. $\dfrac{2.064″}{4.128″} = \dfrac{\angle 1}{120°}$
    $\angle = 60°$

14. Apply Principle 14.
    a. (1) $DB = 5.378″ \div 2 = 2.689″$
      (2) $\overset{\frown}{ACB} = 2(3.782″) = 7.564″$
    b. (1) $AB = 2(3.017″) = 6.034″$
      (2) $\overset{\frown}{CB} = 7.308″ \div 2 = 3.654″$

15. Apply Principle 12.
    $\angle EOF = 214° - (101° + 86°) = 214° - 187° = 27°$
    $\angle EOF = \angle HOK$
    $\overset{\frown}{HK} = \overset{\frown}{EF} = 21.23 \text{ mm}$

16. Apply Principle 13.
    $C = 2(3.1416)(1.3″) = 8.168″$
    a. $\angle AOC = 360° - 240° = 120°$
    $\dfrac{120°}{360°} = \dfrac{\overset{\frown}{ABC}}{8.168′}$
    $\overset{\frown}{ABC} = 2.723″$
    b. $\overset{\frown}{ADC} = 8.168′ - 2.300″ = 5.868″$
    $\dfrac{\angle 1}{360°} = \dfrac{5.868″}{8.168″}$
    $\angle 1 = 258.63″$ *or* $258°38′$

17. Apply Principle 13.

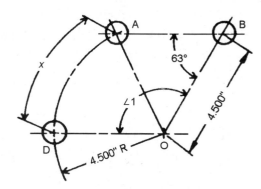

$\triangle$ AOB is isosceles; $\angle AOB = 180° - 2(63)° = 54°$
$C = 2(3.1416)(4.500″) = 28.274″$
a. $\dfrac{5.100″}{28.274″} = \dfrac{\angle AOD}{360°}$
$\angle AOD = 64.936°$ *or* $64°56′$
$\angle 1 = 64°56′ + 54° = 118°56′$
b. $\dfrac{4.750″}{28.274″} = \dfrac{\angle AOD}{360°}$
$\angle AOD = 60.480° = 60°29′$
$\angle 1 = 60°29′ + 54° = 114°29′$

UNIT **47** (*continued*)

18. Apply Principle 14 and the Pythagorean Theorem.

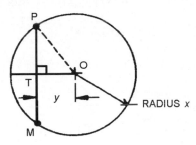

a. PO = radius x = 7.500″

$$PO^2 = y^2 + PT^2$$

$$(7.500 \text{ in})^2 = (4.500 \text{ in})^2 + PT^2$$

$$PT^2 = 56.250 \text{ sq in} - 20.250 \text{ sq in}$$

$$PT^2 = 36 \text{ sq in}$$

$$PT = 6 \text{ in}$$

$$PM = 2PT = 12.000 \text{ in}$$

b. $$PO^2 = y^2 + PT^2$$

$$(8.000 \text{ in})^2 = (4.800 \text{ in})^2 + PT^2$$

$$PT^2 = 64.000 \text{ sq in} - 23.040 \text{ sq in}$$

$$PT^2 = 40.960 \text{ sq in}$$

$$PT = 6.400 \text{ in}$$

$$PM = 2PT = 12.800 \text{ in}$$

19. Apply Principle 13.

a. A circumference = 360°

$$\frac{3.200''}{14.400''} = \frac{\angle 1}{360°}$$

$$\angle 1 = 80°$$

b. $$\frac{x}{14.400''} = \frac{36°}{360°}$$

$$x = 1.440''$$

20. Apply Principle 14 and the Pythagorean Theorem.

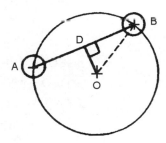

a. OB = radius x = 8.000 in

$$OB^2 = DO^2 + BD^2$$

$$(8.000 \text{ in})^2 = (2.100 \text{ in})^2 + BD^2$$

$$BD^2 = 64.000 \text{ sq in} - 4.410 \text{ sq in}$$

$$BD^2 = 59.590 \text{ sq in}$$

$$BD = 7.719 \text{ in}$$

$$AB = 2(7.719 \text{ in}) = 15.438 \text{ in}$$

b. $$OB^2 = DO^2 + BD^2$$

$$(1.200 \text{ in})^2 = (0.700 \text{ in})^2 + BD^2$$

$$BD^2 = 1.440 \text{ sq in} - 0.490 \text{ sq in}$$

$$BD^2 = 0.950 \text{ sq in}$$

$$BD = 0.975 \text{ in}$$

$$AB = 2(0.975 \text{ in}) = 1.950 \text{ in}$$

21. Apply Principle 15.

a. (1) $\angle E = 180° - (90° + 41° \, 21') = 48°\,39'$

(2) $\angle F = 180° - (48°39' + 107°18') = 24°03'$

b. (1) $\angle E = 180° - (90° + 48°20') = 41°40'$

(2) $\angle F = 180° - (41°40' + 107°18') = 31°02'$

UNIT **47** (*continued*)

22. Apply Principle 16.

a. (1) ∠1 = 67° ÷ 2 = 33°30′

   (2) $x = y$ = 137.20 mm

b. (1) ∠ABC = 2(33.8°) = 67.6°

   (2) $y = x$ = 207.70 mm

23. Apply Principle 15 and the Pythagorean Theorem.

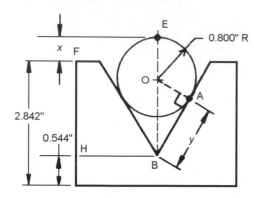

a. ∠OAB = 90°

$OB^2 = OA^2 + y^2$

$OB^2 = (0.800 \text{ in})^2 + (1.400 \text{ in})^2$

$OB^2 = 0.640 \text{ sq in} + 1.960 \text{ sq in}$

$OB^2 = 2.600 \text{ sq in}$

OB = 1.612 in

FH = 2.842 in − 0.544 = 2.298 in

x = OE + OB − FH

x = 0.800 in + 1.612in = 2.298 in

x = 0.114 in

b. $OB^2 = (0.800 \text{ in})^2 + (1.800 \text{ in})^2$

$OB^2 = 0.640 \text{ sq in} + 3.240 \text{ sq in}$

$OB^2 = 3.880 \text{ sq in}$

OB = 1.970 in

x = OE + OB − FH

x = 0.800 in + 1.970 in = 2.298 in

x = 0.472 in

24. Apply Principle 16.

a. ∠F = ∠G = ∠E = 90°

∠FBO = 180° − (90° + 58°) = 32°

∠GBO = ∠FBO = 32°

∠GAO = 180° − (32° + 109°) = 39°

∠EAO = ∠GAO = 39°

  ∠2 = 180° − (90° + 39°) = 51°

b. ∠GBO = ∠FBO = 32°

∠GAO = 180° − (32° + 118°45′) = 29°15′

∠EAO = ∠GAO = 29°15′

  ∠2 = 180° − (90° + 29°15′) = 60°45′

25. Apply Principle 17.

a.   EK(GK) = FK(HK)

(150 mm)(GK) = (75.00 mm)(337.50 mm)

     GK = 168.75 mm

b.   GK(EK) = FK(HK)

(120.00 mm)(EK) = (75.00 mm)(337.50 mm)

     EK = 210.94 mm

26. Apply Principle 17.

a. PM = 2.584 in ÷ 2 + 0.614 in = 1.906 in

PS = 1.292 in − 0.614in = 0.678 in

PE = PT − ET = 1.800 in − 1.200 in = 0.600 in

    PM(PS) = (PE)x

(1.906 in)(0.678 in) = (0.600 in)x

     x = 2.154 in

b. PM = 1.906 in

PS = 0.678 in

PE = 2.000 in − 1.200 in = 0.800 in

    PM(PS) = (PE)x

(1.906 in)(0.678 in) = (0.800 in)x

     x = 1.615 in

UNIT 48 Arcs and Angles of Circles, Tangent Circles

1. Arc Length $= \dfrac{90°}{360°}[2(3.1416)(3.500\text{ in})] = 5.498$ in

2. $\overparen{ADC} = 360° - 85° = 275°$

   Arc Length $= \dfrac{275°}{360°}[2(3.1416)(60.000\text{ mm})] = 287.980$ mm

   (handwritten: 6979)

3. $510.000\text{ mm} = \dfrac{\angle 1}{360°}[2(3.1416)(120.000\text{ mm})]$

   $\angle 1 = 243.506°$ *or* $243°30'$

4. $22.700\text{ in} = \dfrac{\text{Central Angle}}{360°}[2(3.1416)(5.200\text{ in})]$

   Central Angle $= 250.118°$

   $\angle 1 = 360° - 250.118° = 109.882°$ *or* $109°53'$

5. $10.700\text{ in} = \dfrac{72°}{360°}[2(3.1416)r]$

   $r = 14.921$ in

6. $620.700\text{ mm} = \dfrac{69.30°}{360°}[2(3.1416)r]$

   $r = 513.180\text{ mm}$

   (handwritten: .182)

7. Apply Principle 18a.
   a. (1) $\overparen{DC} = \angle 1 = 76°$
      (2) $\angle EOD = 107° - 76° = 31°$
      (3) $\overparen{ABC} = 98° + 36° = 134°$
   b. (1) $\overparen{DC} = \angle 1 = 63.76°$
      (2) $\angle EOD = 107° - 63.76° = 43.24°$
      (3) $\overparen{BCD} = 36° + 63° = 99°$ *(handwritten: .76)*

8. Apply Principle 18a.
   a. (1) $\overparen{HK} = \angle HOK = \angle 1 = 63°$
      (2) $\overparen{HM} = 180° - \angle 1 = 180° - 63° = 117°$
   b. (1) $\overparen{HK} = \angle HOK = \angle 1 = 59°47'$
      (2) $\overparen{HM} = 180° - \angle 1 = 180° - 59°47' = 120°13'$

9. Apply Principle 18b.
   a. (1) $\angle 1 = \dfrac{1}{2}(46° + 36°) = \dfrac{1}{2}(82°) = 41°$
      (2) $\angle 2 = 180° - 41° = 139°$
   b. (1) $\angle 1 = \dfrac{1}{2}(39° + 36°) = \dfrac{1}{2}(75°) = 37°30'$
      (2) $\angle 2 = 180° - 37°30' = 142°30'$

10. Apply Principle 18b.
    a. $82° = \dfrac{1}{2}(\overparen{AB} + \overparen{DC})$

    $82° = \dfrac{1}{2}\overparen{AB} + \dfrac{1}{2}(35°)$

    $\dfrac{1}{2}\overparen{AB} = 82° - 17.5°$

    $\overparen{AB} = 129°$

10. b. $82° = \dfrac{1}{2}(\overparen{AB} + \overparen{DC})$

    $82° = \dfrac{1}{2}(127°) + \dfrac{1}{2}\overparen{DC}$

    $\dfrac{1}{2}\overparen{DC} = 82° - 63°30'$

    $\overparen{DC} = 37°$

11. Apply Principle 18c.
    a. (1) $\overparen{EF} = 2(47°) = 94°$
       (2) $\angle 4 = \dfrac{1}{2}(32°) = 16°$
    b. (1) $\angle 3 = \dfrac{1}{2}(103°) = 51°30'$
       (2) $\overparen{GH} = 2(17°53') = 35°46'$

12. Apply Principle 18c.
    a. (1) $\overparen{KTP} = 2(90°) = 180°$
       (2) $\overparen{PT} = 2(25°) = 50°$
       (3) $\overparen{MP} = \overparen{MPT} - \overparen{PT} = 95° - 50° = 45°$
    b. (1) $\overparen{KTP} = 2(90°) = 180°$
       (2) $\overparen{PT} = 2(17°30') = 35°$
       (3) $\overparen{MP} = \overparen{MPT} - \overparen{PT} = 103° - 35° = 68°$

13. Apply Principle 19.
    a. (1) $\angle 1 = \dfrac{1}{2}(116°) = 58°$
       (2) $\angle 2 = \dfrac{1}{2}\overparen{AC} = \dfrac{1}{2}(180°) = 90°$
    b. (1) $\angle 1 = \dfrac{1}{2}(112°56') = 56°28'$
       (2) $\angle 2 = \dfrac{1}{2}\overparen{AC} = \dfrac{1}{2}(180°) = 90°$

14. Apply Principle 19.
    a. (1) $\angle EFD = \dfrac{1}{2}(84°) = 42°$
       (2) $\angle HFP = 180° - (42° + 87°) = 51°$
          $\overparen{HF} = 2(51°) = 102°$
       (3) $\angle FHP = \dfrac{1}{2}\overparen{HF} = \dfrac{1}{2}(102°) = 51°$
          $\angle 1 = 180° - 51° = 129°$
    b. (1) $\angle EFD = \dfrac{1}{2}(79°) = 39°30'$
       (2) $\angle HFP = 180° - (39°30' + 87°) = 53°30'$
          $\overparen{HF} = 2(53°30') = 107°$
       (3) $\angle FHP = \dfrac{1}{2}\overparen{HF} = \dfrac{1}{2}(107°) = 53°30'$
          $\angle 1 = 180° - 53°30' = 126°30'$

UNIT **48** (*continued*)

15. Apply Principle 20.

    a. (1) $\angle 1 = \frac{1}{2}(113°08' - 20°18') = \frac{1}{2}(92°50') = 46°25'$

       (2) $\angle 2 = \frac{1}{2}(95°23' - 38°07') = \frac{1}{2}(57°16') = 28°38'$

    b. (1) $\angle 1 = \frac{1}{2}(113°08' - 25°17') = \frac{1}{2}(87°51') = 43°56'$

       (2) $\angle 2 = \frac{1}{2}(95°23' - 35°24') = \frac{1}{2}(59°59') = 30°0'$

16. Apply Principle 20.

    a. $\overset{\frown}{ABCD} = \overset{\frown}{AB} + \overset{\frown}{BC} + \overset{\frown}{CD} = 72°20' + 108°19' + 50°18' = 230°57'$

      $\overset{\frown}{AD} = 360° - 230°57' = 129°03'$

      (1) $\angle 1 = \frac{1}{2}(\overset{\frown}{ABCD} - \overset{\frown}{AD}) = \frac{1}{2}(230°57' - 129°03') = \frac{1}{2}(101°54') = 50°57'$

      (2) $\angle 2 = \frac{1}{2}(\overset{\frown}{AD} + \overset{\frown}{CD} - \overset{\frown}{AB}) = \frac{1}{2}(129°03' = 50°18' - 72°20') = \frac{1}{2}(107°01') = 53°31'$

      (3) $\angle 3 = 180$ roman $° - (\angle 1 + \angle 2) = 180° - (50°57' + 53°31') = 180° - 104°28' = 75°32'$

    b. $\overset{\frown}{ABCD} = 360° - \overset{\frown}{AD} = 360° - 106°05' = 253°55'$

      (1) $\angle 1 = \frac{1}{2}(\overset{\frown}{ABCD} - \overset{\frown}{AD}) = \frac{1}{2}(253°55' - 106°05') = \frac{1}{2}(147°50') = 73°55'$

      (2) $\overset{\frown}{AB} = 360° - (106°05' + 43°15' + 108°19') = 360° - 257°39' = 102°21'$

        $\angle 2 = \frac{1}{2}(\overset{\frown}{AD} + \overset{\frown}{CD} - \overset{\frown}{AB}) = \frac{1}{2}(106°05' + 43°15' - 102°21') = \frac{1}{2}(46°59') = 23°30'$

      (3) $\angle 3 = 180° - (\angle 1 + \angle 2) = 180° - (73°55' + 23°30') = 180° - 97°25' = 82°35'$

17. Apply Principle 20.

    a. (1) $144° - 85° = 59°$

          $\angle 1 = \frac{1}{2}(59° - \overset{\frown}{DH})$

          $24° = \frac{1}{2}(59° - \overset{\frown}{DH})$

          $\overset{\frown}{DH} = 11°$

      (2) $\angle 2 = \frac{1}{2}(144° - \overset{\frown}{EDH})$

          $60° = 72° - \frac{1}{2}\overset{\frown}{EDH}$

          $\overset{\frown}{EDH} = 24°$

    b. (1) $\angle 1 = \frac{1}{2}(59° - \overset{\frown}{DH})$

          $29° = 29°30' - \frac{1}{2}\overset{\frown}{DH}$

          $\overset{\frown}{DH} = 1°$

      (2) $\angle 2 = \frac{1}{2}(144° - \overset{\frown}{EDH})$

          $64° = 72° - \frac{1}{2}\overset{\frown}{EDH}$

          $\overset{\frown}{EDH} = 16°$

18. Apply Principle 21a.

    a. $x = \frac{3.756''}{2} - \frac{1.622''}{2} = 1.067''$

    b. Radius A $= 0.975'' + \frac{1.026''}{2} = 0.975'' + 0.513'' = 1.488''$

      Dia A $= 2(1.488'') = 2.976''$

19. Apply Principle 21b.

    a. Radius Circle B = 28.95 mm − 24.93 mm = 4.02 mm

      Radius Circle A = 24.93 mm − 4.02 mm = 20.91 mm

      Dia A = 2(20.91 mm) = 41.82 mm

    b. Radius Circle B = 114.48 mm − 78.36 mm = 36.12 mm

      Radius Circle A = 78.36 mm − 36.12 mm = 42.24 mm

      Dia A = 2(42.24 mm) = 84.48 mm

20. Apply Principle 20.

    a. (1) In $\triangle GHF$:

          $\angle GHF = \angle 1 = 67°$

          $\angle FGH = 70°$

          $\angle F = 180° - (67° + 70° = 43°$

          $\overset{\frown}{AB} = 2(\angle F) = 2(43°) = 86°$

UNIT **48** (*continued*)

20. a. (2) In △PMG:

$\angle G = 70°$

$\angle M = 180° - \angle 2 = 180° - 93° = 87°$

$\angle P = 180° - (70° + 87°) = 180° - 157° = 23°$

$\angle P = \frac{1}{2}(\overset{\frown}{BC} - \overset{\frown}{DE})$

$23° = \frac{1}{2}(62°) - \frac{1}{2}DE$

$\overset{\frown}{DE} = 16°$

b. (1) $\angle F = 180° - (75° + 70°) = 35°$

$\overset{\frown}{AB} = 2(\angle F) = 2(35°) = 70°$

(2) In △PMG:

$\angle G = 70°$

$\angle M = 180° - 85° = 95°$

$\angle P = 180° - (70° + 95°) = 15°$

$\angle P = \frac{1}{2}(62°) - \frac{1}{2}\overset{\frown}{DE}$

$15° = 31° - \frac{1}{2}\overset{\frown}{DE}$

$\overset{\frown}{DE} = 32°$

21. Apply Principle 21b and the Pythagorean Theorem

a. $x^2 = \left(\frac{1.600\ in}{2} + \frac{1.000\ in}{2}\right)^2 + \left(\frac{1.600\ in}{2} + \frac{1.200\ in}{2}\right)^2$

$x^2 = (1.300\ in)^2 + (1.400\ in)^2$

$x^2 = 1.690\ sq\,in + 1.960\ sq\,in$

$x^2 = 3.650\ sq\,in$

$x = 1.911\ in$

b. $x^2 = \left(\frac{1.600\ in}{2} + \frac{0.800\ in}{2}\right)^2 + \left(\frac{1.600\ in}{2} + \frac{1.200\ in}{2}\right)^2$

$x^2 = (1.200\ in)^2 + (1.400\ in)^2$

$x^2 = 1.440\ sq\,in + 1.960\ sq\,in$

$x^2 = 3.400\ sq\,in$

$x = 1.844\ in$

22. Apply Principle 21a and the Pythagorean Theorem.

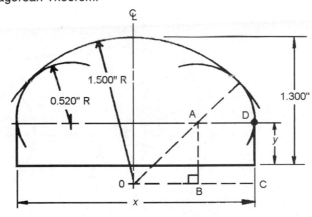

a. $AO = 1.500\ in - 0.520\ in = 0.980\ in$

$AB = 1.500\ in - 1.300\ in + y$

$AB = 1.500\ in - 1.300\ in + 0.350\ in$

$AB = 0.550\ in$

$AO^2 = AB^2 + OB^2$

$(0.980in)^2 = (0.550\ in)^2 + OB^2$

$0.9604\ sq\,in = 0.3025\ sq\,in + OB^2$

$OB^2 = 0.6579\ sq\,in$

$OB = 0.811\ in$

$BC = AD = 0.520\ in$

$x = 2(OB + BC) = 2(0.811\ in + 0.520\ in) = 2.662\ in$

b. $AO = 0.980\ in$

$AB = 1.500\ in - 1.300\ in + 0.140\ in = 0.610\ in$

$AO^2 = AB^2 + OB^2$

$(0.980\ in)^2 = (0.610\ in)^2 + OB^2$

$OB^2 = 0.5883\ sq\,in$

$OB = 0.767\ in$

$BC = AD = 0.520\ in$

$x = 2(OB + BC) = 2(0.767\ in + 0.520\ in) = 2.574\ in$

UNIT **48** *(continued)*

23. Apply Principles 18, 20b, and 16.

a. $\overset{\frown}{ADC} = \frac{1}{2}(360°) = 180°$

$\overset{\frown}{CB} = 2(22°) = 44°$

$\overset{\frown}{ADCB} = \overset{\frown}{ADC} + \overset{\frown}{CB} = 180° + 44° = 224°$

$\overset{\frown}{AB} = 360° - 224° = 136°$

$\angle AEB = \frac{1}{2}(224° - 136°) = 44°$

$\angle 1 = \frac{1}{2}(44°) = 22°$

b. $\overset{\frown}{ADC} = 180°$

$\overset{\frown}{CB} = 2(30°54') = 61°48'$

$\overset{\frown}{ADCB} = 180° + 61°48' = 241°48'$

$\overset{\frown}{AB} = 360° - 241°48' = 118°12'$

$\angle AEB = \frac{1}{2}(241°48' - 118°12') = 61°48'$

$\angle 1 = \frac{1}{2}(61°48') = 30°54'$

24. Apply Principle 21 and the Pythagorean Theorem.

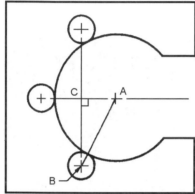

A = 0.270 in + (0.260 in ÷ 2) = 0.400 in

CA = 0.650 in − 0.270 in = 0.380 in

AB = 0.650 in + (0.260 in ÷ 2) = 0.780 in

$$AB^2 = CB^2 + CA^2$$

$$(0.780 \text{ in})^2 = CB^2 + (0.380 \text{ in})^2$$

$$0.6084 \text{ sq in} = CB^2 + 0.1444 \text{ sq in}$$

$$CB = \sqrt{0.4640 \text{ sq in}}$$

$$CB = 0.681 \text{ in}$$

$$B = 2(CB) = 2(0.681 \text{ in}) = 1.362 \text{ in}$$

25. Apply Principles 18a, 16, and 10.

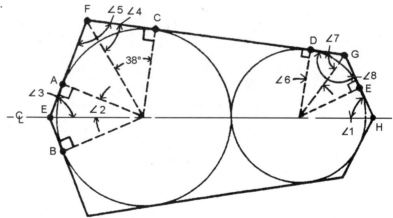

a. $\angle 2 = \frac{1}{2}\overset{\frown}{AB} = \frac{1}{2}(46°) = 23°$

$\angle 3 = 180° - (90° + 23°) = 67°$

$\angle 4 = 180° - (90° + 38°) = 52°$

$\angle 5 = 2(\angle 4) = 104°$

$\angle 6 = \frac{1}{2}\overset{\frown}{DE} = \frac{1}{2}(66°) = 33°$

$\angle 7 = 180° - (90° + 33°) = 57°$

$\angle 8 = 2(\angle 7) = 2(57°) = 114°$

Interior degrees in EFGH $= (N - 2)(180°)$

$= (4 - 2)180° = 360°$

$\angle 1 = 360° - (\angle 3 + \angle 5 + \angle 8)$

$= 360° - (67° + 104° + 114°) = 75°$

b. $\angle 2 = \frac{1}{2}\overset{\frown}{AB} = \frac{1}{2}(53°) = 26°30'$

$\angle 3 = 180° - (90° + 26°30') = 63°30'$

$\angle 5 = 104°$

$\angle 6 = \frac{1}{2}\overset{\frown}{DE} = \frac{1}{2}(70°) = 35°$

$\angle 7 = 180° - (90° + 35°) = 55°$

$\angle 8 = 2(\angle 7) = 2(55°) = 110°$

$\angle 1 = 360° - (\angle 3 + \angle 5 + \angle 8)$

$= 360° - (63°30' + 104° + 110°) = 82°30' \text{ or } 82.50°$

UNIT 48 (*continued*)

26. a. BT = 72.40 mm   2 = 36.20 mm

$AB^2 = AT^2 + BT^2$

$AB^2 = (95.00 \text{ mm})^2 + (36.20 \text{ mm})^2$

$AB^2 = 9025 \text{ mm}^2 + 1310.44 \text{ mm}^2$

$AB = \sqrt{10{,}355.44 \text{ mm}^2}$

C = AB = 101.66 mm

b. TC = 30.80 mm   2 = 15.40 mm

$AC^2 = AT^2 + TC^2$

$AC^2 = (95.00 \text{ mm})^2 + (15.40 \text{ mm})^2$

$AC^2 = 9025 \text{ mm}^2 + 237.16 \text{ mm}^2$

$AC = \sqrt{9262.16 \text{ mm}^2}$

AC = 96.24 mm

D = AC = 96.24 mm

UNIT 49 Fundamental Geometric Constructions

All problems are constructed.

UNIT 50 Achievement Review—Section Four

1. a. 123°41′

   b. 61°89′ = 62°29′

   c. 42°19′13″

   d. 57°74′ − 44°58′ = 13°16′

   e. 108°92′ = 109°32′

   f. 21°69′129″ = 21°71′9″ = 22°11′9″

   g. 43.5° or 42°30′

   h. 25°50′

2. $4\angle A + 46°20′ + 81°55′ + 24°17′ = 360°$

   $\qquad\qquad 4\angle A = 360° − 152°32′$

   $\qquad\qquad 4\angle A = 207°28′$

   $\qquad\qquad \angle A = 51°52′$

3. ∠3 = ∠4 = ∠5 = ∠6.

   Therefore, ∠3 + ∠4 + ∠5 + ∠6 = 4∠4

   $\qquad 4\angle 3 + \angle 1 + \angle 2 = 720°$

   $4\angle 3 + 2(68°42′18″) = 720°$

   $4\angle 3 + 136°84′36″ = 720°$

   $4\angle 3 + 137°24′36″ = 720°$

   $\qquad\qquad 4\angle 3 = 719°59′60″ − 137°24′36″$

   $\qquad\qquad 4\angle 3 = 582°35′24″$

   $\qquad\qquad \angle 3 = 145°38′51″$

4. $0.85° = 0.85 \times 60′ = 51′$

   $68.85° = 68°51′$

5. $0.1420° = 0.1420 \times 60′ = 8.52′$

   $0.52′ = 0.52 \times 60″ = 31″$

   $64.1420° = 64°8′31″$

6. $23′ = 23 \div 60 = 0.38°$

   $37°23′ = 37.38°$

7. $43″ = 43 \div 60 = 0.71667′$

   $38.71667′ = 38.71667 \div 60 = 0.64528°$

   $103°38′43″ = 103.6453°$

8. ∠1 = 58°   ∠4 = 10°   ∠6 = 73°

   ∠2 = 111°   ∠5 = 90°   ∠7 = 198°

   ∠3 = 20°

9. a. 10°30′   b. 19°45′   c. 29°30′

10. a. 23°   b. 72°19′   c. 35°12′07″

11. a. 139°   b. 80°28′   c. 76°56′33″

12. ∠1 = 94°40′

    $\angle 2 = 180° − \angle 1 = 179°60′ − 94°40′ = 85°20′$

    ∠3 = 94°40′

    $\angle 4 = 180° − \angle 3 = 179°60′ − 94°40′ = 85°20′$

    ∠5 = ∠2 = 85°20′

    ∠6 = ∠5 = 85°20′

    ∠7 = 81°

    $\angle 8 = 142° − \angle 7 = 142° − 81° = 61°$

    $\angle 9 = 180° − 142° = 38°$

    ∠10 = 8 = 61°

13. a. (1) ∠1 = 39°43′

    (2) Side *a* = 2 ft ÷ 2 = 1 ft

UNIT 50 (*continued*)

13. b. (1) $\angle 1 = 180° - (90° + 30°) = 180° - 120° = 60°$

    (2) Side $b = 9.6$ in

    (3) Side $c = 9.6$ in $\div 2 = 4.8$ in

  c. (1) $\angle 1 = 35° \div 2 = 17.5° = 17°30'$

    (2) $\angle 2 = (180° - 35°) \div 2 = 145° \div 2 = 72.5° = 72°30'$

14. a. $c^2 = a^2 + b^2$

    $c^2 = (8.400 \text{ in})^2 + (9.200 \text{ in})^2$

    $c^2 = 70.560 \text{ sq in} + 84.640 \text{ sq in}$

    $c^2 = 155.200 \text{ sq in}$

    $c = 12.458$

  b. $c^2 = a^2 + b^2$

    $(150.00 \text{ mm})^2 = a^2 + (90.00 \text{ mm})^2$

    $a^2 = 22{,}500 \text{ mm}^2 - 8{,}100 \text{ mm}^2$

    $a^2 = 14{,}400 \text{ mm}^2$

    $a = 120$ mm

15. $(n - 2)180° = (6 - 2)180° = 720°$

  $\angle 1 = 720° - [90° + 31° + (360° - 77°) + 38° + 80°]$

  $\angle 1 = 720° - 522°$

  $\angle 1 = \cancel{190°}$ $198°$

16. $C = 2(3.1416)(5.360 \text{ in}) = 33.678$ in

17. $360.00 \text{ mm} = 3.1416d$

    $d = 144.59$ mm

18. a. $CF = CD \div 2 = 184 \text{ mm} \div 2 = 92$ mm

    $\overparen{CED} = 2\overparen{CE} = 2(118 \text{ mm}) = 236$ mm

  b. $CD = 2FD = 2(26 \text{ mm}) = 52$ mm

    $\overparen{ED} = \overparen{CED} \div 2 = 78 \text{ mm} \div 2 = 39$ mm

19. a. $AE(EB) = CE(ED)$

    $AE(5.150 \text{ in}) = (3.000 \text{ in})(5.600 \text{ in})$

    $AE = 3.262$ in

  b. $AE(EB) = CE(ED)$

    $(4.200 \text{ in})EB = (3.000 \text{ in})(5.600 \text{ in})$

    $EB = 4.000$ in

    $AB = AE + EB = 4.200 \text{ in} + 4.000 \text{ in} = 8.200$ in

20. $\angle 1$: $\overparen{ABCDE} = 360° - \overparen{AFE} = 360° - 156° = 204°$

    $\angle APE = \dfrac{1}{2}(\overparen{ABCDE} - \overparen{AFE}) = \dfrac{1}{2}(204° - 156°)$

    $= \dfrac{1}{2}(48°) = 24°$

    $\angle 1 = \dfrac{1}{2}(\angle APE) = \dfrac{1}{2}(24°) = 12°$

20. $\angle 2$: In right $\triangle PAO$, $\angle 1 = 12°$ and $\angle PAO = 90°$.

    $\angle 2 = 180° - (90° + 12°) = 78°$

  $\angle 3$: $\angle 3 = \angle 1 = 12°$

  $\angle 4$: $\angle 4 = 90°$

  $\angle 5$: $\overparen{CD} = \overparen{CDE} - \overparen{ED} = 140° - 60° = 80°$

    $\angle 5 = \dfrac{1}{2}\overparen{CD} = \dfrac{1}{2}(80°) = 40°$

  $\angle 6$: $\overparen{BC} = \overparen{BCDE} - \overparen{CDE} = 180° - 140° = 40°$

    $\angle 6 = \dfrac{1}{2}(\overparen{BC}) = \dfrac{1}{2}(40°) = 20°$

  $\angle 7$: $\angle 7 = \dfrac{1}{2}\overparen{ED} = \dfrac{1}{2}(60°) = 30°$

  $\angle 8$: $\angle 8 = \dfrac{1}{2}\overparen{ED} = \dfrac{1}{2}(60°) = 30°$

  $\angle 9$: $\overparen{CD} = \overparen{CDE} - \overparen{ED} = 140° - 60° = 80°$

    $\overparen{BAFE} = 180°$

    $\angle 9 = \dfrac{1}{2}(\overparen{CD} + \overparen{BAFE}) = \dfrac{1}{2}(80° + 180°)$

    $= \dfrac{1}{2}(260°) = 130°$

  $\angle 10$: $\angle 10 = 180° - \angle 9 = 180° - 130° = 50°$

21. a. Arc Length $= \dfrac{110°}{360°}[2(3.1416)(4.700 \text{ in})]$

    $= 9.023$ in

  b. $478.60 \text{ mm} = \dfrac{\angle 1}{360°}[2(3.1416)(105.00 \text{ mm})]$

    $\angle 1 = 261.17°$

22. a. Dia $H \div 2 = 14.520 \text{ in} \div 2 = 7.260$ in

    Dia $M = 2(7.260 \text{ in} + d)$

    $= 2(7.260 \text{ in} + 8.300 \text{ in}) = 31.120$ in

  b. Dia $M \div 2 = 36.900 \text{ in} \div 2 = 18.450$ in

    $18.450 \text{ in} - d = 18.450 \text{ in} - 12.620 \text{ in}$

    $= 5.830$ in

    $d = 6.790$ in

    $18.450 - 2(5.830) = 6.790$

    $f = 6.790 \text{ in} + e = 6.790 \text{ in} + 15.840 \text{ in}$

    $= 22.630$ in

23. Problem to be laid out using construction methods.

UNIT **50** (*continued*)

23. $\overset{\frown}{BC} = 2(\angle BEC) = 2(40°) = 80°$

$\overset{\frown}{AB} = \overset{\frown}{ABC} - \overset{\frown}{BC} = 130° - 80° = 50°$

$\angle 1 = \frac{1}{2}(\overset{\frown}{AB}) = \frac{1}{2}(50°) = 25°$

$\angle 2 = \frac{1}{2}(\overset{\frown}{CDE}) = \frac{1}{2}(134°) = 67°$

$\overset{\frown}{AE} = 360° - (\overset{\frown}{ABC} + \overset{\frown}{CDE} = 360° - (130° + 134°) = 96°$

$\angle 3 = \frac{1}{2}(\overset{\frown}{AE}) = \frac{1}{2}(96°) = 48°$

$\angle EAC = \frac{1}{2}\overset{\frown}{CDE} = \frac{1}{2}(134°) = 67°$

$\angle 4 = \angle EAC - \angle CAD = 67 - 38° - 17° = 29°$

$\angle 5 = \frac{1}{2}\overset{\frown}{AE} = \frac{1}{2}(96°) = 48°$

$\angle 6 = \frac{1}{2}(\overset{\frown}{DC} + \overset{\frown}{AE}) = \frac{1}{2}(76° + 96°) = \frac{1}{2}(172°) = 86°$

$\angle 7 = 180° - \angle 6 = 180° - 86° = 94°$

$\angle 8 = \frac{1}{2}(\overset{\frown}{BCD} + \overset{\frown}{AE}) = \frac{1}{2}[(180° + 76°) + 96°] = \frac{1}{2}(252°) = 126°$

$\angle 9 = 180° - \angle 8 = 180° - 126° = 54°$

$\angle 10 = \frac{1}{2}(\overset{\frown}{BC} + \overset{\frown}{AE}) - \frac{1}{2}(80° + 96°) - \frac{1}{2}(176°) = 88°$

24. a. $y - x = 5.10 \text{ in} - 1.50 \text{ in}$

Dia A $= 2(1.50 \text{ in}) = 3.00 \text{ in}$

24. b. Dia A $\div 2 = 8.76 \text{ in} \div 2 = 4.38 \text{ in}$

$x - 4.38 = 10.52 \text{ in} - 4.38 \text{ in} = 6.14 \text{ in}$

Dia B $= 2(6.14 \text{ in}) = 12.28 \text{ in}$

$t - \text{Dia A} + \text{Dia B} = 8.76 \text{ in} + 12.128 \text{ in} = 21.04 \text{ in}$

25. $\overset{\frown}{ADEFC} = 360° - \overset{\frown}{AHC} = 360° - 116 = 244°$

$\angle ABC = \frac{1}{2}(\overset{\frown}{ADEFC} - \overset{\frown}{AHC}) = \frac{1}{2}(244° - 116°) = 64°$

$\angle 1 = \frac{1}{2}(\angle ABC) = \frac{1}{2}(64°) = 32°$

$\angle 2 = 180° - (\angle OAB + \angle 1) = 180° - 90° + 32° = 58°$

$\overset{\frown}{FC} = \overset{\frown}{EFC} - \overset{\frown}{EF} = 140° - 64° = 76°$

$\angle 3 = \frac{1}{2}(\overset{\frown}{FC} - \overset{\frown}{CH}) = \frac{1}{2}(76° - 42°) = 17°$

$\angle CBO = \angle 1 = 32°$

$\angle 4 = \angle CBO - \angle 3 = 32° - 17° = 15°$

$\angle 5 = \frac{1}{2}\overset{\frown}{EF} = \frac{1}{2}(64°) = 32°$

$\overset{\frown}{ED} = \overset{\frown}{DEFC} - \overset{\frown}{EFC} = 180° - 140° = 40°$

$\angle 6 = \frac{1}{2}\overset{\frown}{ED} = \frac{1}{2}40° = 20°$

$\angle 7 = \frac{1}{2}\overset{\frown}{FC} = \frac{1}{2}76° = 38°$

$\angle 8 = \frac{1}{2}\overset{\frown}{CH} = \frac{1}{2}42° = 21°$

$\overset{\frown}{DFC} = \frac{1}{2}\overset{\frown}{DAHC} = \frac{1}{2}(180°) = 90°$

$\angle 9 = \angle DFC - \angle 8 = 90° - 21° = 69°$

$\angle 10 = \frac{1}{2}(\overset{\frown}{DAHC} + \overset{\frown}{EF}) = \frac{1}{2}(180° + 64°) = 122°$

UNIT **50** *(continued)*

26.

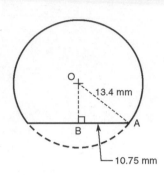

$$BA = \frac{1}{2}(21.5\ mm) = 10.75\ mm$$

$$OA = 26.8\ mm \div 2 = 13.4\ mm$$

$$OA^2 = OB^2 + BA^2$$

$$(13.4\ mm)^2 = OB^2 + (10.75\ mm)^2$$

$$(179.56\ mm)^2 = OB^2 + 115.5625\ mm^2$$

$$OB = \sqrt{63.9975\ mm^2}$$

$$OB = 8.0\ mm$$

$$x = 8.0\ mm$$

27. Pitch circle circumference $= \pi$(Pitch diameter)

$$= \pi(4.1250\ in)$$

$$= 12.95907\ in$$

Circular Pitch $= 12.95907\ in \div$ number of spaces between teeth

$$= 12.95907\ in \div 26$$

$$= 0.4984\ in$$

28.

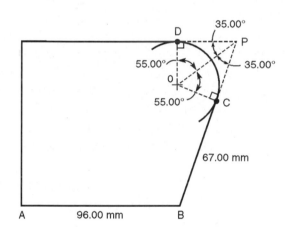

$$\angle DPO = \angle CPO = 70.00° \div 2 = 35.00°$$

$$Rt \triangle PDO \cong rt \triangle PCO$$

$$\angle DOP = \angle COP = 180° - (90° + 35.00°) = 55.00°$$

$$\angle DOC = 2(55.00°) = 110.00°$$

$$Circumference = 2\pi r = 2(\pi)(50.00\ mm) = 314.159\ mm$$

$$\frac{\overset{\frown}{DC}}{314.159\ mm} = \frac{110°}{360°}$$

$$360\overset{\frown}{DC} = 314.159\ mm(110)$$

$$\overset{\frown}{DC} = 95.993\ mm$$

29.

$$AO^2 = AG^2 + OG^2$$

$$AO^2 = (68.00\ cm)^2 + (20.00\ cm)^2$$

$$AO = \sqrt{5,024\ cm^2}$$

$$AO = 70.88\ cm$$

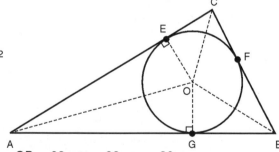

$$GB = 98\ cm - 68\ cm = 30\ cm$$

$$OB^2 = OG^2 + GB^2$$

$$OB^2 = (20.00\ cm)^2 + (30.00\ cm)^2$$

$$OB = \sqrt{1300.00\ cm^2}$$

$$OB = 36.06\ cm$$

$$EC = AC - AE - 87.00\ cm - 68.00\ cm = 19.00\ cm$$

$$OC^2 = EC^2 + EO^2$$

$$OC^2 = (19.00\ cm)^2 + (20.00\ cm)^2$$

$$OC = \sqrt{761.00\ cm^2}$$

$$OC = 27.59\ cm$$

UNIT **50**   (*continued*)

30.   Radius = 2.620 in ÷ 2 = 1.310 in

MP = MO + OP = 1.310 in = 1.924 in

SP = MS – MP = 2.6200 in – 1.924 in = 0.696 in

PE = PT – ET = 1.9000 in – 1.200 in = 0.700 in

PE(*x*) = MP(SP)

(0.700 in)*x* = 1.924 in (0.696 in)

x = 1.913 in

31.

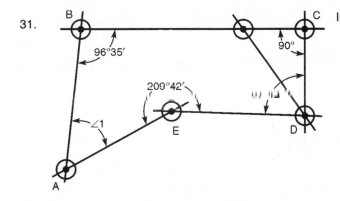

In pentagon ABCDE, ∠B = 180° – 83°25′ = 96°35′

∠C = 180° – 90° = 90°

∠D = 51°10′ = 36°32′ = 87°42′

∠E – 360° – 150°18′ = 209°42′

(5 – 2)180° = 3(180°) = 540°

∠1 = 540° – (96°35′ + 90° + 87°42′ + 209°42′)

∠1 = 56°01′

32.

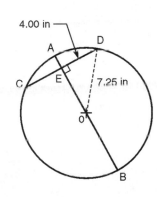

4.00 in

7.25 in

ED = CE = CD ÷ 2 = 8.00 in ÷ 2 = 4.00 in

OD = AB ÷ 2 = 14.5 in ÷ 2 = 7.25 in

OD² = OE² = ED²

(7.25 in)² = OE² + (4.00 in)²

52.562 sq in = OE² + 16.0 sq in

MO = √36.5625 sq in

OE = 6.05 in

Chord is 6.05 in from the center.

33.   MO = 8.6 in ÷ 2 = 4.3 in

MT = 4.3 in + 1.4 in = 5.7 in

TS = 4.3 in – 1.4 in = 2.9 in

TP = 6.7 in – 3.8 in = 2.9 in

TP(*x*) = MT(TS)

2.9 in(*x*) = 5.7 in (2.9 in)

x = 5.7 in

34.   Problem to be laid out using construction methods.

Section Five
Geometric Figures: Areas and Volumes

UNIT 51   Areas of Rectangles, Parallelograms, and Trapezoids

1. $A = 8.5 \text{ in} \times 6.0 \text{ in}$
    $A = 51 \text{ sq in}$

2. $A = 5.0 \text{ m} \times 9.0 \text{ m}$
    $A = 4.5 \text{ m}^2$

3. $11.7 \text{ sq in} = 2.61 \text{ in} (w)$
    $w = \dfrac{117 \text{ sq in}}{2.6 \text{ in}}$
    $w = 4.5 \text{ in}$

4. $200.1 \text{ mm}^2 = (l)23 \text{ mm}$
    $l = \dfrac{200.1 \text{ mm}^2}{23 \text{ mm}}$
    $l = 8.7 \text{ in}$

5. $0.2 \text{ m}^2 = 0.4 \text{ m} (w)$
    $w = \dfrac{20.2 \text{ m}^2}{0.4 \text{ m}}$
    $w = 0.5 \text{ m}$

6. $0.136 \text{ sq in} = (l)0.086 \text{ in}$
    $l = \dfrac{0.136 \text{ sq in}}{0.086 \text{ sq in}}$
    $l = 1.6 \text{ in}$

7. $366.8 \text{ mm}^2 = 26.2 \text{ mm} (w)$
    $w = \dfrac{366.8 \text{ mm}^2}{26.2 \text{ mm}}$
    $w = 14.0 \text{ mm}$

8. $31.7 \text{ sq in} = (l)39.8 \text{ in}$
    $l = \dfrac{31.7 \text{ sq in}}{39.8 \text{ in}}$
    $l = 0.8 \text{ in}$

9. $3,762 \text{ mm}^2 = 64.2 \text{ mm} (w)$
    $w = \dfrac{3,762 \text{ mm}^2}{64.2 \text{ mm}}$
    $w = 58.6 \text{ mm}$

10. $A = 2.95 \text{ in} \times 0.76 \text{ in}$
     $A = 2.2 \text{ sq in}$

11. $6.7 \text{ sq ft} = 7.4 \text{ ft} (w)$
     $w = \dfrac{6.7 \text{ sq ft}}{7.4 \text{ ft}}$
     $w = 0.9 \text{ ft}$

12. $26,160 \text{ sq ft} = (l)125.0 \text{ ft}$
     $l = \dfrac{26,160 \text{ sq ft}}{125.0 \text{ ft}}$
     $l = 209.3 \text{ ft}$

13. $9.00 \text{ in} = 0.750 \text{ ft}$
     $A = 6.50 \text{ ft} \times 0.750 \text{ ft}$
     $A = 4.88 \text{ sq ft}$

16. Area of ①.
     $A = 29.00 \text{ in} \times 12.00 \text{ in} = 348 \text{ sq in}$
     Area of ②.
     $A = 39.00 \text{ in} \times 14.00 \text{ in} = 540 \text{ sq in}$
     Area of ③
     $A = 25.00 \text{ in} \times 10.00 \text{ in} = 250 \text{ sq in}$
     Total Area.
     $A = 348 \text{ in} + 546 \text{ sq in} + 250 \text{ sq in}$
     $A = 1,144 \text{ sq in}$

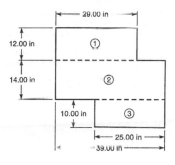

17. ① $A = 740 \text{ mm} \times 81.00 \text{ mm}$
     $A = 5994 \text{ mm}^2$
     ② $A = 6,350 \text{ mm}^2 - 5994 \text{ mm}^2$
     $A = 356 \text{ mm}^2$
     $A = lw$
     $356 \text{ mm}^2 = 20.00 \text{ mm} (x)$
     $x = \dfrac{356 \text{ mm}^2}{20.0 \text{ mm}}$
     $x = 17.8 \text{ mm}$

18. $l = 1.5w$
     $A = lw$
     $2,250 \text{ mm}^2 = 1.5w(w)$
     $2,250 \text{ mm}^2 = 1.5w^2$
     $w^2 = \dfrac{2,250 \text{ mm}^2}{1.5}$
     $w = \sqrt{1,500 \text{ mm}^2}$
     $w = 38.73 \text{ mm}$
     $l = 1.5(38.73 \text{ mm})$
     $l = 58 \text{ mm}$

14. $\sqrt{729 \text{ sq in}} = 27 \text{ in}$

15. $A = 3.0 \text{ ft} \times 4.0 \text{ ft}$
     $A = 12 \text{ sq ft}$
     $\dfrac{\$45}{12 \text{ sq ft}} = \$3.75 / \text{sq ft}$
     $A = 6.0 \text{ ft} \times 8.0 \text{ ft}$
     $A = 48 \text{ sq ft}$
     $\$3.75 / \text{sq ft} \times 48 \text{ sq ft} = \$180$

19. $A = 20.00 \text{ mm} \times 5.20 \text{ mm}$
     $A = 104 \text{ mm}^2$

20. $A = 6.00 \text{ in} \times 9.80 \text{ in}$
     $A = 58.8 \text{ sq in}$

21. $A = 486.6 \text{ sq in} = 26.0 \text{ in} (h)$
     $h = \dfrac{486.2 \text{ sq in}}{26.0 \text{ in}}$
     $h = 18.7 \text{ in}$

UNIT **51** (*continued*)

22. $2{,}057 \text{ mm}^2 = b(37.4 \text{ mm})$

$$b = \frac{2{,}057 \text{ mm}^2}{37.4 \text{ mm}}$$

$b = 55 \text{ mm}$

23. $0.014 \text{ m}^2 = 0.07 \text{ m}(h)$

$$h = \frac{0.014 \text{ m}^2}{0.07 \text{ m}}$$

$h = 0.2 \text{ m}$

24. $A = 24.0 \text{ in} \times 4.50 \text{ in}$

$A = 108 \text{ sq in}$

25. $312.5 \text{ sq in} = 18.5 \text{ in}(h)$

$$h = \frac{312.5 \text{ sq in}}{18.5 \text{ in}}$$

$h = 16.9 \text{ in}$

26. $5.1 \text{ sq ft} = b(0.60 \text{ ft})$

$$b = \frac{5.1 \text{ sq ft}}{0.60 \text{ ft}}$$

$b = 8.5 \text{ ft}$

27. $A = 56.0 \text{ mm} \times 6.800 \text{ mm}$

$A = 380.8 \text{ mm}^2$

28. $A = 17.00 \text{ in} \times 18.30 \text{ in}$

$A = 311.1 \text{ in}$

29. $1{,}887.2 \text{ mm}^2 = b(38.0 \text{ mm})$

$$b = \frac{1{,}887.2 \text{ mm}^2}{38.0 \text{ mm}}$$

$b = 49.7 \text{ mm}$

30. $A = 0.380 \text{ m} \times 0.266 \text{ m}$

$A = 0.010 \text{ m}^2 = 0.0 \text{ m}^2$

31. Compute the altitude:

$$c^2 = a^2 + b^2$$

$(1.25 \text{ in})^2 = (0.50 \text{ in})^2 + h^2$

$h^2 = 1.3125 \text{ sq in}$

$h = \sqrt{1.3125 \text{ sq in}} = 1.1456 \text{ in}$

$A = bh$

$A = 1.50 \text{ in} \times 1.1456 \text{ in}$

$A = 1.72 \text{ sq in}$

32. Since AB ‖ CD, the altitues of the 2 cutouts are equal.
The bases are given equal.
Therefore, the two cutouts have equal areas.

33. Area of groove $= 14.0 \text{ mm} \times 26.0 \text{ mm} = 364 \text{ mm}^2$
Area of top before cutting groove $= 35.0 \text{ mm} \times 26.0 \text{ mm}$
$= 910 \text{ mm}^2$
Area of top after cutting groove $= 910 \text{ mm}^2 - 364 \text{ mm}^2$
$= 546 \text{ mm}^2$

34. ① $A = 310 \text{ mm} \times 100 \text{ mm} = 31{,}000 \text{ mm}^2$

② $A = 310 \text{ mm} \times 115 \text{ mm} = 35{,}650 \text{ mm}^2 34.$

③ $A = 85 \text{ mm} \times 75 \text{ mm} = 6{,}375 \text{ mm}^2$

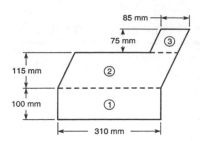

Total area $= 31{,}000 \text{ mm}^2 + 35{,}650 \text{ mm}^2 + 6{,}375 \text{ mm}^2$
Total area $= 73{,}025 \text{ mm}^2$

35. $A = 0.5(8.00 \text{ in})(16.00 \text{ in} + 10.00 \text{ in})$
$A = 4.00 \text{ in}(26.00 \text{ in})$
$A = 104 \text{ sq in}$

36. $A = 0.5(28.0 \text{ mm})(47.0 \text{ mm} + 38.0 \text{ mm})$
$A = 14.0 \text{ mm}(85.0 \text{ mm})$
$A = 1{,}190 \text{ mm}^2$

37. $64.0 \text{ sq ft} = 0.5h(8.00 \text{ ft} + 4.00 \text{ ft})$
$64.0 \text{ sq ft} = 0.5h(12.00 \text{ ft})$

37. $64.0 \text{ sq ft} = 6.00 \text{ ft}(h)$

$$h = \frac{64.0 \text{ sq ft}}{6.0 \text{ ft}}$$

$h = 10.7 \text{ ft}$

38. $7.7 \text{ sq ft} = 0.5(1.2 \text{ ft})(b_1 + 5.5 \text{ ft})$
$7.7 \text{ sq ft} = 0.6 \text{ ft}(b_1 + 5.5 \text{ ft})$
$7.7 \text{ sq ft} = 0.6 \text{ ft}(b_1) + 3.3 \text{ sq ft}$
$0.6 \text{ sq ft}(b_1) = 7.7 \text{ sq ft} - 3.3 \text{ sq ft}$

$$b_1 = \frac{4.4 \text{ sq ft}}{0.6 \text{ ft}}$$

$b_1 = 7.3 \text{ ft}$

39. $0.4 \text{ m}^2 = 0.5(0.6 \text{ m})(0.8 \text{ m} + b_2)$
$0.4 \text{ m}^2 = 0.3 \text{ m}(0.8 \text{ m} + b_2)$
$0.4 \text{ m}^2 = 0.24 \text{ m}^2 + 0.3 \text{ m}(b_2)$

$$b_2 = \frac{0.16 \text{ m}^2}{0.3 \text{ m}}$$

$b_2 = 0.5 \text{ m}$

40. $738.4 \text{ m}^2 = 0.5h(56.00 \text{ m} + 48.00 \text{ m})$
$738.4 \text{ m}^2 = 0.5h(104.00 \text{ m}^2)$
$738.4 \text{ m}^2 = 52.00 \text{ m}(h)$

$$h = \frac{738.4 \text{ m}^2}{52.00 \text{ m}}$$

$h = 14.2 \text{ m}$

UNIT **51** (*continued*)

41. $A = 0.5(18.70\text{ in})(36.00\text{ in} + 28.40\text{ in})$
$A = 9.350\text{ in}(64.40\text{ in})$
$A = 602.1\text{ sq in}$

42. $62.1\text{mm}^2 = 0.5(38\text{ mm})(b_1 + 8.7\text{ mm})$
$62.1\text{mm}^2 = 19\text{ mm}(b_1 + 8.7\text{ mm})$
$62.1\text{mm}^2 = 19\text{ mm}(b_1 + 16.53\text{ mm}^2)$
$19\text{ mm}(_1) = 45.57\text{ mm}^2$
$b_1 = \dfrac{45.57\text{ mm}^2}{19\text{ mm}}$
$b_1 = 2.4\text{ mm}$

43. $A = 0.5(0.10\text{ m})(1.2\text{ m} + 0.6\text{ m})$
$A = 0.05\text{ m}(1.8\text{ m})$
$A = 0.1\text{mm}^2$

44. $2,125\text{ sq in} = 0.5h(66.37\text{ in} + 43.86\text{ in})$
$2,125\text{ sq in} = 0.5h(110.23\text{ in})$
$2,125\text{ sq in} = 55.115\text{ in}(h)$
$h = \dfrac{2,125\text{ sq in}}{55.115\text{ in}}$
$h = 38.6\text{ in}$

45. $0.2\text{ m}^2 = 0.5(0.3\text{ m})(0.8\text{ m} + b_2)$
$0.2\text{ m}^2 = 0.15\text{ m}(0.8\text{ m} + b_2)$
$0.2\text{ m}^2 = 0.12\text{ m}^2 + 0.115\text{ m}(b_2)$
$b_2 = \dfrac{0.08\text{ m}^2}{0.15\text{ m}}$
$b_2 = 0.5\text{ m}$

46. a $A = 0.5(14.00\text{ in})(20.00\text{ in} + 3.200\text{ in})$
$A = 7.000\text{ in}(23.200\text{ in})$
$A = 162.4\text{ sq in}$

47. a. $A = 0.5(6\text{ in})(5.25\text{ in} + 2.25\text{ in})$
$A = 3\text{ in}(7.50\text{ in})$
$A = 22.5\text{ sq in}$

b.

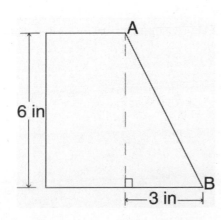

47. b. $AB^2 = (6.00\text{ in})^2 + (3.00\text{ in})^2$
$AB^2 = 36\text{ sq in}^2 + 9\text{ sq in}$
$AB = \sqrt{45\text{ sq in}}$
$AB = 6.71\text{ in}$

48. ① $A = 42\text{in}(46\text{in} - 12.5\text{in}) = 1,407\text{ sq in}$
② $A = 28\text{in} \times 12.5\text{ln} = 350\text{ sq in}$
③ $A = 0.5(6.5\text{in})(16\text{ ft}) = 87.75\text{ sq in}$
④ $A = 0.5(6.5\text{in})(14\text{ ft} + 9\text{in}) = 74.75\text{ sq ft}$
⑤ $A = 74.75\text{ in}$

Total Area

$= 1,407\text{ sq in} + 350\text{ sq in} + 87.75\text{ sq in} + 2(74.75\text{ sq in})$

Total Area $= 1,994.25\text{ sq in} \div 144 = 13.8\text{ sq ft}$

49. $b_1 = h$

$b_2 = 0.75h$

$0.420\text{m}^2 = 0.5h(h + 0.75h)$

$0.420\text{ m}^2 = 0.5h(1.75h)$

$0.420\text{ m}^2 = 0.875h^2$

$h^2 = \dfrac{0.420\ m^2}{0.875}$

$h = \sqrt{0.488\text{ m}^2}$

$h = 0.6928\text{ m} = 0.6928\text{ m} \times 1000 = 692.8\text{ mm}$

$b_1 = 692.8\text{ mm}$

$b_2 = (692.8\text{ mm}) = 519.6\text{ mm}$

UNIT 52   Areas of Triangles

1. $A = 0.5(21.00 \text{ mm})(17.00 \text{ mm})$
    $A = 178.5 \text{ mm}^2$

2. $78.2 \text{ sq ft} = 0.5(b)6.0 \text{ ft}$
    $b = \dfrac{78.2 \text{ sq ft}}{0.5(6.0 \text{ ft})}$
    $b = 26.1 \text{ ft}$

3. $0.02 \text{ m}^2 = 0.5(0.2 \text{ m})h$
    $0.02 \text{ m}^2 = 0.1\text{m}(h)$
    $h = \dfrac{0.02 \text{ m}^2}{0.1\text{ m}}$
    $h = 0.2 \text{ m}$

4. $3.22 \text{ sq in} = 0.5b(1.40 \text{ in})$
    $3.22 \text{ sq in} = 0.70 \text{ in}(b)$
    $b = \dfrac{3.22 \text{ sq in}}{0.70 \text{ in}}$
    $bh = 4.6 \text{ in}$

5. $A = 0.5(0.8 \text{ m})(0.4 \text{ m})$
    $A = 0.2 \text{ m}^2$

6. $A = 0.5(18.5 \text{ in})(7.25 \text{ in})$
    $A = 37.1 \text{ sq in}$
    $A = 65.3 \text{ sq ft}$

7. $427 \text{ mm}^2 = 0.5(30.5 \text{ mm})h$
    $427 \text{ mm}^2 = 15.25 \text{ mm}(h)$
    $h = \dfrac{427 \text{ mm}^2}{15.25 \text{ mm}}$
    $h = 28 \text{ mm}$

8. $1{,}919 \text{ mm}^2 = 0.5b(38.0 \text{ mm})$
    $1{,}919 \text{ mm}^2 = 19.0 \text{ mm}(b)$
    $b = \dfrac{1{,}919 \text{ mm}^2}{19.0 \text{ mm}}$
    $b = 101 \text{ mm}$

9. $A = 0.5(17.00 \text{ in})(9.80 \text{ in})$
    $A = 83.3 \text{ sq in}$

10. $16 \text{ sq ft} = 0.5b(0.8 \text{ ft})$
    $16 \text{ sq ft} = 0.4 \text{ ft}(b)$
    $b = \dfrac{16 \text{ sq ft}}{0.4 \text{ ft}}$
    $b = 40 \text{ ft}$

11. $249.7 \text{ sq in} = 0.5(45.41 \text{ in})h$
    $249.7 \text{ sq in} = 22.705 \text{ in}(h)$
    $h = \dfrac{249.7 \text{ sq in}}{22.705 \text{ in}}$
    $b = 11.0 \text{ in}$

12. $1.76 \text{ sq in} = 0.5b(3.43 \text{ in})$
    $1.76 \text{ sq in} = 1.715 \text{ in}(b)$
    $b = \dfrac{1.76 \text{ sq in}}{1.715 \text{ in}}$
    $b = 1.0 \text{ in}$

13. $s = 0.5(4\text{in} + 6 \text{ in} + 8 \text{ in}) = 9 \text{ in}$
    $A = \sqrt{9 \text{ in}(9 \text{ in} - 4 \text{ in})(9 \text{ in} - 6 \text{ in})(9 \text{ in} - 8 \text{ in})}$
    $A = \sqrt{135 \text{ in}^4}$
    $A = 11.6 \text{ in}^2$

14. $s = 0.5(2 \text{ ft} + 5 \text{ ft} + 6 \text{ ft}) = 6.5 \text{ ft}$
    $A = \sqrt{6.5 \text{ ft}(6.5 \text{ ft} - 2 \text{ ft})(6.5 \text{ in} - 5 \text{ in})(6.5 \text{ ft} - 6 \text{ ft})}$
    $A = \sqrt{21.937 \text{ ft}^4}$
    $A = 4.7 \text{ ft}$

15. $s = 0.5(3.5\text{in} + 4 \text{ in} + 2.5 \text{ in}) = 5 \text{ in}$
    $A = \sqrt{5 \text{ in}(5 \text{ in} - 3.5 \text{ in})(5 \text{ in} - 4 \text{ in})(5 \text{ in} - 2.5 \text{ in})}$
    $A = \sqrt{18.75 \text{ in}^4}$
    $A = 4.3 \text{ sq in}$

16. $s = 0.5(3.5\text{mm} + 15 \text{ mm} + 25 \text{ mm}) = 30 \text{ mm}$
    $A = \sqrt{30 \text{ mm}(30 \text{ mm} - 20 \text{ mm})(30 \text{ mm} - 15 \text{ mm})(30 \text{ mm} - 25 \text{ mm})}$
    $A = \sqrt{22{,}500 \text{ mm}^4}$
    $A = 150 \text{ mm}^2$

17. $s = 0.5(3.2 \text{ ft} + 3.6 \text{ ft} + 0.8 \text{ ft}) - 3.8 \text{ ft}$
    $A = \sqrt{3.8 \text{ ft}(3.8 \text{ ft} - 3.2 \text{ ft})(3.8 \text{ ft} - 3.6 \text{ ft})(3.8 \text{ ft} - 0.8 \text{ ft})}$
    $A = \sqrt{1.368 \text{ ft}^4}$
    $A = 1.2 \text{ sq ft}$

18. $s = 0.5(9.100 \text{ in} + 30.86 \text{ in} + 28.57 \text{ in}) = 34.265 \text{ in}$
    $A = \sqrt{34.265 \text{ in}(34.265 \text{ in} - 9.100 \text{ in})(34.265 \text{ in} - 30.86 \text{ in})(344.265 \text{ in} - 28.57 \text{ in})}$
    $A = \sqrt{16{,}720.86 \text{ in}^4}$
    $A = 129.3 \text{ sq in}$

19. $s = 0.5(7.2 \text{ mm} + 10 \text{ mm} + 90 \text{ mm}) = 13.18 \text{ mm}$
    $A = \sqrt{13.1\text{mm}(13.1\text{mm} - 7.2 \text{ mm})(13.1\text{mm} - 10 \text{ mm})(13.1\text{mm} - 9 \text{ mm})}$
    $A = \sqrt{982.355\,9 \text{ mm}^4}$
    $A = 31.3 \text{ mm}^2$

UNIT **52**   (*continued*)

20. $s = 0.5(0.5 \text{ m} + 1.0 \text{ m} + 0.8 \text{ m}) = 1.15 \text{ m}$

$A = \sqrt{1.15 \text{ m}(1.15 \text{ m} - 0.5 \text{ m})(1.15 \text{ m} - 1.0 \text{ m})(1.15 \text{ m} - 0.8 \text{ m})}$

$A = \sqrt{0.039 \ 2 \text{ m}^4}$

$A = 0.2 \text{ m}^2$

21. Outside area $= 0.5(38.4 \text{ mm})(33.3 \text{ mm}) = 639.36 \text{ mm}^2$
Inside area $= 0.5(25.8 \text{ mm})(22.4 \text{ mm}) = 288.96 \text{ mm}^2$
Cross-sectional area $= 639.36 \text{ mm}^2 - 288.96 \text{ mm}^2 = 350.40 \text{ mm}^2, 350 \text{ mm}^2$

22. Area of sheet $= 4 \text{ ft} \times 8 \text{ ft} = \text{sq ft}$
Area of small triangle $= 0.5(5.5 \text{ ft})(3.5 \text{ ft}) = 12.5 \text{ sq ft}$
Area of sheet wasted $= 32 \text{ sq ft} - 8.25 \text{ sq ft} + 12.25 \text{ sq ft}) = 11.5 \text{ sq ft}$

23. ① $A = 0.5(72.0 \text{ mm})(50.0 \text{ mm}) = 1{,}800 \text{ mm}^2$

② $A = 0.5(68.0 \text{ mm})(55.3 \text{ mm}) = 1{,}880.2 \text{ mm}^2$

Total area $= A = 1{,}800 \text{ mm}^2 + 1{,}880.2 \text{ mm}^2 - 0{,}000.2 \text{ mm}^2, 3{,}680 \text{ mm}^2$

24. ① Area of bottom trapezoid section:

$h = 10.0 \text{ in}$

$b_1 = 22.5 \text{ in} + 2(5.0 \text{ in}) = 32.5 \text{ in}$

$b_2 = 22.5 \text{ in}$

$A = 0.5(10.0 \text{ in} + 22.5 \text{ in}) = 275 \text{ sq in}$

② Area of top triangle section:

$h = 18.0 \text{ in} - 10.0 \text{ in} = 8.0 \text{ in}$

$A = 0.5(22.5 \text{ in})(8.0 \text{ in}) = 90 \text{ sq in}$

Total Area:
$275 \text{ sq in} + 90 \text{ sq in} = 365 \text{ sq in}, 370 \text{ sq in}$

25. ① $A = 0.5(13.00 \text{ cm})(18.00 \text{ cm}) = 117.0 \text{ cm}^2$

② $A = 0.5(25.00 \text{ cm})(23.00 \text{ cm}) = 278.5 \text{ cm}^2$

③ $A = 0.5(62.00 \text{ cm})(12.00 \text{ cm}) = 372.0 \text{ cm}^2$

④ $b = (25.00 \text{ cm} + 20.00 \text{ cm} + 62.00 \text{ cm}) - (13.00 \text{ cm} + 70.00 \text{ cm}) = 24.00 \text{ cm}$
$A = 0.5(24.00 \text{ cm})(21.00 \text{ in}) = 252.0 \text{ cm}^2$

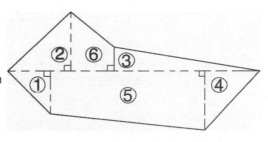

⑤ $A = 0.5(70.00 \text{ cm})(18.00 \text{ cm} + 21.00 \text{ cm}) = 1{,}365 \text{ cm}^2$

⑥ $A = 0.5(20.00 \text{ cm})(23.00 \text{ cm} + 12.00 \text{ cm}) = 350 \text{ cm}^2$
Total area $= 117.0 \text{ cm}^2 + 287.5 \text{ cm}^2 + 372.0 \text{ cm}^2 + 252.0 \text{ cm}^2 + 1{,}365 \text{ cm}^2 + 350.0 \text{ cm}^2 = 2{,}743.5 \text{ cm}^2, 2744 \text{ cm}^2$

UNIT 53   Areas of Circles, Sectors, and Segments

1. $A = 3.1416(7.000 \text{ in})^2 = 3.1416(49 \text{ sq in}) = 153.9 \text{ sq in}$
2. $A = 3.1416(10.80 \text{ cm})^2 = 3.1416(116.64 \text{ cm}^2) = 366.4 \text{ cm}$
3. $A = 0.7854(15.5 \text{ in})^2 = 0.7854(240.25 \text{ sq in}) = 188.7 \text{ sq in}$
4. $A = 0.7854(17.23 \text{ mm})^2 = 0.7854(296.88 \text{ mm}^2) = 233.2 \text{ mm}^2$

5. $3.4 \text{ sq ft} = 3.1416 r^2$

    $r^2 = \dfrac{3.4 \text{ sq ft}}{3.1416}$

    $r^2 = 1.08225 \text{ sq ft}$
    $r = 1.0 \text{ ft}$

6. $218.3 \text{ cm}^3 = 0.7854 d^2$

    $d^2 = \dfrac{218.3 \text{ cm}^2}{0.7854}$

    $d^2 = 277.9475 \text{ cm}^2$
    $d = 16.7 \text{ cm}$

7. $380 \text{ mm}^2 = 3.1416 r^2$

    $r^2 = \dfrac{380.0 \text{ mm}^2}{3.1416}$

    $r^2 = 120.957474 \text{ mm}^2$
    $r = 11.0 \text{ mm}$

8. $A = 3.1416(2.78 \text{ in})^2 = 3.1416(67.7284 \text{ sq in}) = 24.3 \text{ sq in}$

9. $A = 0.7854(0.75 \text{ ft})^2 = 0.7854 \text{ sq ft}) = 0.4 \text{ sq ft}$

10. $102.6 \text{ cm}^2 = 0.7854 d^2$

    $d^2 = \dfrac{102.6 \text{ cm}^2}{0.7854}$

    $d^2 = 130.6341 \text{ cm}^2$
    $d = 11.4 \text{ cm}$

11. $36.8 \text{ sq in} = 0.7854 d^2$

    $d^2 = \dfrac{36.8 \text{ sq in}}{0.7854}$

    $d^2 = 46.085511 \text{ sq in}$
    $d = 6.8 \text{ in}$

12. $A = 3.1416 \times (0.026 \text{ m})^2$
    $A = 0.00214 \text{m}^2 ; 0.0 \text{ m}^2$

13. $A_1 = 15.10(12.45 \text{ in}) = 187.995 \text{ sq in}$
    $A_2 = 0.7854(4.65 \text{ in}) = 3.65211 \text{ sq in}$
    $184.995 \text{ sq in} - 3(3.65211 \text{ sq in}) = 174.0387 \text{ sq in}$

    $19.4 \text{ lb.} \div 187.995 \text{ sq in} = 0.103194 \text{ lb} / \text{sq in}$
    $174.0387 \text{ sq in} \times 0.103194 \text{ lb} / \text{sq in} = 18.0 \text{ lb}$

14. $A = 0.7854(3.150 \text{ in})^2 = 7.79313 \text{ sq in}$
    $7.79313 \text{ sq in} \times 705.0 \text{ lb} / \text{sq in} = 5494 \text{ lb}$

15. $A_1 = 0.7854(230.00 \text{ mm})^2 = 41,547.66 \text{ mm}^2$
    $A_2 = 0.7854(45.00 \text{ mm})^2 = 1590.435 \text{ mm}^2$
    $A_3 = 0.7854(25.00 \text{ mm})^2 = 490.875 \text{ mm}^2$

    $41,547.66 \text{ mm}^2 - (1590.435 \text{ mm}^2) + 6(490.875 \text{ mm}^2) = 37011.975 \text{ mm}^2$

    $37011.975 \text{ mm}^2 = 0.037011975 \text{ m}^2$
    $0.037011975 \text{ m}^2 \times 34 \text{ kg} / \text{m}^2 = 1.3 \text{ kg}$

16. ① $A = 0.5[3.1416(3.2 \text{ in})^2] = 16.085 \text{ sq in}$

    ② $A = 4.5(3.2 \text{ in}) = 14.400 \text{ sq in}$

    ③ $A = 0.5(3.000 \text{ in})(11.400 \text{ in} + 3.200 \text{ in}) = 21.900 \text{ sq in}$

    ④ $A = 0.5[3.1416(5.700 \text{ in})^2] = 51.035 \text{ sq in}$

    $16.085 \text{ sq in} + 14.400 \text{ sq in} + 21.900 \text{ sq in} + 51.035 \text{ sq in} = 103.4 \text{ sq in}$

17. $A = 0.7854(1.800 \text{ in})^2 = 2.544696 \text{ sq in}$

    $62,125 \text{ lb} \div 2.544696 \text{ sq in}$
    $= 24,413.5 \text{ lb} / \text{sq in}, 24,414 \text{ lb} / \text{sq in}$

18. a. $A_1 = (128 \text{ mm})^2 = 16,384 \text{ mm}^2$

    $A_2 = 3.1416(64 \text{ mm})^2 = 12,867.99 \text{ mm}^2$

    $16,384 \text{ mm}^2 - 12,867.99 \text{ mm}^2 = 3,516 \text{ mm}^2$

    b. Percent wasted: $\dfrac{12,868 \text{ mm}^2}{16,384 \text{ mm}^2} \times 100 = 78.5\%$

19. $A = \dfrac{120.0°}{360°}(\pi)(10.00 \text{ cm})^2 = 104.7 \text{ cm}^2$

20. $A = \dfrac{90.0°}{360°}(\pi)(3.5 \text{ ft})^2 = 9.6 \text{ sq ft}$

21. $A = \dfrac{40.00°}{360°}(\pi)(15.3 \text{ in})^2 = 81.7 \text{ sq in}$

22. $300.0 \text{ sq in} = \dfrac{65°}{360°}(\pi) r^2$

    $300.0 \text{ sq in} = 0.567 r^2$
    $r^2 = 528.88 \text{ sq in}$
    $r = 23.0 \text{ in}$

UNIT **53**   *(continued)*

23. $750.0 \text{ mm}^2 = \dfrac{180.5°}{360°}(\pi)r^2$

    $750.0 \text{ mm}^2 = 1.575r^2$

    $r^2 = 476.14 \text{ mm}^2$

    $r = 21.8 \text{ mm}$

24. $94.62 \text{ sq in} = \dfrac{\theta}{360°}(\pi)(9.570 \text{ in})^2$

    $94.62 \text{ sq in} = 0.799 \text{ sq in} / 1°(\theta)$

    $\theta = 118.4°$

25. $1{,}028 \text{ sq in} = \dfrac{\theta}{360°}(\pi)(20.25 \text{ in})^2$

    $1{,}028 \text{ sq in} = 3.5785 \text{ sq in} / 1°(\theta)$

    $\theta = 287.3°$

26. $A = \dfrac{220°}{360°}(\pi)(0.2 \text{ m})^2 = 0.1 \text{ m}^2$

27. $A = \dfrac{26.20°}{360°}(\pi)(54.08 \text{ cm})^2 = 671.2 \text{ cm}^2$

28. $79.4 \text{ sq in} = \dfrac{307.20°}{360°}(\pi)r^2$

    $79.4 \text{ sq in} = 2.68083\,r^2$

    $r^2 = 29.61769 \text{ sq in}$

    $r = 5.4 \text{ in}$

29. $15.882 \text{ sq in} = \dfrac{\theta}{360°}(\pi)(3.273 \text{ in})^2$

    $15.882 \text{ sq mi} = 0.093484 \text{ sq in} / 1°(\theta)$

    $\theta = 169.9°$

30. $A = \dfrac{15.286°}{360°}(\pi)(150.78 \text{ mm})^2 = 3{,}032.7 \text{ mm}^2$

31. $A = \dfrac{(360° - 48°)}{360°}(\pi)(37.5 \text{ mm})^2 = 3{,}829 \text{ mm}^2,\ 3{,}800 \text{ mm}^2$

32. $A_1 = \dfrac{90°}{360°}(\pi)(0.65 \text{ m})^2 = 0.33183 \text{ m}^2$

    $A_2 = \dfrac{32.0°}{360°}(\pi)(1.05 \text{ m})^2 = 0.30788 \text{ m}^2$

    $A_3 = \dfrac{80.0°}{360°}(\pi)(0.45 \text{ m})^2 = 0.14137 \text{ m}^2$

    $A_4 = 1.60(0.65 \text{ m}) = 1.04 \text{ m}^2$

    $1.04 \text{ m}^2 - 0.78108 = 0.259 \text{ m}^2,\ 0.3 \text{ m}^2$

33. $A_1 = \dfrac{360° - (137° + 90°)}{360°}(\pi)(8.460 \text{ in} - 4.640 \text{ in})^2$

    $A_1 = \dfrac{133°}{360°}(\pi)(14.5924 \text{ in}^2)$

    $A_1 = 16.93658 \text{ in}^2$

    $A_2 = (15.810 \text{ in} - 3.820 \text{ in})(8.460 \text{ in} - 4.640 \text{ in})$

    $A_2 = (11.99 \text{ in})(3.82 \text{ in})$

    $A_2 = 45.8018 \text{ in}^2$

    $A_3 = 3.820 \text{ in}(4.640 \text{ in})$

    $A_3 = 17.7248 \text{ in}^2$

    $16.93658 \text{ in}^2 + 45.8018 \text{ in}^2 + 17.7248 \text{ in}^2$

    $= 80.4632 \text{ in}^2,\ 80.5 \text{ sq in}$

34. $A_1 = \dfrac{298.5°}{360°}(\pi)(4.280 \text{ in})^2$

    $A_1 = 47.7177 \text{ sq in}$

34. $A_2 = \dfrac{298.5°}{360°}(\pi)(4.280 \text{ in} - 2.095 \text{ in})^2$

    $A_2 = 12.4364 \text{ sq in}$

    $47.7177 \text{ sq in} - 12.4364 \text{ sq in} = 35.281 \text{ sq in},\ 35.3 \text{ sq in}$

35. $2.48 \text{ sq ft} - 1.65 \text{ sq ft} = 0.83 \text{ sq ft}$

36. $9.35 \text{ sq in} - 6.98 \text{ sq in} = 2.37 \text{ sq in}$

37. $213.5 \text{ mm}^2 - 156 \text{ mm}^2 = 57.5 \text{ mm}^2$

38. $109.27 \text{ sq in} - 85.33 \text{ sq in} = 23.94 \text{ sq in}$

39. $0.39 \text{ m}^2 - 0.26 \text{ m}^2 = 0.13 \text{ m}^2$

40. Area of sector:

    $A = \dfrac{150.0°}{360°}(\pi)(6.00 \text{ in})^2 = 47.124 \text{ in}^2$

    Area of triangle:

    $c^2 = a^2 + b^2$

    $(6.00 \text{ in})^2 = (1.55 \text{ in})^2 + b^2$

    $36.0 \text{ in}^2 = 2.4025 \text{ in}^2 + b^2$

    $b^2 = 33.5975 \text{ in}^2$

    $b = 5.7963 \text{ in}$

    $\text{Base} = 2(5.7963 \text{ in}) = 11.5926 \text{ in}$

    $A = 0.5(11.5926 \text{ in})(1.55 \text{ in}) = 8.984 \text{ in}^2$

    Area of segment:

    $47.124 \text{ in}^2 - 8.984 \text{ in}^2 = 38.1 \text{ in}^2$

41. Area of sector:

    $A = \dfrac{92.00°}{360°}(\pi)(20.3 \text{ mm})^2 = 330.847 \text{ mm}^2$

    Area of triangle:

    $c^2 = a^2 + b^2$

    $(20.3 \text{ mm})^2 = (12.8 \text{ mm})^2 + h^2$

    $412.09 \text{ mm}^2 = 163.84 \text{ mm}^2 + h^2$

    $h^2 = 248.25 \text{ mm}^2$

    $h = 15.75595 \text{ mm}$

    $A = 0.5(25.6 \text{ mm})(15.75595 \text{ mm}) = 201.676 \text{ mm}^2$

    Area of segment:

    $330.847 \text{ mm}^2 - 201.676 \text{ mm}^2 = 129.2 \text{ mm}^2$

42. a. Area of sector:

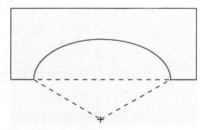

    $A = \dfrac{130°18'}{360°}(\pi)(22.05 \text{ cm})^2 = 552.852 \text{ cm}^2$

    Area of triangle: $c^2 = a^2 + b^2$

    $(22.05 \text{ cm})^2 = (18.09 \text{ cm})^2 + h^2$

    $486.2025 \text{ cm}^2 = 327.2481 \text{ cm}^2 + h^2$

    $h^2 = 158.9544 \text{ cm}^2$

    $h = 12.6077 \text{ cm}$

UNIT 53   (*continued*)

42. $A = 0.5(36.18 \text{ cm})(12.6077 \text{ cm}) = 228.0733 \text{ cm}^2$

   Area of segment: $552.852 \text{ cm}^2 - 228.0733 \text{ cm}^2 = 324.7787 \text{ cm}^2$

   Area of rectangular pattern before cut: $56.18 \text{ cm}(26.16 \text{ cm}) = 1,413.4888 \text{ cm}^2$

   Area of pattern: $1413.4888 \text{ cm}^2 - 324.7787 \text{ cm}^2 = 1,089 \text{ cm}^2$

   b. $1,089 \text{ cm}^2 = 0.1089 \text{ m}^2$

   $0.1089 \text{ m}^2 \times 7.85 \text{ kg} / \text{m}^2 = 0.85 \text{ kg}$

43. Area of sector: $A = 2 \dfrac{62.0°}{360°}(\pi)(20.00 \text{ in})^2 = 432.843 \text{ sq in}$

   Area of triangle: $c^2 = a^2 + b^2$

   $(20.00 \text{ in})^2 = (9.40 \text{ in})^2 + b^2$

   $400 \text{ sq in} = 88.36 \text{ sq in} + b^2$

   $b^2 = 311.64 \text{ sq in}$

   $b = 17.653 \ 3 \text{ in}$

   Base $= 2(17.6533 \text{ in}) = 35.3066 \text{ in}$

   $A = 0.5(35.3066 \text{ in})(9.4 \text{ in}) = 165.94 \text{ sq in}$

   Area of segment: $432.843 \text{ sq in} - 165.94 \text{ sq in} = 266.903 \text{ sq in}$

   Area of price: $0.5(266.903 \text{ sq in}) = 133.45 \text{ sq in}, 133.5 \text{ sq in}$

UNIT 54   Volumes of Prisms and Cylinders

➤ Answers may vary slightly due to rounding within the solutions.

1. $V = 125 \text{ sq in}(8 \text{ in}) = 1,000 \text{ cu in}$

2. $V = 610.00 \text{ cm}^2(26.500 \text{ cm}) = 16,165 \text{ cm}^2$

3. $V = 48 \text{ sq in}(5.3 \text{ in}) = 254.4 \text{ cu in}$

   $254.4 \text{ cu in} \times 0.26 \text{ lb} / \text{cu in} = 66 \text{ lb}$

4. $V = (38.50 \text{ sq ft})(4.25 \text{ ft}) = 163.625 \text{ cu ft}$

   $7.5 \text{ gal} \times 163.625 = 1227.187 \text{ gal}, 1227 \text{ gal}$

6. a. ① $A_B = 8.25 \text{ in}(0.75 \text{ in}) = 6.1875 \text{ sq in}$

   ② $A_B = (8.25 \text{ in} - 0.75 \text{ in})(0.75 \text{ in}) = 5.625 \text{ sq in}$

   $V = (6.1875 \text{ sq in} + 5.625 \text{ sq in}(67.75 \text{ in} = 800.30 \text{ in}, 800 \text{ cu in}$

   b. $800 \text{ cu in} \div 1,728 \text{ cu in} / \text{cu ft} = 0.463137 \text{ cu ft}$

   Weight $= 0.463137 \text{ cu ft} \times 490 \text{ lb} / \text{cu ft} = 226.94$, ~~230 lb~~ 227lbs QUESTION ASKS FOR NEAREST lb.

5. Base height: $(9.08 \text{ cm})^2 = (4.54 \text{ cm})^2 + h^2$

   $h^2 = (82.4464 \text{ cm}^2) - 20.6116 \text{ cm}^2$

   $h = \sqrt{61.8348 \text{ cm}^2} = 7.86351 \text{ cm}^2$

   Base area: $0.5(9.08 \text{ cm})(7.86351 \text{ cm}) = 35.70034 \text{ cm}^2$

   $V = (35.70034 \text{ cm}^2)(13.82 \text{ cm})$

   $V = 493.38 \text{ cm}^2, 493 \text{ cm}^3$

7. a. $A_b = 0.5(5.75 \text{ in})(3.90 \text{ in} + 1.52 \text{ in}) = 15.5825 \text{ sq in}$

   $V = (15.5825 \text{ sq in})(23.60 \text{ in}) = 367.747 \text{ cu in}, 368 \text{ cu in}$

   b. $1 \text{ cu in} = 1728 \text{ cu in}$

   $368 \text{ cu in} \div 1728 \text{ cu in} = 0.21296$

   $0.21296 \times 488.5 \text{ lb} = 104.03 \text{ lb}, 104 \text{ lb}$

UNIT **54**   *(continued)*

8. Base height: $(17.80 \text{ cm})^2 = (8.90 \text{ cm})^2 + h^2$

$$h^2 = (316.84 \text{ cm}^2) - 79.21 \text{ cm}^2$$

$$h = \sqrt{237.63 \text{ cm}^2} = 15.4153 \text{ cm}^2$$

Base area: $0.5(17.80 \text{ cm})(15.4153 \text{ cm}) = 137.1957 \text{ cm}^2$

$V = (137.1957 \text{ cm}^2)(16.23 \text{ cm})$

$V = 2226.6862 \text{ cm}^3$

Weight: $(2226.6862)(8.8 \text{ g}) = 19,594.8 \text{ g}$

$19,549.8 \text{ g} \div 1000 = 19.5948 \text{ kg}, 19.59 \text{ kg}$

9.

$A_1 = 0.5(40.80 \text{ cm})(83.60 \text{ cm} + 48.74 \text{cm}) = 2699.736 \text{ cm}^2$

$A_2 = (65.98 \text{ cm})(36.05 \text{ cm}) = 2,378.579 \text{ cm}^2$

$A_3 = (40.80 \text{ cm})(6.10 \text{ cm}) = 248.88 \text{ cm}^2$

Total area $= 2699.736 \text{ cm}^2 + 2378.579 \text{ cm}^2 + 248.88 \text{ cm}^2 = 5327.195 \text{ cm}^2$

$V = (5327.195 \text{ cm}^2)(3.20 \text{ cm}^2) = 17,047.024 \text{ cm}^3$

$V = 17,047 \text{ cm}^3 \div 1,000,000 = 0.017047, 0.017 \text{ m}^3$

10. $A_1 = (25.00 \text{ cm})(3.00 \text{ cm}) = 75.00 \text{ cm}^2$

$A_2 = A_1 = 75.00 \text{ cm}^2$

$A_3 = (26.00 \text{ cm})(3.00 \text{ cm}) = 78.00 \text{ cm}^2$

Total area $= 75.00 \text{ cm}^2 + 75.00 \text{ cm}^2 + 78.00 \text{ cm}^2$

Total area $= 228.00 \text{ cm}^2$

$V = (228.00 \text{ cm}^2)(500 \text{ cm})$

$V = 114,000 \text{ cm}^3 = 0.114 \text{ m}^3$

Weight $= 7,800 \text{ kg} \times 0.114 = 889 \text{ kg}$

11. $V = 76.00 \text{ sq in}(8.600 \text{ in}) = 653.6 \text{ cu in}$

12. $V = 0.30 \text{ m}^2(0.40 \text{m}) = 0.12 \text{m}^3$

13. $V = 154.0 \text{ sq in}(16.00 \text{ in}) = 2,464 \text{ cu in}$

$2,464 \text{ cu in} \div 231 \text{ cu in / gal} = 10.67 \text{ gal}$

14. $V = \pi(1.920 \text{ cm})^2(59.00 \text{ cm}) = 683.3 \text{ cm}^3$

UNIT 54 *(continued)*

15. $V = \pi(1.5625 \text{ in})^2(4.570 \text{ in}) = 35.05146 \text{ cu in}$
    $6(35.05146 \text{ cu in}) = 210.3 \text{ cu in}$

16. a. $V = \pi(0.230 \text{ in})^2(101.219 \text{ in}) = 16.8 \text{ cu in}$
    b. $40 \times 0.300 \text{ lb} / \text{cu in} \times 16.822 \text{ cu in} = 201.9 \text{ lb}$ ~~201.9 lbs.~~

17. a. $V_1 = \pi(0.9500 \text{ m})^2(2.750 \text{ in}) = 7.7970 \text{ cu in}$
    $V_2 = \pi(0.9500 \text{ in} - 0.350 \text{ in})^2(2.750 \text{ in}) = 3.1102 \text{ cu in}$
    $7.7970 \text{ cu in} - 3.1102 \text{ cu in} = 4.69 \text{ cu in}$
    b. $1.50 \text{ lb} \div 4.69 \text{ cu in} = 0.32 \text{ lb} / \text{cu in}$

18. $A_1 = \pi(9.84 \text{ cm})^2 = 304.1866 \text{ cm}^2$
    $A_2 = \pi(2.93 \text{ cm})^2 = 26.9703 \text{ cm}^2$
    $A_3 = \pi(0.125 \text{ cm})^2 = 0.04909 \text{ cm}^2$
    Total area of plate $= 304.1866 \text{ cm}^2 - (26.97703 \text{ cm}^2) + 4(0.04909 \text{ cm}^2) = 277.01994 \text{ cm}^2$
    $V = (277.01994 \text{ cm}^2)(4.73 \text{ cm}) = 1310.30 \text{ cm}^3$

19. $V_1 = \pi(0.2625 \text{ in})^2(1.25 \text{ in}) = 0.27059 \text{ cu in}$
    $V_2 = \pi(0.1875 \text{ in})^2(1.25 \text{ in}) = 0.13806 \text{ cu in}$
    Volume of one bushing $= 0.27059 \text{ cu in} - 0.13806 \text{ cu in} = 0.1325 \text{ cu in}$
    Volume of 2,600 bushings $= (2,600)(0.1325 \text{ cu in}) = 344.5 \text{ cu in}$
    $344.5 \text{ cu in} \times \dfrac{1 \text{ cu ft}}{1728 \text{ cu in}} = 0.1994 \text{ cu ft}$
    Total weight $= 0.1994 \times 546.2 \text{ lb} = 108.9 \text{ lb}, 109 \text{ lb}$

20. $V_1 = \pi(22.75 \text{ mm})^2(10 \text{ mm}) = 16,259.7055 \text{ mm}^3$
    $V_2 = \pi(19.35 \text{ mm})^2(22.8 \text{ mm}) = 26,819.2518 \text{ mm}^3$
    $V_3 = \pi(12.8 \text{ mm})^2(10 \text{ mm} + 22.8 \text{ mm} + 10 \text{ mm}) = 22,029.9535 \text{ mm}^3$
    Volume of material $= 2(16,259.7055 \text{ mm}^3) + 26,819.2518 \text{ mm}^3 - 22,029.9535 \text{ mm}^3 = $ ~~21,049 mm³~~ $37,309 \text{ mm}^3$

21. $512.70 \text{ cu in} = (67.84 \text{ sq in})h$
    $h = 7.56 \text{ in}$

22. $119.62 \text{ cm}^3 = A_b(18.25 \text{ cm})$
    $A_b = 6.55 \text{ cm}^2$

23. $104 \text{ cu in} = A_b(27.60 \text{ in})$
    $A_b = 3.7681 \text{ sq in}$
    $3.7681 \text{ sq in} = s^2$
    $s = 1.94 \text{ in}$

24. $1 \text{ gal} = 231 \text{ cu in}$
    $1 \text{ qt} = 231 \text{ cu in} \div 4 = 57.75 \text{ cu in}$
    $A_B = \pi(3.86 \text{ in} \div 2)^2 = \pi(1.93 \text{ in})^2 = 11.702 \text{ sq in}$
    $57.75 \text{ cu in} = 11.702 \text{ sq in}(h)$
    $h = 4.94 \text{ in}$

25. $V = 176 \times 1000 \text{ cm}^3 = 1760 \text{ cm}^3$
    $1760 \text{ cm}^3 = A_b(26.20 \text{ cm})$
    $A_b = 67.18 \text{ cm}^2$

26. $15.30 \text{ lb} \div 526.7 \text{ lb} / \text{cu ft} = 0.02905 \text{ cu ft}$
    $0.02905 \text{ cu ft} = 0.02905 \times 1728 \text{ cu in} = 50.1984 \text{ cu in}$
    $A_b = 0.5(10.87 \text{ in})(7.52 \text{ in}) = 40.8712 \text{ sq in}$
    $50.1984 \text{ cu in} = (40.8712 \text{ sq in})(h)$
    $h = 1.23 \text{ in}$

27. $505.5 \text{ lb} \div 168.5 \text{ lb} / \text{cu ft} = 3.000 \text{ cu ft}$
    $A_b = (5.0 \text{ ft})(4.0 \text{ ft}) = 20 \text{ sq ft}$
    $3,000 \text{ cu ft} = (20 \text{ sq ft})(h)$
    $h = 0.15 \text{ ft} = 1.8 \text{ in}$

28. $V = 3.72 \text{ lb} \div 0.284 \text{ lb} / \text{cu ft} = 13.0986 \text{ cu in}$
    $13.0986 \text{ cu in} = A_b(3.67 \text{ in})$
    $A_b = 3.57 \text{ sq in}$

29. $8.67 \text{ lb} \div 3.66 \text{ lb} / \text{cu ft} = 2.36885 \text{ ft} = 28.4262 \text{ in}$
    $56.67 \text{ cu in} = A_b(28.4262 \text{ in})$
    $A_b = 1.99 \text{ sq in}$

30. $A = (2.598)(0.875 \text{ in})^2 = 1.98909 \text{ sq in}$
    $31.2 \text{ cu in} = (1.98909 \text{ sq in})h$
    $h = 15.69 \text{ in}$

UNIT 55   Volumes of Pyramids and Cones

1. $V = \dfrac{(236.90 \text{ sq in})(12.84 \text{ in})}{3} = 3041.80 \text{ cu in}$

2. $V = \dfrac{(38.60 \text{ cm}^2)(5.000 \text{ cm})}{3} = 64.33 \text{ cm}^2$

3. $V = \dfrac{(98.00 \text{ sq in})(10.80 \text{ in})}{3} = 352.8 \text{ cu in}$

4. $V = (63.60 \text{ sq in})(7.65 \text{ in}) = 486.54 \text{ cu in}$
   $486.54 \text{ cu in} \div 231 \text{ cu in} / \text{gal} = 2.11 \text{ gal}$

5. $V = \pi(4.13 \text{ cm})^2(18.36 \text{ cm}) = 327.945 \text{ cm}^3, \ 328 \text{ cm}^3$

6. Volume of 2-inch diameter piece:

   $V = \dfrac{\pi(1 \text{ in})^2(6 \text{ in})}{3} = 6.28 \text{ cu in}$

   Volume of 4-inch diameter piece:

   $V = \dfrac{\pi(2 \text{ in})^2(6 \text{ in})}{3} = 25.13 \text{ cu in}$

   $25.13 \text{ cu in} \div 6.28 \text{ cu in} = 4.00$

7. Volume of vessel:

   $V = \dfrac{\pi(7.50 \text{ cm})^2(18.2 \text{ cm})}{3} = 1,072.068 \text{ cm}^3$

   Volume of liquid in container:

   $V = \dfrac{\pi(5.00 \text{ cm})^2(12.8 \text{ cm})}{3} = 335.103 \text{ cm}^3$

   $1,072.068 \text{ cm}^3 - 335.103 \text{ cm}^3 = 0.74 \text{ L}$

8. a. Compute the base heights:
   $(5.7 \text{ in})^2 = (2.85 \text{ in})^2 + h^2$
   $32.49 \text{ sq in} = 8.1225 \text{ sq in} + h^2$
   $h^2 = 24.3675 \text{ sq in}$
   $h = 4.9363 \text{ in}$
   $A_B = 0.5(5.7 \text{ in})(4.9363 \text{ in}) = 14.0684 \text{ sq in}$
   $V = \dfrac{(14.0684 \text{ sq in})(4.65 \text{ in})}{3} = 21.806 \text{ cu in}, \ 21.81 \text{ cu in}$

   b. $5.82 \text{ lb} \div 21.806 \text{ lb}, \ 0.2669 \text{ lb}, \ 0.27 \text{ lb}$

9. $A_b = \pi(0.2885 \text{ in})^2 = 0.26148 \text{ sq in}$
   $V = \dfrac{(0.26148 \text{ sq in})(0.500 \text{ in})}{3}$
   $V = 0.04 \text{ cu in}$

10. a. $A_b = (4.828)(9.36 \text{ in})^2 = 422.979 \text{ sq in}$
    $V = \dfrac{(422.979 \text{ sq in})(7.08 \text{ in})}{3} = 2994.6913 \text{ cu in}, \ 2995 \text{ cu in}$

10. b. $2994.6913 \text{ cu in} \div 1728 \text{ cu in} / \text{cu ft} = 1.733 \text{ cu ft}$
    $547.9 \text{ lb} / \text{cu ft} \times 1.733 \text{ cu ft} = 949.51 \text{ lb}, \ 950 \text{ lb}$

11. $152.08 \text{ cu in} = \dfrac{(32.87 \text{ sq in})h}{3}$
    $h = 13.88 \text{ in}$

12. $198.7 \text{ cm}^3 = \dfrac{A_b(12.7 \text{ cm})}{3}$
    $A_b = 46.937 \text{ cm}^2, \ 47 \text{ cm}^3$

13. $323 \text{ cu in} = \dfrac{(49 \text{ sq in})h}{3}$
    $h = 19.776 \text{ in}, \ 20 \text{ in}$

14. $V = 231 \text{ cu in} / \text{gal} \times 6.00 \text{ gal} = 1386 \text{ cu in}$
    $1386 \text{ cu in} = \dfrac{A_b(17.80 \text{ in})}{3}$
    $A_b = 233.596 \text{ sq in}, \ 233.60 \text{ sq in}$

15. $1152 \text{ cm}^3 = \dfrac{A_b(8.64 \text{ cm})}{3}$
    $A_b = 400 \text{ cm}^2$
    $s = \sqrt{400 \text{ cm}^2} = 20 \text{ cm}$

16. $922.4 \text{ cm}^3 = \dfrac{A_b(14.85 \text{ cm})}{3}$
    $A_b - 186.34343 \text{ cm}^2$
    $186.34343 \text{ cm}^3 = \pi r^2$
    $r^2 = 59.31496 \text{ cm}^2$
    $r = \sqrt{59.31496 \text{ cm}^2} = 7.7016 \text{ cm}$
    $d = 2(7.7016 \text{ cm}) = 15.403 \text{ cm}, \ 15.40 \text{ cm}$

17. $A_b = (9.71 \text{ in})^2 = 94.2841 \text{ sq in}$
    $V = 204.8 \text{ lb} \div 490.5 \text{ lb} / \text{ft} = 0.417533 \text{ cu ft}$
    $0.417533 \text{ cu ft} \times 1728 = 721.49725 \text{ cu in}$
    $721.49725 \text{ cu in} = \dfrac{(94.2841 \text{ sq in})h}{3}$
    $h = 22.9571 \text{ in}, \ h = 22.96 \text{ in}$

18. $3174 \text{ cm}^3 = \dfrac{A_b(16.91 \text{ cm})}{3}$
    $A_b = 563.09876 \text{ cm}^2$
    $563.09876 \text{ cm}^2 = (0.5)(s)(0.5s)$
    $563.09876 \text{ cm}^2 = 0.25s^2$
    $s = \sqrt{2252.39504 \text{ cm}^2} = 47.4594 \text{ cm}, \ 47.46 \text{ cm}$

19. $V = \dfrac{(16.29 \text{ in})[31.76 \text{ sq in} + 14.05 \text{ sq in} + \sqrt{(31.76 \text{ sq in})(14.05 \text{ sq in})}]}{3}$

    $V = \dfrac{(16.29 \text{ in})(45.81 \text{ sq in} + 21.12411 \text{ sq in})}{3}$

    $V = 363.34 \text{ cu in}, \ 363 \text{ cu in}$

UNIT 55   (*continued*)

20. $V = \dfrac{\pi(29.5 \text{ cm})[875 \text{ cm}^2 + 426 \text{ cm}^2 + \sqrt{(875 \text{ cm}^2)(426 \text{cm}^2)}]}{3}$

$V = \dfrac{(\pi)(29.5 \text{ cm})(1301 \text{ cm}^{2)} + 610.53255 \text{ cm}^{2)}}{3}$

$V = 59{,}051.69 \text{ cm}^3$, 59.1 L

21. $V = \dfrac{(5.10 \text{ in})[58.30 \text{ sq in} + \sqrt{(58.30 \text{ sq in})(40.0 \text{ sq in})}]}{3}$

$V = \dfrac{(5.10 \text{ sq in})(98.30 \text{ sq in} + 48.2908 \text{ sq in})}{3}$

$V = 747.613 \text{ cu in} = 0.4326 \text{ cu ft}$

Weight = $490.3 \text{ lb} / \text{cu ft} \times 0.4326 \text{ cu ft} = 212.1 \text{ lb}$

22. $V = \dfrac{\pi(24.52 \text{ cm})[(155.68 \text{ cm}^2) + (126.98 \text{ cm})^2 + (155.68 \text{ cm})(126.98 \text{ cm})]}{3}$

$V = \dfrac{(\pi)(24.52 \text{ cm})(60{,}128.4249 \text{ cm}^2)}{3}$

$V = 1{,}543{,}934 \text{ cm}^3 = 1.54 \text{ m}^3$

23. height = $14.10 \text{ cm} - 0.62 \text{ cm} = 13.48 \text{ cm}$

side of large base = $20.48 \text{ cm} - 2(0.62 \text{ cm}) = 19.24 \text{ cm}$

side of small base = $16.64 \text{ cm} - 2(0.62 \text{ cm}) = 15.40 \text{ cm}$

$A_B = (19.24 \text{ cm})^2 = 370.1776 \text{ cm}^2$

$A_b = (15.4 \text{ cm})^2 = 237.16 \text{ cm}^2$

$V = \dfrac{(\pi)(13.48 \text{ cm})[370.1775 \text{ cm}^2 + 237.16 \text{ cm}^2 + \sqrt{(370.1775 \text{ cm}^2)(237.16 \text{ cm}^2)}]}{3}$

$V = \dfrac{\pi(13.48 \text{ cm})(903.633 \text{ cm}^2)}{3}$

$V = 12{,}755.88 \text{ cm}^3$, 12,756 cm^3

24. $h = 18.40 \text{ in} - 13.60 \text{ in} = 4.80 \text{ in}$

$V = \dfrac{(\pi)(4.80 \text{ in})[(0.925 \text{ in})^2 + (0.625 \text{ in})]}{3}$

$V = \dfrac{(\pi)(4.80 \text{ in})(0.8556 \text{ sq in} + 0.3906 \text{ sq in} + 0.5781 \text{ sq in})}{3}$

$V = 9.17 \text{ cu in}$

25. a. $V = \dfrac{(\pi)(3.50 \text{ in})[(1.40 \text{ in})^2 + (1.15 \text{ in})^2 + (1.40 \text{ in})(1.15 \text{ in})]}{3}$

$V = \dfrac{(\pi)(3.50 \text{ in})(4.8925 \text{ sq in})}{3}$

$V = 17{,}93195$, 17.9 cu in

b. Weight = $17.93195 \text{ cu in} \times 0.256 \text{ lb} / \text{cu in}$

Weight = 4.5906 lb, 4.6 lb

26. $A_B = 4.828(8.17 \text{ cm})^2 = 322.26369 \text{ cm}^2$

$A_b = 4.828(6.77 \text{ cm})^2 = 221.28124 \text{ cm}^2$

$V = \dfrac{(\pi)(23.84 \text{ cm})[322.26369 \text{ cm}^2 + 221.2812 \text{ cm}^2 + \sqrt{(322.26369 \text{ cm}^2)(221.2812 \text{ cm}^2)}]}{3}$

$V = \dfrac{(\pi)(23.84 \text{ cm})(810.58589 \text{ cm})^2}{3}$

$V = 20{,}236.43 \text{ cm}^3$, 20,236 cm^3

UNIT 55   (*continued*)

27. $V_1 = \dfrac{(\pi)(5.06 \text{ cm})[(5.66 \text{ cm})^2 + (4.64 \text{ cm})^2 + (5.66 \text{ cm})(4.64 \text{ cm})]}{3}$

$V_1 = \dfrac{(\pi)(5.06 \text{ cm})(79.8276 \text{ cm}^2)}{3} = 422.992 \text{ cm}^3$

$V_2 = \dfrac{(\pi)(5.06 \text{ cm})[(3.94 \text{ cm})^2 + (2.92 \text{ cm})^2 + (3.94 \text{ cm})(2.92 \text{ cm})]}{3}$

$V_2 = \dfrac{(\pi)(5.06 \text{ cm})(35.5548 \text{ cm}^2)}{3} = 188.398 \text{ cm}^3$

$V = 422.992 \text{ cm}^3 - 188.398 \text{ cm}^3$

$V = 234.594 \text{ cm}^3, 234.6 \text{ cm}^3$

28. $(6.77 \text{ in})^2 = (3.385 \text{ in})^2 + h^2$

$h^2 = 34.37468 \text{ sq in}$

$h = 5.8630 \text{ in}$

$(4.98 \text{ in})^2 = (2.49 \text{ in})^2 + h^2$

$h^2 = 18.6003 \text{ in}^2$

$h = 4.3128 \text{ in}$

$A_1 = 0.5(6.77 \text{ in})(5.8630 \text{ in}) = 19.8463 \text{ sq in}$

$A_2 = 0.5(4.98 \text{ in})(2.49 \text{ in}) = 6.2001 \text{ sq in}$

$240.5 \text{ cu in} = \dfrac{(\pi)(h)[19.8463 \text{ sq in} + 6.200 \text{ sq in} + \sqrt{(19.8463 \text{ sq in})(6.2001 \text{ sq in})}]}{3}$

$240.5 \text{ cu in} = \dfrac{(\pi)(h)(37.13896 \text{ sq in})}{3}$

$h = 6.1841 \text{ in}, 6.18 \text{ in}$

UNIT 56   Volumes of Spheres and Composite Solid Figures

1. $V = \dfrac{4(\pi)(2.154 \text{ cm})}{3} = 41.6298 \text{ cm}^3, 41.63 \text{ cm}^3$

2. $V = \dfrac{4(\pi)(0.14 \text{ m})^3}{3} = 0.01149 \text{ m}^3, 0.01 \text{ m}^3$

3. $V = \dfrac{4(\pi)(3.80 \text{ in})^3}{3} = 229.8473 \text{ cu in}, 229.85 \text{ cu in}$

4. $V = \dfrac{4(\pi)(0.12 \text{ ft})^3}{3} = 7.2382 \text{ cu ft}, 7.24 \text{ cu ft}$

5. $V = \dfrac{4(\pi)(4.78 \text{ in})^3}{3} = 457.48 \text{ cu in}$

6. $V = \dfrac{4(\pi)(0.0375 \text{ m})^3}{3} = 0.00066 \text{ m}^3, 0.\bar{0} \text{ m}^3$

7. $V = \dfrac{4(\pi)(8.10 \text{ cm})^3}{3} = 2226.09 \text{ cm}^3$

8. $V = \dfrac{4(\pi)(0.625 \text{ f})^3}{3} = 1.0227 \text{ cu ft}^3 = 1.0227 \text{ cu ft}, 1.02 \text{ cu ft}$

9. $V = \dfrac{4(\pi)(0.120 \text{ in})^3}{3} = 0.00724 \text{ cu in}$

$0.00724 \text{ cu in} \times 18 \times 0.283 \text{ lb} / \text{cu in} = 0.0369 \text{ lb}$

10.   Volume of the sphere:

$V = \dfrac{4(\pi)(9.0 \text{ in})^3}{3} = 3,053.628 \text{ cu in}$

10.   Volume of the hemisphere:

$V = 0.5(3,053.628 \text{ cu in}) = 1,526.814 \text{ cu in}$

$1,526.814 \text{ cu in} \div 231 \text{ cu in} / \text{gal} = 6.61 \text{ gal}$

11. $V = \dfrac{4(\pi)(3.13 \text{ cm})^3}{3} = 128.446 \text{ cm}^3$

$128.446 \text{ cm}^3 \times 0.94 = 121 \text{ cm}^3$

12. $V_1 = \dfrac{4(\pi)(0.73 \text{ in})^3}{3} = 1.6295 \text{ cu in}$

$V_2 = \dfrac{4(\pi)(1.135 \text{ in})^3}{3} = 6.1246 \text{ cu in}$

$0.523 \text{ lb} / 1.6295 \text{ cu in} = 0.3210 \text{ lb} / \text{cu in}$

$6.1246 \text{ cu in} \times 0.3210 \text{ lb} / \text{cu in} = 1.996 \text{ lb}$

13. $27.50 \text{ lb} \div 707.7 \text{ lb} / \text{cu in} = 0.038858 \text{ cu ft}$

$0.38858 \text{ cu ft} = \dfrac{4\pi r^3}{3}$

$4\pi r^3 = 0.116574 \text{ cu ft}$

$r^3 = \dfrac{0.116574 \text{ cu ft}}{4\pi} = 0.009277 \text{ cu ft}$

$r = 0.210118 \text{ ft} = 2.5215 \text{ in}$

$d = 5.04929 \text{ in}, 5.04 \text{ in}$

UNIT **56**   (*continued*)

14. $V_1 = \left(\dfrac{1}{2}\right)\dfrac{4\pi(19.3\ \text{cm})^3}{3}$

$V_1 = 15{,}056.72577\ \text{cm}^3$

$V_2 = \left(\dfrac{1}{2}\right)4\pi(19.3\ \text{cm} - 0.05\ \text{cm})^3$

$V_2 = 14{,}940.00749\ \text{cm}^3$

Volume of cover $= 15{,}056.72577\ \text{cm}^3 - 14{,}940.007\ \text{cm}^3 = 116.7182812\ \text{cm}^3$

Material expense $= \$0.0014\,/\,\text{cm}^3(116.7182812\ \text{cm}^3) \times 55{,}000 = \$8{,}987$

15. Volume of the solid plate: $V = (14.00\ \text{in})^2(2.00\ \text{in}) = 392\ \text{cu in}$

Volume of one 1.50-inch diameter hole: $V = \pi(0.750\ \text{in})^2(2.00\ \text{in}) = 3.5343\ \text{cu in}$

Volume of the 3.20-inch diameter hole: $V = \pi(1.60\ \text{in})^2(2.00\ \text{in}) = 16.08495\ \text{cu in}$

Volume of the plate: $V = 392\ \text{cu in} - [4(3.5343\ \text{cu in}) + 16.08495\ \text{cu in}] = 361.77792\ \text{cu in}$

$361.77792\ \text{cu in} \div 1{,}728\ \text{cu in}\,/\,\text{ft} = 0.2094\ \text{cu ft}$

$0.2094\ \text{cu ft} \times 490\ \text{lb}\,/\,\text{cu ft} = 103\ \text{lb}$

16. Volume of cylindrical section: $V = \pi(11.2\ \text{cm})^2(20.0\ \text{cm}) = 7{,}881.628\ \text{cm}^3$

Volume of the frustum of the cone section: $V = \dfrac{\pi(16.0\ \text{cm})[(11.2\ \text{cm})^2 + (2.0\ \text{cm})^2 + (11.2\ \text{cm})(2.0\ \text{cm})]}{3}$

$$V = \dfrac{\pi(16.0\ \text{cm})(125.44\ \text{cm}^2 + 4\ \text{cm}^2 + 22.4\ \text{cm})}{3}$$

$$V = 2{,}544.104\ \text{cm}^3$$

Total Volume: $V = 7{,}881.628\ \text{cm}^3 + 2{,}544.104\ \text{cm}^3 = 10{,}425.732\ \text{cm}^3$

$10{,}425.732\ \text{cm}^3 \div 1{,}000\ \text{cm}^3\,/\,\text{L} = 10.43\ \text{L};\ 10.4\ \text{L}$

17. Volume of tube:

$V_1 = 0.7854(3.875\ \text{in})^2(19.37\ \text{in} + 1.250\ \text{in})$

$V_1 = 243.17727\ \text{cu in}$

$V_2 = 0.7854[3.875\ \text{in} - 2(0.238\ \text{in})]^2(19.37\ \text{in} + 1.250\ \text{in})$

$V_2 = 187.10349\ \text{cu in}$

Volume of tube $= 243.17727\ \text{cu in} - 187.10349\ \text{cu in} = 56.07378\ \text{cu in}$

Volume of plate $= [(18.63\ \text{in}^2 - (0.7854)(3.875\ \text{cu in})^2] \times 1.250\ \text{in} = 419.10454\ \text{cu in}$

Volume of assembly $= 56.07378\ \text{cu in} + 419.10454\ \text{cu in} = 475.17832\ \text{cu in}$

Weight $= (475.17832\ \text{cu in})(0.305\ \text{lb}\,/\,\text{cu in}) = 144.929\ \text{lb},\ 144.9\ \text{lb}$

18. Volume of solid 2.580-cm diameter cylinder: $V = \pi(1.290\ \text{cm})^2(2.520\ \text{cu in} - 0.730\ \text{cm}) = 9.35798\ \text{cm}^3$

Volume of solid 3.140-cm diameter cylinder: $V = \pi(1.570\ \text{cm})^2(0.730\ \text{cm}) = 5.6529\ \text{cm}^3$

18. Volume of 0.960-cm diameter cylinder through hole: $V = \pi(0.480\ \text{cm})^2(2.520\ \text{cm}) = 1.8240\ \text{cm}^3$

Volume of bushing: $V = 9.35798\ \text{cm}^3 + 5.6529\ \text{cm}^3 - 1.8240\ \text{cm}^3 = 13.187\ \text{cm}^3,\ 13.2\ \text{cm}^3$

19. Volume of angle iron without webb:

$[(11.95\ \text{in})(1\ \text{in}) + (9.88\ \text{in} - 1.00\ \text{in})(1\ \text{in})](9.00\ \text{in}) = 187.47\ \text{cu in}$

Volume of one triangular webb:

$0.5(9.88\ \text{in} - 1.00\ \text{in})(11.95\ \text{in} - 1.00\ \text{in})(1.50\ \text{in}) = 72.927\ \text{cu in}$

Total Volume $= 187.47\ \text{cu in} + 2(72.927\ \text{cu in}) = 333.324\ \text{cu in}$

Weight $= 333.324\ \text{cu in} \times 0.284\ \text{lb}\,/\,\text{cu in} = 94.664\ \text{lb},\ 94.7\ \text{lb}$

UNIT 56   (*continued*)

20. Prism volume $= (3.470 \text{ in})^2 (3.512 \text{ in}) = 42.28764$ cu in

Cylinder volume $= \pi (4.505 \text{ in})^2 (5.870 \text{ in}) = 374.26358$ cu in

Frustum of one Volume $= \left(\dfrac{1}{3}\right)(\pi)(4.425 \text{ in})[(4.505 \text{ in})^2 + (1.345 \text{ in})^2 + (4.505 \text{ in})] = 130.50437$ cu in

Total Volume $= 42.2876$ cu in $+ 374.2636$ cu in $+ 130.5044$ cu in $= 547.0556$ cu in, 547.1 cu in

21. Volume of large cylinder:

$V = \pi (3.1875 \text{ in})^2 (0.375 \text{ in}) = 11.96965$ cu in

Volume of small cylinder without hole:

$V = \pi (1.5625 \text{ in})^2 (0.750 \text{ in}) = 5.752428$ cu in

Volume of hole:

$V = \pi (0.8125 \text{ in})^2 (0.750 \text{ in}) = 1.55546$ cu in

Volume of one rib:

Triangle base $= \dfrac{6.075\text{ in} - 1.115\text{ in}}{2} = 1.625$ in

$V = 0.5(1.625 \text{ in})(0.750 \text{ in})(0.375 \text{ in}) = 0.22852$ cu in

Total Volume $= 11.96965$ cu in $+ 5.752428$ cu in $- 1.55546$ cu in $+ 4(0.22852$ cu in$) = 17.0807$ cu in

Weight $= 17.0807$ cu in $\times 0.283$ lb / cu in $= 4.8338$ lb, 4.83 lb

22.

① $V = (1.50 \text{ cm})(1.00 \text{ cm})(6.50 \text{ cm}) = 9.75 \text{ cm}^3$

② Volume of solid prism: $V = (1.00 \text{ cm})(6.00 \text{ cm})(6.50 \text{ cm}) = 39.0 \text{ cm}^3$

③ $V = 4.50 \text{ cm}(2.50 \text{ cm})(6.50 \text{ cm}) = 73.125 \text{ cm}^3$

④ Volume of solid prism: $V = 1.00 \text{ cm}(6.00 \text{ cm})(6.50 \text{ cm}) = 39.0 \text{ cm}^3$

⑤ Volume of semicircle cutout: $V = \pi (1.50 \text{ cm})^2 (1.00 \text{ cm}) \div 2 = 3.5343 \text{ cm}^3$

⑥ Volume of V-cutout: $V = 0.5(2.50 \text{ cm})(2.00 \text{ cm})(1.00 \text{ cm}) = 2.50 \text{ cm}^3$

Total Volume: $9.75 \text{ cm}^3 + 39.0 \text{ cm}^3 + 73.125 \text{ cm}^3 + 39.0 \text{ cm}^3 - 3.5343 \text{ cm}^3 - 2.50 \text{ cm}^3 = 154.84 \text{ cm}^3, 155 \text{ cm}^3$

UNIT 57   Achievement Review—Section 5

1. $A = 17.500 \text{ in} \times 9.000 \text{ in}$

$A = 157.5$ sq in

2. $0.12 \text{ m}^2 = l(0.20 \text{ m})$

$l = \dfrac{0.12 \text{ m}^2}{0.20 \text{ m}}$

$l = 0.6$ m

3. $851.6 \text{ mm}^2 = 43.70 \text{ mm}(w)$

$w = \dfrac{851.6 \text{ mm}^2}{43.70 \text{ mm}}$

$w = 19.487$ mm, 19.5 mm

4. $A = 17.71 \text{ cm}(12.07 \text{ cm})$

$A = 213.7597 \text{ cm}^2, 213.8$ cm

5. $13.83 \text{ sq in} = 3.56 \text{ in}(h)$

$h = \dfrac{13.83 \text{ sq in}}{3.56 \text{ in}}$

$h = 3.8848$ in, 3.9 in

6. $0.22 \text{ sq ft} = (b)0.25 \text{ ft}$

$b = \dfrac{0.22 \text{ sq ft}}{0.25 \text{ ft}} = 0.88 \text{ ft}, 0.9 \text{ ft}$

UNIT **57** (*continued*)

7. $A = 0.5(14.75 \text{ cm})(23.06 \text{ cm} + 17.66 \text{ cm})$
$A = 300.31 \text{ cm}^2, 300.3 \text{ cm}^3$

8. $0.87 \text{ m}^2 = 0.5(0.42 \text{ m})(2.98 \text{ m} + b_2)$
$0.87 \text{ m}^2 = 0.21 \text{m}(2.98 \text{m} + b_2)$
$0.87 \text{ m}^2 = 0.6258 \text{ m}^2 + 0.21 \text{m}(b_2)$
$0.21 \text{m}(b_2) = 0.87 \text{ m}^2 - 0.6407 \text{ m}^2$

$b_2 = \dfrac{0.87 \text{ m}^2 - 0.6258 \text{ m}^2}{0.21 \text{m}}$

$b_2 = 1.165 \text{ m}, 1.2 \text{ m}$

9. $202.7 \text{ sq in} = 0.5h(24.82 \text{ in} + 21.77 \text{ in})$

$0.5h = \dfrac{202.7 \text{ sq in}}{46.59 \text{ in}}$

$0.5h = 4.35072 \text{ in}$

$h = 8.7014 \text{ in}, 8.7 \text{ in}$

10. $A = 0.5(7.60 \text{ cm})(5.50 \text{ cm})$
$A = 20.9 \text{ cm}^2$

11. $32.7 \text{ sq in} = 0.5(b)(4.36 \text{ in})$

$b = \dfrac{32.7 \text{ sq in}}{0.5(4.36 \text{ in})}$

$b = 15 \text{ in}$

12. $s = 0.5(12.62 \text{ cm} + 8.04 \text{ cm} + 16.56 \text{ cm}) = 18.61 \text{ cm}$

$A = \sqrt{18.61 \text{ cm}(18.61 \text{ cm} - 12.62 \text{ cm})(18.61 \text{ cm} - 8.04 \text{ cm})(18.61 \text{ cm} - 16.56 \text{ cm})}$

$A = \sqrt{2{,}415.472 \text{ cm}^4}$

$A = 49.1 \text{ cm}^2$

13. Area of strip:
$A = 72.0 \text{ in}(2.40 \text{ in}) = 172.8 \text{ sq in}$
Area of one stamped piece:
$h = 240 \text{ in} - 2(0.30 \text{ in}) = 1.80 \text{ in}$
$A = 2.60 \text{ in}(1.80 \text{ in}) = 4.68 \text{ sq in}$
Area of strip wasted:
$172.8 \text{ sq in} - 24(4.68 \text{ in}) = 60.5 \text{ sq in}$

14. Area of rectangular cross section:
$A = 17.90 \text{ cm}(6.40 \text{ cm}) = 114.56 \text{ cm}^2$
Area of dovetail cutout:
$h = 6.40 \text{ cm} - 4.20 \text{ cm} = 2.20 \text{ cm}$
$b_1 = 17.90 \text{ cm} - 2(3.40 \text{ cm}) = 11.1 \text{ cm}$
$b_2 = 17.90 \text{ cm} - 2(5.20 \text{ cm}) = 7.50 \text{ cm}$
$A = 0.5(2.20 \text{ cm})(11.1 \text{ cm} + 7.50 \text{ cm}) = 20.46 \text{ cm}^2$
After cutting dovetail:
$114.56 \text{ cm}^2 - 20.46 \text{ cm}^2 = 94.1 \text{ cm}^2$

15.

① $A = 0.5(10.00 \text{ cm})(21.08 \text{ cm}) = 105.4 \text{ cm}^2$

② $A = 0.5(37.66 \text{ cm} - 10.00 \text{ cm})(21.08 \text{ cm} + 12.56 \text{ cm}) = 465.24 \text{ cm}^2$

③ $b = (67.98 \text{ cm} - 37.66 \text{ cm})(12.56 \text{ cm}) = 30.32 \text{ cm}(12.56 \text{ cm}) = 380.82 \text{ cm}^2$

④ $A = 0.5(16.87 \text{ cm})[28.12 \text{ cm} + (28.12 \text{ cm} - 15.36 \text{ cm})]$
$A = 0.5(16.87 \text{ cm})(28.12 \text{ cm} + 12.76 \text{ cm})$
$A = 8.435 \text{ cm}(40.86 \text{ cm})$
$A = 344.82 \text{ cm}^2$

⑤ $A = 0.5(46.75 \text{ cm} - 28.12 \text{ cm})(29.26 \text{ cm} + 16.87 \text{ cm}) = 429.705 \text{ cm}^2$

⑥ $A = 0.5(67.98 \text{ cm} - 46.75 \text{ cm})(29.26 \text{ cm}) = 310.59 \text{ cm}^2$

Total area $= 105.4 \text{ cm}^2 + 465.24 \text{ cm}^2 + 380.82 \text{ cm}^2 + 344.82 \text{ cm}^2 + 429.70 \text{ cm}^2 + 310.59 \text{ cm}^2 = 2{,}037 \text{ cm}^2$

16. $A = \pi r^2$
$A = (\pi)(14.86 \text{ in})^2$
$A = 693.725 \text{ sq in}, 693.7 \text{ sq in}$

UNIT **57**   (*continued*)

17. $A = 0.7854(28.600 \text{ cm})^2$
     $A = 642.426 \text{ cm}^2, 642.4 \text{ cm}^2$

18. $0.62 \text{ sq ft} = \pi r^2$

$$r^2 = \frac{0.62 \text{ sq ft}}{\pi} = 0.197352 \text{ sq ft}$$

$$r = 0.444 \text{ sq ft}, 0.4 \text{ ft}$$

19. $A = \dfrac{120.0°}{360°}\pi(5.50 \text{ in})^2 = 0.3333(\pi)(30.25 \text{ sq in}) = 31.7 \text{ sq in}$

20. $54.36 \text{ sq in} = \dfrac{230.0°25'}{360°}\pi r^2$
     $54.36 \text{ sq in} = 2.01076 r^2$
     $r^2 = 27.03455 \text{ sq in}$
     $r = 5.2 \text{ in}$

21. $0.0300 \text{ m}^2 = \dfrac{\theta}{360°} = \pi(0.200 \text{ m})^2$

$$\theta = \frac{0.0300 \text{ m}^2(360°)}{\pi(0.200 \text{ m})^2}$$

$$\theta = 85.9437°, 85.9°$$

22. $A = 72.3 \text{ cm}^2 - 58.0 \text{ cm}^2 = 14.3 \text{ cm}^2$

23. $A = 207.8 \text{ sq in} - 135.3 \text{ sq in} = 72.5 \text{ sq in}$

24. $A = 719.5 \text{ sq in} - 587.0 \text{ sq in} = 132.5 \text{ sq in}$

25. Area of sector:
$$A = \frac{160.0°}{360.0°}(\pi)(2.400 \text{ in})^2 = 8.0425 \text{ in}^2$$

Area triangle:
$$c^2 = a^2 + b^2$$
$$(2.400 \text{ in}) = (0.420 \text{ in})^2 + b^2$$
$$5.76 \text{ in}^2 = 0.1764 \text{ in}^2 + b^2$$
$$b_2 = 5.5836 \text{ in}$$
$$b = 2.3630 \text{ in}$$
Base $= 2(2.3630 \text{ in}) = 4.726 \text{ in}$
$A = 0.5(4.726 \text{ in})(0.420 \text{ in}) = 0.992 \text{ in}^2$
Area of segment:
$8.0425 \text{ in}^2 - 0.992 \text{ in}^2 = 7.05 \text{ sq in}$

26. Area of circular plate:
$A = \pi(15.00 \text{ in})^2 = 706.86 \text{ sq in}$

$706.86 \text{ sq in} \div 144 \text{ sq in} / \text{sq ft} = 4.909 \text{ sq ft}$

Area of rectangular plate:
$A = 4.00 \text{ ft}(3.00 \text{ ft}) = 12.0 \text{ sq ft}$

Weight of circular plate:
$30.00 \text{ lb} \div 12.0 \text{ sq ft} = 2.50 \text{ lb} / \text{sq ft}$
$2.50 \text{ lb} / \text{sq ft} \times 4.909 \text{ sq ft} = 12.3 \text{ lb}$

27. ① $\dfrac{90°}{360°}(3.1416)(1.250 \text{ in})^2 = 1.2272 \text{ sq in}$

② $A = 1.227\ 2 \text{ sq in}$

③ $A = 4.800 \text{ in}(1.250 \text{ in}) = 6 \text{ sq in}$

Area of block before cut:
$A = 9.000 \text{ in}(3.100 \text{ in}) = 27.900 \text{ sq in}$

Area of block after cut:
$27.900 \text{ sq in} - [2(1.2272 \text{ sq in}) + 6 \text{ sq in}] = 19.5 \text{ sq in}$

28.

① $A = \dfrac{78.0°}{360°} = (\pi)(8.20 \text{ cm})^2 = 45.769 \text{ cm}^2$

② $A = 0.5(8.02 \text{ cm})[7.10 \text{ cm} + (13.60 \text{ cm} - 8.20 \text{ cm})] = 50.125 \text{ cm}^2$

③ $A = (21.00 \text{ cm} - 8.02 \text{ cm})(13.60 \text{ cm}) = 176.528 \text{ cm}^2$

④ $A = \dfrac{90°}{360°}(\pi)(13.60 \text{ cm})^2 = 145.268 \text{ cm}^2$

Total area $= 45.769 \text{ cm}^2 + 50.125 \text{ cm}^2 + 176.528 \text{ cm}^2 + 145.268 \text{ cm}^2 = 417.69 \text{ cm}^2, 418 \text{ cm}^2$

29. $V = 220.0 \text{ cm}^2 (7.600 \text{ cm}) = 1,672 \text{ cm}^3$

30. $V = 53.00 \text{ sq in}(4.600 \text{ in}) = 243.8 \text{ cu in}$

31. $4.86 \text{ cu ft} = 2.7 \text{ sq ft}(h)$
     $h = 1.8 \text{ ft}$

UNIT 57   *(continued)*

32. $V = A_B h$

    $1910 \text{ cm}^3 = A_B(9.55)$

    $A_B = 200 \text{ cm}^2$

33. $V = A_B h$

    $V = (8.70 \text{ in})^2(2.85 \text{ in})$

    $V = 215.7165 \text{ cu in}, 215.75 \text{ cu in}$

34. $V = A_B h$

    $V = 0.7854(22.08 \text{ in})^2(2.63 \text{ in})$

    $V = 1007.03551 \text{ cu in}$

    $\dfrac{1007.03551 \text{ cu in}}{1728 \text{ cu in} / \text{cu ft}} = 0.582775 \text{ cu ft}$

    $168.5 \text{ lb} / \text{cu ft} \times 0.582775 \text{ cu ft} = 98.1976 \text{ lb}, 98 \text{ lb}$

35. $V = A_B h$

    $V = 0.7854(6.75 \text{ in})^2(8.12 \text{ in})$

    $V = 290.57247 \text{ cu in}$

    $290.57247 \text{ cu in} \div 1728 \text{ cu in} / \text{cu ft} = 0.168155 \text{ cu ft}$

    $0.168155 \text{ cu ft} \times 7.5 \text{ gal} / \text{cu ft} = 1.2612 \text{ gal}, 1.26 \text{ gal}$

36. $A_B = \pi(2.500 \text{cm})^2 = 19.635 \text{ cm2}$

    $1.000 \text{ L} = 1,000 \text{ cm}^3$

    $1.000 \text{ cm}^3 = 19.635 \text{ cm}^2(h)$

    $h = 50.93 \text{ cm}$

41. $210.5 \text{ cu in} = \dfrac{(54.6 \text{ sq in})h}{3}$

    $h = 11.5659 \text{ in}, 11.57 \text{ in}$

42. $1070 \text{ cm}^3 = \dfrac{A_B(15.8 \text{ cm})}{3}$

    $A_B = 203.1646 \text{ cm}^2, 203.16 \text{ cm}$

43. $V = \dfrac{(22.0 \text{ cm})[40.0 \text{ cm}^2 + 19.0 \text{ cm}^2 + \sqrt{40.0 \text{ cm}^2(19.0 \text{ cm}^2)}]}{3}$

    $V = \dfrac{(22.0 \text{ cm})(40.0 \text{ cm}^2 + 19.0 \text{ cm}^2 + 27.568 \text{ cm}^2)}{3}$

    $V = 635 \text{ cm}^3$

44. $A_B = (\dfrac{26.10 \text{ in}}{4})^2 = 43.56 \text{ sq in}$

    $A_B = (\dfrac{18.60 \text{ in}}{4})^2 = 21.6225 \text{ sq in}$

    $V = \dfrac{(5.63 \text{ in})(43.56 \text{ sq in} + 21.6225 \text{ sq in} + \sqrt{(43.56 \text{ sq in})(21.6225 \text{ sq in})}}{3}$

    $V = \dfrac{(5.63 \text{ in})(43.56 \text{ sq in} + 21.6225 \text{ sq in} + 30.69 \text{ sq in})}{3}$

    $V = 179.9207 \text{ cu in}, 179.92 \text{ cu in}$

45. $V = \dfrac{(\pi)(2.18 \text{ in})^2(3.94 \text{ in})}{3}$

    $V = \dfrac{(\pi)(4.7524 \text{ sq in})(3.94 \text{ in})}{3}$

    $V = 19.608 \text{ cu in}$

    $19.608 \text{ cu in} \times 0.302 \text{ lb} / \text{cu in} = 5.92 \text{ lb}$

37. $V = A_B h$

    $A_B = 0.5(10.30 \text{ cm})(9.48 \text{ cm} + 6.25 \text{ cm})$

    $A_B = 81.0095 \text{ cm}^2$

    $V = 81.0095 \text{ cm}^2(18.36)$

    $V = 1487.3344 \text{ cm}^3, 1487.33 \text{ cm}$

38. a. Area of 1.90-in diameter circle:

    $A = (\pi)(0.950 \text{ in})^2 = 2.83529 \text{ sq in}$

    Area of 1.5-in diameter circle:

    $A = (\pi)(0.750 \text{ in})^2 = 1.76715 \text{ sq in}$

    $A_B = 2.83529 \text{ sq in} - 1.76715 \text{ sq in} = 1.06814 \text{ sq in}$

    $30 \text{ ft} = 360 \text{ in}$

    $V = 1.06814 \text{ sq in}(360 \text{ in}) = 384.53 \text{ cu in}, 385 \text{ cu in}$

    b. $384.53 \text{ cu in} \div 1,728 \text{ cu in} / \text{cu ft} = 0.2225 \text{ cu ft}$

    $0.2225 \text{ cu ft} \times 526 \text{ lb} / \text{cu ft} = 117.035 \text{ lb}, 117 \text{ lb}$

39. $V = \dfrac{(0.800 \text{ sq in})(1.240 \text{ in})}{3} = 0.331 \text{ sq in}, 0.33 \text{ sq in}$

40. $V = \dfrac{(2010.3 \text{ cm}^2)(13.70 \text{ cm})}{3} = 9180.37 \text{ cm}^3$

    $\dfrac{9180.37 \text{ cm}^3}{1,000,000} = 0.00918 \text{ m}^3, 0.10 \text{ m}^3$

UNIT 57   (*continued*)

46. $0.690 \text{ L} = 690 \text{ cm}^3$

$690 \text{ cm}^3 = \dfrac{(\pi)(6.15 \text{ cm})^2(h)}{3}$

$h = 17.4209 \text{ cm}, 17.42 \text{ cm}$

47. $V_1 = \dfrac{(\pi)(13.65 \text{ cm})[(1.92 \text{ cm})^2 + 1.05 \text{ cm})^2 + (1.92 \text{ cm})(1.05 \text{ cm})]}{3}$

$V_1 = \dfrac{(\pi)(13.65 \text{ cm})(6.8049 \text{ cm}^2)}{3}$

$V_1 = 97.72092 \text{ cm}^3$

$V_2 = \dfrac{(\pi)(13.65 \text{ cm})[(1.35 \text{ cm}^2) + (0.48 \text{ cm}^2) + (1.35 \text{ cm})(0.48 \text{ cm})]}{3}$

$V_2 = \dfrac{(\pi)(13.65 \text{ cm})(2.7009 \text{ cm}^2)}{3}$

$V_2 = 38.60733 \text{ cm}^3$

Nozzle volume $= 97.72092 \text{ cm}^3 - 38.60733 \text{ cm}^3 = 59.11359 \text{ cm}^3$

$59.11359 \times 7.8 \text{ grams} = 461.086 \text{ grams}, 461.1 \text{ grams}$

48. $A_B = (21.50 \text{ cm} - 2.80 \text{ cm})^2 = 349.69 \text{ cm}^2$

$A_b = (10.20 \text{ cm} - 2.80 \text{ cm})^2 = 54.76 \text{ cm}^2$

$V = \dfrac{14.60 \text{ cm}[349.692 \text{ cm}^2 + 54.76 \text{ cm}^2 + \sqrt{(3.49.69 \text{ cm}^2)(54.76 \text{ cm}^2)}]}{3}$

$V = \dfrac{14.60 \text{ cm}(349.69 \text{ cm}^2 + 54.76 \text{ cm}^2 + 138.8 \text{ cm}^2)}{3}$

$V = \dfrac{14.60 \text{ cm}(542.83 \text{ cm}^2)}{3} = 2641.773 \text{ cm}^3$

$V = \dfrac{2641.773 \text{ cm}^3}{1000} = 2.641, 2.6 \text{ L}$

49. $V = \dfrac{4}{3}\pi(1.935 \text{ in})^3$

$V = \dfrac{4}{3}\pi(7.24508 \text{ in}^{3)}$

$V = 30.3481 \text{ cu in}, 30.3 \text{ cu in}$

50. $V = \dfrac{4}{3}\pi(4.525 \text{ cm})^3$

$V = \dfrac{4}{3}\pi(92.6522 \text{ cm}^{3)}$

$V = 388.1006 \text{ cm}^3, 388 \text{ cm}^3$

51. $V = \dfrac{4}{3}\pi(0.154 \text{ ft})^3$

$V = \dfrac{4}{3}\pi(0.003652 \text{ cu ft})$

$V = 0.015299 \text{ cu ft}, 0.02 \text{ cu ft}$

52. $42.98 \text{ cu in} = \dfrac{4}{3}\pi r^3$

$r^3 = \dfrac{3(42.98 \text{ cu in})}{4\pi}$

$r^3 = 10.260719 \text{ cu in}$

$r = 2.173 \text{ in}$

Dia. $= 4.346 \text{ in}, 4.35 \text{ in}$

UNIT 57   (*continued*)

53. $775 \text{ cm}^3 = \dfrac{4}{3}\pi r^3$

$r^3 = \dfrac{3(775 \text{ cm}^3)}{4\pi}$

$r^3 = 185.01762 \text{ cm}^3$

$r = 5.6982 \text{ cm}$

Dia. $= 11.3964 \text{ cm}, 11.4 \text{ cm}$

54.   Volume of head: $V = \dfrac{4(\pi)(0.450 \text{ in})^3}{3} \div 2$

$V = \dfrac{4(\pi)(0.091125 \text{ cu in}}{3} \div 2$

$V = 0.19085 \text{ cu in}$

Volume of stem: $V = \pi(0.250 \text{ in})^2(1.500 \text{ in}) = 0.29452 \text{ cu in}$

Weight: $(0.19085 \text{ cu in} + 0.29452 \text{ cu in}(0.283 \text{ lb} / \text{cu in}) = 0.137 \text{ lb}$

55.   Volume of 3.80 - cm diameter sphere: $V = \dfrac{4(\pi)(1.90 \text{ cm})^3}{3} = 28.73093 \text{ cm}^3$

$\$1.05 \div 28.7309 \text{ cm}^3 = \$0.036546 / \text{cm}^3$

Volume of 5.70 - cm diameter sphere: $V = \dfrac{4(\pi)(2.85 \text{ cm})^3}{3} = 96.96683 \text{ cm}^3$

$96.96683 \text{ cm}^3 \times \$0.036546 / \text{cm}^3 = \$3.54$

56.   Volume of solid sphere: $23.80 \text{ cm} = \pi d$

$d = 7.57578 \text{ cm}$

$r = 3.78789 \text{ cm}$

$V = \dfrac{4(\pi)(3.78789 \text{ cm})^3}{3} = 227.6568 \text{ cm}^3$

56.   Volume of air space: $V = \dfrac{4(\pi)(3.78789 \text{ cm} - 0.50 \text{ cm})^3}{3} = 148.881 \text{ cm}^3$

a.   Volume of hollow sphere: $227.6568 \text{ cm}^3 - 148.881 \text{ cm}^3 = 78.7758 \text{ cm}^3, 78.8 \text{ cm}^3$

b.   Weight $= 78.77584 \text{ cm}^3, \times 1.5 \text{ g} / \text{cm}^3 = 118.16 \text{ g}, 118.2 \text{ g}$

57.   (Top) $V_1 = (8.52 \text{ in})^2(6.73 \text{ in}) = 488.53339 \text{ cu in}$

(Bottom) $V_2 = (13.86 \text{ in})^2(10.08 \text{ in}) = 1936.36397 \text{ cu in}$

(Middle) $V_3 = \dfrac{(11.38 \text{ in})[(13.86 \text{ in})^2 + (8.52 \text{ in})^2 + \sqrt{(13.86 \text{ in})^2 (8.52 \text{ in})^2}}{3}$

$V_3 = 1452.0015 \text{ cu in}$

Total Volume $= 488.53339 \text{ cu in} + 1936.36397 \text{ cu in} + 1452.0015 \text{ cu in}$

Total Volume $= 3876.89887 \text{ cu in}$

$3876.89887 \text{ cu in} \div 1728 \text{ cu in} / \text{cu ft} = 2.2436 \text{ cu ft}, 2.24 \text{ cu ft}$

58.   ① $A = 0.5(81.0 \text{ cm})(40.0 \text{ cm}) = 1{,}620 \text{ cm}^2$

② $A = \dfrac{150°}{360°} \pi (40.0 \text{ cm})^2 = 2{,}094.395 \text{ cm}^2$

③ $A = 0.5(50.0 \text{ cm})(115.0 \text{ cm} + 40.0 \text{ cm}) = 3{,}875 \text{ cm}^2$

Total area $= 1{,}620 \text{ cm}^2 + 2{,}094.395 \text{ cm}^2 + 3{,}875 \text{ cm}^2 = 7{,}589.95 \text{ cm}^2$

$V = (7{,}589.95 \text{ cm}^2)(3.50 \text{ cm}) = 26{,}564.825 \text{ cm}^3, 26.565 \text{ cm}^3$

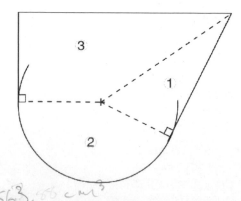

Section Six
Trigonometry

UNIT 58 Introduction to Trigonometric Functions

1. r is hyp
    x is adj
    y is opp

2. r is hyp
    x is opp
    y is adj

3. a is adj
    b is opp
    c is hyp

4. a is opp
    b is hyp
    c is adj

5. a is hyp
    b is opp
    c is adj

6. d is hyp
    m is opp
    p is adj

7. d is hyp
    m is opp
    p is adj

8. e is hyp
    f is adj
    g is opp

9. h is adj
    k is hyp
    l is opp

10. h is adj
    k is hyp
    l is opp

11. m is opp
    p is hyp
    s is adj

12. m is hyp
    p is opp
    s is adj

13. m is hyp
    r is adj
    t is opp

14. m is adj
    r is opp
    t is hyp

15. f is opp
    g is hyp
    h is adj

16. f is hyp
    g is opp
    h is adj

17. $\sin \angle 1 = \dfrac{y}{r}$

    $\cos \angle 1 = \dfrac{x}{r}$

    $\tan \angle 1 = \dfrac{y}{x}$

    $\cot \angle 1 = \dfrac{x}{y}$

    $\sec \angle 1 = \dfrac{r}{x}$

    $\csc \angle 1 = \dfrac{r}{y}$

18. $\sin \angle 1 = \dfrac{f}{d}$

    $\cos \angle 1 = \dfrac{e}{d}$

    $\tan \angle 1 = \dfrac{f}{e}$

    $\cot \angle 1 = \dfrac{e}{f}$

    $\sec \angle 1 = \dfrac{d}{e}$

    $\csc \angle 1 = \dfrac{d}{f}$

19. $\sin \angle 1 = \dfrac{k}{g}$

    $\cos \angle 1 = \dfrac{h}{g}$

    $\tan \angle 1 = \dfrac{k}{h}$

    $\cot \angle 1 = \dfrac{h}{k}$

    $\sec \angle 1 = \dfrac{g}{h}$

    $\csc \angle 1 = \dfrac{g}{k}$

20. $\sin \angle 1 = \dfrac{s}{m}$

    $\cos \angle 1 = \dfrac{l}{m}$

    $\tan \angle 1 = \dfrac{s}{l}$

    $\cot \angle 1 = \dfrac{l}{s}$

    $\sec \angle 1 = \dfrac{m}{l}$

    $\csc \angle 1 = \dfrac{m}{s}$

21. $\sin \angle 1 = \dfrac{r}{s}$

    $\cos \angle 1 = \dfrac{p}{s}$

    $\tan \angle 1 = \dfrac{r}{p}$

    $\cot \angle 1 = \dfrac{p}{r}$

    $\sec \angle 1 = \dfrac{s}{p}$

    $\csc \angle 1 = \dfrac{s}{r}$

22. $\sin \angle 1 = \dfrac{w}{t}$

    $\cos \angle 1 = \dfrac{y}{t}$

    $\tan \angle 1 = \dfrac{w}{y}$

    $\cot \angle 1 = \dfrac{y}{w}$

    $\sec \angle 1 = \dfrac{t}{y}$

    $\csc \angle 1 = \dfrac{t}{w}$

23. Group 1: a, b, d
    Group 2: a, c
    Group 3: a, c, d

24. 0.58779
25. 0.60182
26. 1.07237
27. 0.95106
28. 0.98163
29. 0.99756
30. 2.16222
31. 0.45492
32. 0.11010
33. 0.99674
34. 3.45553
35. 0.76661
36. 0.95747
37. 0.01501
38. 1.72440
39. 0.49083
40. 0.22250
41. 0.18173
42. 0.44594
43. 0.11985
44. 0.94147
45. 0.95097
46. 0.91955
47. 0.34966
48. 0.99402
49. 0.76557
50. 0.15983
51. 0.06086
52. 0.80667
53. 2.88168
54. 2.20269
55. 1.78829
56. 2.90421
57. 1.49448
58. 9.31921
59. 2.92910
60. 1.32849
61. 4.47246
62. 18.61149
63. 1.43756
64. 8.31904
65. 1.65896
66. 1.06600
67. 1.37974
68. 3.20734
69. 0.28853
70. 1.00691
71. 1.03059
72. 19.18972
73. 1.75552
74. 2.98520
75. 56.82°
76. 76.29°
77. 30.68°
78. 13.17°
79. 75.84°
80. 50.69°
81. 1.45°
82. 57.39°
83. 5.50°
84. 77.94°
85. 28.67°
86. 6.05°
87. 67.30°
88. 34.17°
89. 39.52°
90. 86.94°
91. 50.95°

UNIT **58** (*continued*)

92. 28.68°	99. 76°39′	106. 43°37′	113. 45°0′	118. 29°30′
93. 48.16°	100. 29°34′	107. 89°43′	114. 25°11′	119. 84°12′
94. 9.36°	101. 67°7′	108. 25°51′	115. 46°10′	120. 7°6′
95. 9.70°	102. 76°17′	109. 17°47′	116. 78°35′	121. 19°14′
96. 12.31°	103. 87°43′	110. 82°30′	117. 74°22′	122. 68°22′
97. 11.70°	104. 5°35′	111. 46°8′		
98. 19.03°	105. 47°3′	112. 71°44′		

UNIT **59** Analysis of Trigonometric Functions

1. a. side y and side r are almost the same length
   b. side x is very small compared to side r
   c. side x is very small compared to side y

2. a. side $x = 0$
   b. side $y =$ side r

3. a. side y is very small compared to side r
   b. side x and side r are almost the same length
   c. side x is very large compared to side y

4. a. side $y = 0$
   b. side $x =$ side r

5. a. $\angle 1 = 45°$
   b. $\tan \angle 1 = \dfrac{\text{opp side}}{\text{adj side}} = \dfrac{y}{x} = 1.000\ldots$
   c. $\cot \angle 1 = \dfrac{\text{adj side}}{\text{opp side}} = \dfrac{x}{y} = 1.000\ldots$

6. a. $\sin \angle 1 = \dfrac{y}{r} = \dfrac{0}{r} = 0$
   b. $\sec \angle 1 = \dfrac{r}{x} = 1.000\ldots$
   c. $\cos \angle 1 = \dfrac{x}{r} = 1.000\ldots$
   d. $\tan \angle 1 = \dfrac{y}{x} = \dfrac{0}{x} = 0$

7. a. $\sin \angle 1 = \dfrac{y}{r} = 1.000\ldots$
   b. $\cot \angle 1 = \dfrac{x}{y} = \dfrac{0}{y} = 0$
   c. $\cos \angle 1 = \dfrac{x}{r} = \dfrac{0}{r} = 0$
   d. $\csc \angle 1 = \dfrac{r}{y} = 1.000\ldots$

8. sin 43°	30. tan 82°50′
9. tan 18°	31. csc 53°54′
10. cos 78°	32. sec 89°22′
11. cot 36°	33. cos 84.11°
12. sec 8°	34. sin 86.24°
13. csc 22°	35. tan 90°
14. tan 21°40′	36. cot 0°
15. cos 81°19′	37. csc 46°41′
16. sin 0.42°	38. sin 89.99°
17. csc 40.45°	39. cos 0°1′
18. cot 27°23′	40. cos 48°
19. sec 55°	41. sin 40°
20. cot 67°	42. tan 30°
21. cos 41°	43. cot 45°
22. sin 64°	44. sec 42°
23. csc 8°	45. sec 43°
24. tan 55°	46. sin 14°
25. sec 39°	47. cos 75°
26. sin 0°	48. tan 1°20′
27. cos 90°	49. tan 2°40′
28. cot 32.5°	50. sec 0.2°
29. sin 77.8°	51. csc 89.0°

UNIT 60 Basic Calculations of Angles and Sides of Right Triangles

1. $\tan \angle A = \dfrac{1.700}{2.300} = 0.73913$

   $\angle A = 36°28'$

2. $\tan \angle B = \dfrac{1.620}{1.090} = 1.4862$

   $\angle B = 56°4'$

3. $\cos \angle 1 = \dfrac{4.360}{5.870} = 0.74276$

   $\angle 1 = 42°2'$

4. $\sin \angle x = \dfrac{10.00}{18.50} = 0.54054$

   $\angle x = 32°43'$

5. $\tan \angle 1 = \dfrac{126.00}{73.00} = 1.00$

   $\angle 1 = 59.24°$

6. $\sin \angle A = \dfrac{89.00}{143.50} = 0.62021$

   $\angle A = 38.33°$

7. $\cos \angle y = \dfrac{25.62}{42.45} = 0.60353$

   $\angle y = 52.88°$

8. $\tan \angle B = \dfrac{185.20}{116.30} = 1.5924$

   $\angle B = 57.87°$

9. a. $\tan \angle 1 = \dfrac{9.750}{23.720} = 0.41105$

   $\angle 1 = 22°21'$

   b. $\angle 2 = 90° - 22°21' = 67°39'$

10. a. $\sin \angle A = \dfrac{5.070}{5.630} = 0.90053$

    $\angle A = 64°14'$

    b. $\angle B = 90° - 64°14' = 25°46'$

11. a. $\tan \angle x = \dfrac{10.460}{17.070} = 0.61277$

    $\angle x = 31°30'$

    b. $\angle y = 90° - 31°30' = 58°30'$

12. a. $\sin \angle C = \dfrac{37.670}{39.820} = 0.94601$

    $\angle C = 71°5'$

    b. $\angle D = 90° - 71°5' = 18°55'$

13. $\tan 40° = \dfrac{b}{6.800}$

    $0.83910 = \dfrac{b}{6.800}$

    $b = 5.706$ in

14. $\sin 27° = \dfrac{8.950}{c}$

    $0.45399 = \dfrac{8.950}{c}$

    $c = 19.714$ in

15. $\cot 17°20' = \dfrac{x}{15.750}$

    $3.2041 = \dfrac{x}{15.750}$

    $x = 50.465$ in

16. $\cos 15°12' = \dfrac{d}{9.200}$

    $0.96502 = \dfrac{d}{9.200}$

    $d = 8.878$ in

17. $\cot 62.70° = \dfrac{y}{263.80}$

    $0.51614 = \dfrac{y}{263.80}$

    $y = 136.16$ mm

18. $\sin 55.30° = \dfrac{f}{90.45}$

    $0.82214 = \dfrac{f}{90.45}$

    $f = 74.36$ mm

19. $\cos 45.80° = \dfrac{52.64}{p}$

    $0.69717 = \dfrac{52.64}{p}$

    $p = 75.51$ mm

20. $\tan 56.04° = \dfrac{y}{83.00}$

    $1.4848 = \dfrac{y}{83.00}$

    $y = 123.24$ mm

21. a. $\sin 23°10' = \dfrac{0.877}{d}$

    $0.39341 = \dfrac{0.877}{d}$

    $d = 2.229$ in

    b. $\cot 23°10' = \dfrac{e}{0.877}$

    $2.3369 = \dfrac{e}{0.877}$

    $e = 2.049$ in

22. a. $\cos 72°40' = \dfrac{s}{19.500}$

    $0.29793 = \dfrac{s}{19.500}$

    $s = 5.810$ in

    b. $\sin 72°40' = \dfrac{t}{19.500}$

    $0.95459 = \dfrac{t}{19.500}$

    $t = 18.615$ in

23. a. $\sec 19°54' = \dfrac{x}{6.850}$

    $1.0635 = \dfrac{x}{6.850}$

    $x = 7.285$ in

    b. $\tan 19°54' = \dfrac{y}{6.850}$

    $0.36199 = \dfrac{y}{6.850}$

    $y = 2.480$ in

24. a. $\sin 49°10' = \dfrac{p}{21.090}$

    $0.75661 = \dfrac{p}{21.090}$

    $p = 15.957$ in

    b. $\cos 49°10' = \dfrac{n}{21.090}$

    $0.65386 = \dfrac{n}{21.090}$

    $n = 13.790$ in

UNIT **60** (*continued*)

➤ Note To Instructor: Unknown sides are solved using trigonometric functions. Because angles are rounded off to the nearer minute or hundredth degree, there may be a slight difference in answers computed using functions and those computed using the Pythagorean Theorem.

25. a. $\angle B = 90° - 72°30' = 17°30'$

   b. $\sec 72°30' = \dfrac{x}{16.610}$

   $3.3255 = \dfrac{x}{16.610}$

   $x = 55.237$ in

   c. $\tan 72°30' = \dfrac{y}{16.610}$

   $3.1716 = \dfrac{y}{16.610}$

   $y = 52.680$ in

26. a. $\sin \angle 1 = \dfrac{5.210}{6.314} = 0.82515$

   $\angle 1 = 55°36'$

   b. $\angle 2 = 90° - \angle 1 = 90° - 55°36' = 35°24'$

   c. $\cot \angle 1 = \dfrac{a}{5.210}$

   $\cot 55°36' = \dfrac{a}{5.210}$

   $0.68471 = \dfrac{a}{5.210}$

   $a = 3.567$ in

27. a. $\cos 18.70° = \dfrac{a}{87.40}$

   $0.94721 = \dfrac{a}{87.40}$

   $a = 82.79$ mm

   b. $\sin 18.70° = \dfrac{b}{87.40}$

   $0.32061 = \dfrac{b}{87.40}$

   $b = 28.02$ mm

   c. $\angle 2 = 90° - 18.70° = 71.30°$

28. a. $\cot \angle A = \dfrac{36.40}{29.80} = 1.22148$

   $\angle A = 39.31°$

   b. $\angle B = 90° - 39.31° = 50.69°$

28. c. $\cos \angle A = \dfrac{36.40}{r}$

   $\cos 39.31° = \dfrac{36.40}{r}$

   $0.77373 = \dfrac{36.40}{r}$

   $r = 47.04$ mm

29. a. $\angle B = 90° - 73°30' = 16°30'$

   b. $\cot 73°30' = \dfrac{b}{5.330}$

   $0.29621 = \dfrac{b}{5.330}$

   $b = 1.579$ in

   c. $\csc 73°30' = \dfrac{c}{5.330}$

   $1.0429 = \dfrac{c}{5.330}$

   $c = 5.559$ in

30. a. $\tan \angle D = \dfrac{0.087}{0.212} = 0.41038$

   $\angle D = 22°19'$

   b. $\angle E = 90° - \angle D = 90° - 22°19' = 67°41'$

   c. $\sec \angle D = \dfrac{m}{0.212}$

   $1.0810 = \dfrac{m}{0.212}$

   $m = 0.229$ in

31. a. $\angle 1 = 90° - 80°50' = 9°10'$

   b. $\sin 9°10' = \dfrac{g}{6.900}$

   $0.15931 = \dfrac{g}{6.900}$

   $g = 1.099$ in

   c. $\cos 9°10' = \dfrac{h}{6.900}$

   $0.98723 = \dfrac{h}{6.900}$

   $h = 6.812$ in

UNIT 61   Simple Practical Machine Applications

1. a. 5.7358 in   d. 1.6906 in   g. 0.0582 in
   b. 2.2778 in   e. 4.7767 in   h. 0.4246 in
   c. 5.9949 in   f. 6.9883 in   i. 3.3956 in

2. a. 3.2583 in   d. 0.0437 in   g. 3.1601 in
   b. 0.6094 in   e. 1.8690 in   h. 3.5253 in
   c. 1.0538 in   f. 1.1502 in   i 0.7203 in

3. In right △ABC: BC = 5.200 in

   $$AB = \frac{1.500\,in - 0.700\,in}{2} = 0.400\,in$$

   Compute ∠ACB.

   $$\tan \angle ACB = \frac{AB}{BC} = \frac{0.400}{5.200} = 0.07692$$

   $$\angle ACB = 4°24'$$

   $$\angle x = 2(4°24') = 8°48'$$

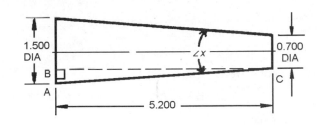

4. In right △DEF: $\angle EFD - \frac{4°50'}{2} = 2°25'$

   $$DE = \frac{2.400\,In - 1.620\,in}{2} = 0.390\,in$$

   Compute x.

   $$\cot 2°25' = \frac{x}{0.390}$$

   $$23.695 = \frac{x}{0.390}$$

   $$x = 23.695\,(0.390)$$

   $$x - 9.241\,in$$

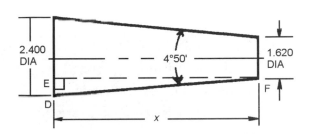

5. In right △GHK: $\angle GKH = \frac{3°}{2} = 1.50° = 1°30'$

   HK = 118.00 mm

   Compute GH.

   $$\tan 1°30' = \frac{GH}{118.00}$$

   $$0.02619 = \frac{GH}{118.00}$$

   $$GH = 0.02619\,(118.00)$$

   $$GH = 3.0904\,mm$$

   Dia y = 19.30 mm – 2(3.0904 mm) = 13.12 mm

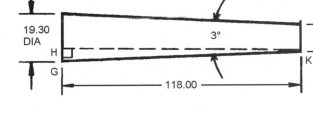

6. In right △MSP: ∠MPS = 42°50'

   MS = 0.785 in – 0.250 in = 0.535 in

   Compute MP.

   $$\cot 42°50' = \frac{MP}{0.535}$$

   $$1.0786 = \frac{MP}{0.535}$$

   $$MP = 1.0786\,(0.535)$$

   $$MP = 0.5771$$

   Dia x = 2.125 in – 2(0.5771 in) = 0.971 in

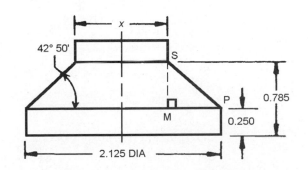

UNIT **61** (*continued*)

7. In right △ABC: ∠BAC = ∠x

$$AB = \frac{0.625\text{ in} - 0.325\text{ in}}{2} = 0.150\text{ in}$$

$$BC = 2.125\text{ in} - (0.375\text{ in} + 1.562\text{ in}) = 0.188\text{ in}$$

Compute ∠x.

$$\tan \angle x = \frac{0.188}{0.150} = 1.2533$$

$$\angle x = 51°25'$$

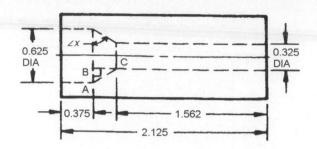

8. In right △DEF: ∠E = 58°20′

$$DE = 0.930\text{ in} - 0.400\text{ in} = 0.530\text{ in}$$

Compute DF.

$$\tan 58°20' = \frac{DF}{0.530}$$

$$1.6213 = \frac{DF}{0.530}$$

$$DF = 1.6213(0.530)$$

$$DF = 0.8593\text{ in}$$

$$y = 2.188\text{ in} - 0.8593\text{ in} = 1.329\text{ in}$$

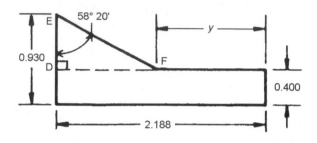

9. △ABC is isosceles, therefore, BD bisects AC and ∠ABC.

$$\angle ABC = \frac{360°}{3} = 120°$$

In right △ABD: $AB = \dfrac{295.00\text{ mm}}{2} = 147.50\text{ mm}$

$$\angle ABD = \frac{120°}{2} = 60°$$

Compute AD.

$$\sin 60° = \frac{AD}{147.50}$$

$$0.86603 = \frac{AD}{147.50}$$

$$AD = 0.86603\,(147.50)$$

$$AD = 127.739\text{ mm}$$

$$y = 2(127.739\text{ mm}) = 255.48\text{ mm}$$

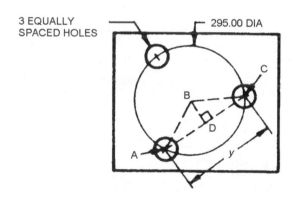

3 EQUALLY SPACED HOLES

295.00 DIA

10. △EFG is isosceles, therefore, FH bisects EG and ∠EFG.

$$\angle EFG = 2\left(\frac{360°}{8}\right) = 90°$$

In right △FGH: $FG = \dfrac{1.500\text{ in}}{2} = 0.750\text{ in}$

$$\angle GFH = \frac{90°}{2} = 45°$$

Compute GH.

$$\sin 45° = \frac{GH}{0.750}$$

$$0.70711 = \frac{GH}{0.750}$$

$$GH = 0.70711(0.750)$$

$$GH = 0.5303\text{ in}$$

$$x = 2(0.5303\text{ in}) - 0.312\text{ in} = 0.749\text{ in}$$

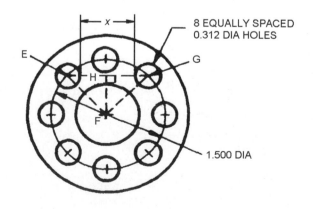

8 EQUALLY SPACED 0.312 DIA HOLES

1.500 DIA

UNIT **61** *(continued)*

11. △HLK is isosceles, therefore, LM bisects HK and ∠HLK.

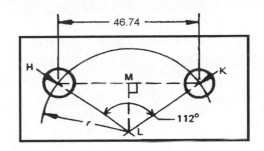

In right △HML: $HM = \dfrac{46.74 \text{ mm}}{2} = 23.37 \text{ mm}$

$$\angle HLM = \dfrac{112°}{2} = 56°$$

Compute HL.

$$\csc 56° = \dfrac{HL}{23.37}$$

$$1.2062 = \dfrac{HL}{23.37}$$

$$HL = 1.2062 (23.37)$$

$$HL = 28.189 \text{ mm}$$

$$r = HL = 28.19 \text{ mm}$$

12. △ABC is isosceles, therefore, CD bisects AB and ∠ACB.

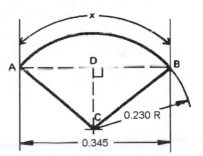

In right △BCD: $BD = \dfrac{0.345 \text{ in}}{2} = 0.1725 \text{ in}$

$$BC = 0.230 \text{ in}$$

Compute ∠BCD.

$$\sin \angle BCD = \dfrac{0.1725}{0.230} = 0.75000$$

$$\angle BCD = 48°35'$$

$$\angle ACB = 2(48°35') = 97°10' = 97.167°$$

Compute circumference. $C = 2\pi r = 2(3.1416)(0.230 \text{ in}) = 1.445 \text{ in}$

$$\dfrac{97.167°}{360°} = \dfrac{x}{1.445 \text{ in}}$$

$$360x = (97.167)(1.445 \text{ in})$$

$$x = 0.390 \text{ in}$$

13. △HEF is isosceles, therefore, GE bisects HF and ∠HEF.

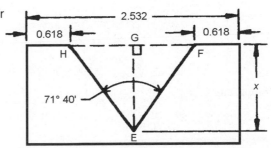

In right △EFG: $GF = \dfrac{2.532 \text{ in} - 2(0.618 \text{ in})}{2} = 0.648 \text{ in}$

$$\angle FEG = \dfrac{71°40'}{2} = 35°50'$$

Compute EG.

$$\cot 35°50' = \dfrac{EG}{0.648}$$

$$1.3848 = \dfrac{EG}{0.648}$$

$$EG = 1.3848 (0.648)$$

$$EG = 0.8974 \text{ in}$$

$$x = EG = 0.897 \text{ in}$$

UNIT **61** *(continued)*

14. In right △PST: ST = 4.814 in − (0.850 in + 0.933 in) = 3.031 in

   PS = 7.528 in − (5.050 in − 1.477 in) = 3.955 in

   Compute ∠x.

$$\tan \angle x = \frac{3.031}{3.955} = 0.76637$$

$$\angle x = 37°28'$$

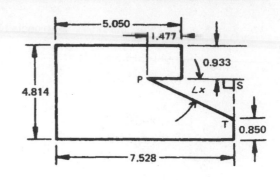

15. In right △ABC: $\angle ACB = \dfrac{67.33°}{2} = 33.665°$ (Geo. Principle 16)

$$AB = \frac{37.50\ mm}{2} = 18.75\ mm$$

   Compute BC.

$$\csc 33.665° = \frac{BC}{18.75}$$

$$1.8039 = \frac{BC}{18.75}$$

$$BC = 1.8039\ (18.75)$$

$$BC = 33.8231\ mm$$

$$y = 20.25\ mm + 33.8231\ mm + 18.75\ mm − 67.40\ mm = 5.42\ mm$$

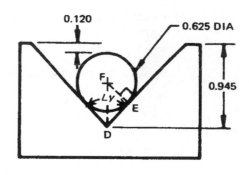

16. In right △DEF: $EF = 0.945\ in − \left(0.120 + \dfrac{0.625\ in}{2}\right) = 0.5125\ in$

$$EF = \frac{0.625\ in}{2} = 0.3125\ in$$

   Compute ∠EDF.

$$\sin \angle EDF = \frac{0.3125}{0.5125} = 0.60976$$

$$\angle EDF = 37°34'$$

$$\angle y = 2(37°34') = 75°8'\ (\text{Geo. Principle 16})$$

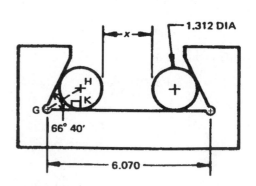

17. In right △GHK: $HK = \dfrac{1.312\ in}{2} = 0.656\ in$

$$\angle HGK = \frac{66°40'}{2} = 33°20'\ (\text{Geo. Principle 16})$$

   Compute GK.

$$\cot 33°20' = \frac{GK}{0.656}$$

$$1.5204 = \frac{GK}{0.656}$$

$$GK = 1.5204\ (0.656)$$

$$GK = 0.9974$$

$$x = 6.070\ in − [2(0.9974\ in) + 1.312\ in] = 2.763\ in$$

UNIT **61**   *(continued)*

18. In right △ABC: BC = $\dfrac{50.00\,mm}{2}$ = 25.00 mm

    AC = $\dfrac{207.30\,mm - (40.00\,mm + 50.00\,mm)}{2}$ = 58.65 mm

    Compute ∠BAC.

    tan ∠BAC = $\dfrac{25.00}{58.65}$ = 0.42626

    ∠BAC = 23.087 °

    x = 2(23.087°) = 46.17° (Geo. Principle 16)

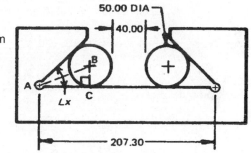

19. In right △DEF: DE = $\dfrac{0.750\,in}{2}$ = 0.375 in

    ∠DFE = $\dfrac{57°}{2}$ = 28°30′ (Geo. Principle 16)

    Compute DF.

    cot 28°30′ = $\dfrac{DF}{0.375}$

    1.8418 = $\dfrac{DF}{0.375}$

    DF = 1.8418 (0.375)

    DF = 0.6907 in

    y = 4.708 in − [0.750 in + 2(0.6907 in)] = 2.577 in

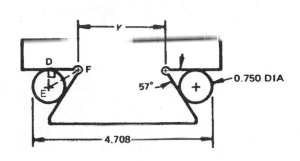

20. In right △GHK: HK = 6.080 in − 2(0.500 in) = 5.080 in

    GH = 3.310 in − 2(0.500 in) = 2.310 in

    Compute ∠G.

    tan ∠G = $\dfrac{5.080}{2.310}$ = 2.1991

    ∠G = 65°33′

    ∠y = ∠G = 65°33′ (Geo. Principle 4)

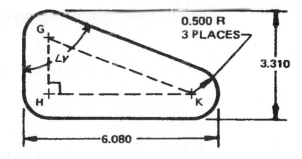

21. ∠PST = 360° − 278° = 82°

    △PTS is isosceles, therefore, MS bisects PT and ∠PST.

    In right △PMS: PS = $\dfrac{82.74\,mm}{2}$ = 41.37 mm

    ∠MSP = $\dfrac{82°}{2}$ = 41°

    Compute PM.

    sin 41° = $\dfrac{PM}{41.37}$

    0.65606 = $\dfrac{PM}{41.37}$

    PM = 0.65606 (41.37)

    PM = 27.1412 mm

    x = 2(27.1412 mm) = 54.28 mm

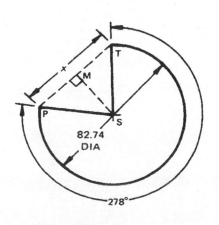

UNIT **61** (*continued*)

22. In △ABC: ∠B is a right angle. (Geo. Principle 21)

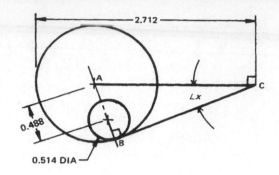

In right △ABC: AB = 0.488 in + $\dfrac{0.514\,\text{in}}{2}$ = 0.745 in

AC = 2.712 in − 0.745 in = 1.967 in

Compute ∠x.

$$\sin \angle x = \frac{0.745}{1.967} = 0.37875$$

$$\angle x = 22°15'$$

23. Compute ∠1. ∠1 = $180° - (96° + 72°) = 12°$

In right △DEF: ∠EDF = $90° - (37° + 12°) = 41°$

DE = 298.00 mm

Compute EF.

$$\tan 41° = \frac{EF}{298.00}$$

$$0.86929 = \frac{EF}{298.00}$$

$$EF = 0.86929\,(298.00)$$

$$EF = 259.048 \text{ mm}$$

$$y = EF = 259.05 \text{ mm}$$

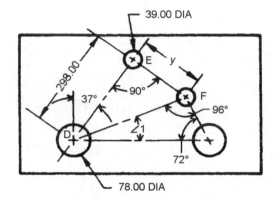

24. In right △GHK: HK = $2(0.438$ in$) = 0.876$ in

∠HGK = $70°10'$ (Geo. Principle 2)

Compute GH.

$$\csc 70°10' = \frac{GH}{0.876}$$

$$1.0630 = \frac{GH}{0.876}$$

$$GH = 1.0630\,(0.876)$$

$$GH = 0.9312$$

$$y = 1.123 \text{ in} + 0.9312 \text{ in} + 1.485 \text{ in} = 3.539 \text{ in}$$

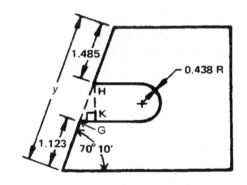

UNIT 62 Complex Practical Machine Applications

1. Analysis: $x = 1.000$ in + AC + 0.875 in + DE

    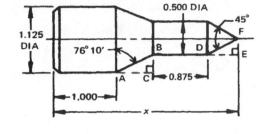

    Compute AC. In right $\triangle$ACB: BC $= \dfrac{1.125\,in - 0.500\,in}{2} = 0.3125$ in

    $$\angle BAC = 90° - 76°10' = 13°50'$$

    $$\cot 13°50' = \frac{AC}{0.3125}$$

    $$AC = 4.0611(0.3125)$$

    $$AC = 1.2691\,in$$

    Compute DE. In right $\triangle$DEF: $\angle EDF = 22°30'$ (Geo. Principle 2)

    $$EF = \frac{0.500\,in}{2} = 0.250\,in$$

    $$\cot 22°30' = \frac{DE}{0.250}$$

    $$DE = 2.4142\,(0.250)$$

    $$DE = 0.6036$$

    $x = 1.000$ in + 1.2691 in + 0.875 in + 0.6036 in = 3.748 in

2. Analysis: In right $\triangle$PST compute PS. In right $\triangle$HKS HS = 196 mm − PS. Compute $\angle x$ using sides HS and HK.
    Compute PS. In right $\triangle$PST:

    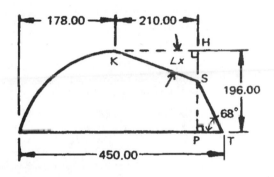

    $$\angle T = 68°$$

    $$PT = 450.00\,mm - (178.00\,mm + 210.00\,mm) = 62.00\,mm$$

    $$\tan 68° = \frac{PS}{62.00}$$

    $$PS = 2.4751\,(62.00)$$

    $$PS = 153.4562\,mm$$

    Compute $\angle x$. In right $\triangle$HKS:

    HS = 196.00 mm   153.4502 mm = 42.5438 mm

    HK = 210.00 mm

    $$\tan \angle x = \frac{42.5438\,mm}{210.00} = 0.20259$$

    $$\angle x = 11.45°$$

3. Analysis: In $\triangle$ABC compute $\angle$BAC and AC. In $\triangle$ACD use AC and DC to compute $\angle$CAD. $\angle x = 90° - (\angle BAC + \angle CAD)$

    Compute $\angle$BAC and AC. In right $\triangle$ABC: AB = 3.312 in − 2.062 in = 1.250 in

    BC = 2.873 in − (0.510 in + 1.000 in + 0.500 in) = 0.863 in

    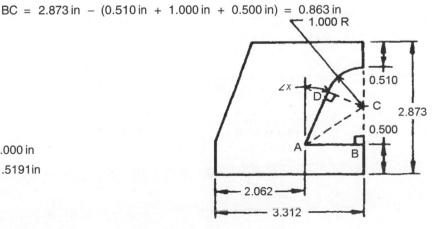

    $$\tan \angle BAC = \frac{0.863}{1.250} = 0.69040$$

    $$\angle BAC = 34°37'$$

    $$\csc 34°37' = \frac{AC}{0.863}$$

    $$AC = 1.7603\,(0.863)$$

    $$AC = 1.5191\,in$$

    Compute $\angle$CAD. In right $\triangle$ACD: DC = 1.000 in

    AC = 1.5191 in

    $$\csc \angle CAD = \frac{1.5191}{1.000} = 1.5191$$

    $$\angle CAD = 41°10'$$

    Ðx = 90° − ($\angle$BAC + $\angle$CAD) = 90° − (34°37′ + 41°10′) = 14°13′

UNIT 62   (*continued*)

4. Analysis: In right △GHF compute ∠GHF and FH. In right △EFH compute ∠EHF.

$$\angle y = \angle GHF + \angle EHF$$

Compute ∠GHF and FH. In right △GHF:

GH = 101.00 mm − 38.00 mm = 63.00 mm

GF = 143.30 mm − 97.50 mm = 45.80 mm

$$\tan \angle GHF = \frac{45.80}{63.00} = 0.72698$$

∠GHF = 36°1′

$$\csc 36°1′ = \frac{FH}{45.80}$$

FH = 1.7006 (45.80)

FH = 77.8875 mm

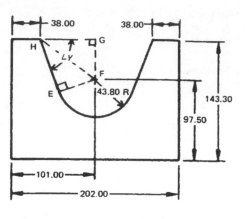

Compute ∠EHF. In right △EFH:

FH = 77.8875 mm

FE = 43.80 mm

$$\sin \angle EHF = \frac{43.80}{77.8875} = 0.56235$$

∠EHF = 34°13.1′

∠y = 36°1′ + 34°13.1′ = 70°14.1′ = 70.24°

5. Analysis: In right △MST compute ST. In right △PRS compute PS.

$$y = (ST + 0.750 \text{ in}) − PS$$

Compute ST. In right △MST:

$$MT = \frac{1.500 \text{ in}}{2} = 0.750 \text{ in}$$

$$\angle MST = \frac{67°20′}{2} = 33°40′ \text{ (Geo. Principle 16)}$$

$$\csc 33°40′ = \frac{ST}{0.750}$$

ST = 1.8039 (0.750)

ST = 1.3529 in

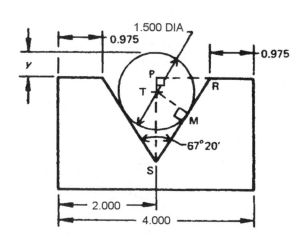

Compute PS. In right △PRS:

∠PSR = 33°40′

PR = 2.000 in − 0.975 in = 1.025 in

$$\cot 33°40′ = \frac{PS}{1.025}$$

PS = 1.5013 (1.025)

PS = 1.5388 in

y = 1.3529 in + 0.750 in − 1.5388 in = 0.564 in

UNIT **62** (*continued*)

6. Analysis: In right △ABC compute BC. In right △ADE compute AE.

$$x = (3.400 \text{ in} - BC) + AE + \frac{2.250 \text{ in}}{2}$$

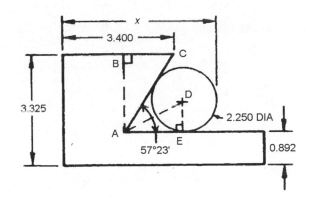

Compute BC. In right △ABC:

AB = 3.325 in − 0.892 in = 2.433 in

∠BAC = 90° − 57°23′ = 32°37′

$$\tan 32°37′ = \frac{BC}{2.433}$$

BC = 0.63994 (2.433)

BC = 1.55697 in

Compute AE. In right △ADE:

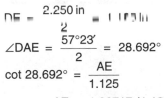

$$\angle DAE = \frac{57°23′}{2} = 28.692°$$

$$\cot 28.692° = \frac{AE}{1.125}$$

AE = 1.82717 (1.125)

AE = 2.0556 in

x = (3.400 in − 1.55697 in) + 2.0556 in + 1.125 in = 5.024 in

7. Analysis: In right △GHF compute FG. In right △DEF compute DE. In right △ABC,
BC = (2.930 in − 0.562 in + FG) − (DE + 0.750 in)

Compute ∠x using sides AB and BC.

Compute FG. In right △GHF:

FH = 1.840 in

ÐGHF = 14° (Geo. Principle 5)

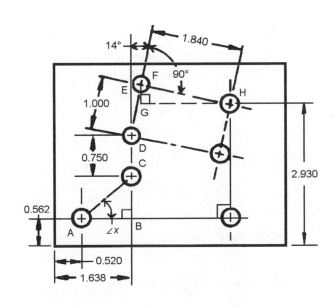

$$\sin 14° = \frac{FG}{1.840}$$

FG = 0.24192 (1.840)

FG = 0.4451 in

Compute DE. In right △DEF:

∠EDF = 14°

DF = 1.000 in

$$\cos 14° = \frac{DE}{1.000}$$

DE = cos 14°

DE = 0.97030

Compute ∠x. In right △ABC:

AB = 1.638 in − 0.520 in = 1.118 in

BC = (2.930 in − 0.562 in + 0.4451 in) − (0.97030 in + 0.750 in) = 1.0928 in

$$\tan \angle x = \frac{0.0928}{0.97746}$$

∠x = 44°21′

UNIT **62** (*continued*)

8. Analysis: In right △MPS compute PS. In right △MTK compute ∠KMT when KT = PS + 1.480 in

$$\angle y = 90° - \angle KMT$$

Compute PS. In right △MPS:

∠PMS = 42°50′

MS = 4.646 in

$$\sin 42°50′ = \frac{PS}{4.646}$$

PS = 0.67987 (4.646)

PS = 3.1587 in

Compute ∠KMT. In right △KMT:

KM = 4.646 in

KT = 3.1587 in + 1.480 in = 4.6387 in

$$\sin \angle KMT = \frac{4.6387}{4.646} = 0.99843$$

∠KMT = 86°48′

∠y = 90° − 86°48′ = 3°12′

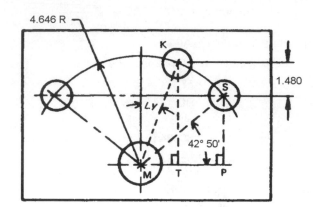

9. Analysis: In right △ABC compute BC. In right △CDE compute CD. In right △FGH compute GH.

$$x = BC + CD + EF + GH + 36.80 \text{ mm}$$

Compute BC. In right △ABC:

∠B = 80.50 °

AC = 70.00 mm (Geo. Principle 15)

$$\csc 80.50° = \frac{BC}{70.00}$$

BC = 1.1039 (70.00)

BC = 70.973 mm

Compute CD. In right △CDE:

ED = 80.00 mm

∠ECD = 80.50° (Geo. Principle 3)

$$\cot 80.50 ° = \frac{CD}{80.00}$$

CD = 0.16734 (80.00)

CD = 13.3872 mm

Compute EF.

EF = 70.00 mm + 41.70 mm = 111.70 mm (Geo. Principle 21)

Compute GH. In right △FGH:

FG = 80.00 mm − 37.50 mm = 42.50 mm

FH = 41.70 mm + 36.80 mm = 78.50 mm (Geo. Principle 21)

$$\sin \angle FHG = \frac{42.50}{78.50} = 0.54140$$

∠FHG = 32°47′

$$\cot 32°47′ = \frac{GH}{42.50}$$

GH = 1.5527 (42.50)

GH = 65.990 mm

x = 70.973 mm + 13.3872 mm + 111.70 mm + 65.990 mm + 36.80 mm = 295.85 mm

UNIT **62** *(continued)*

10. Analysis: KM passes through tangent point P (Geo. Principle 21). ∠KPT and ∠MPT are right angles (Geo. Principle 15). In right △KPT compute PT. In right △MPT compute ∠MTP.

$$\angle y = 2(\angle MTP)$$

Compute PT. In right △KPT:

$$KP = \frac{2.3850 \text{ in}}{2} = 1.925 \text{ in}$$

$$\angle KTP = \frac{48°40'}{2} = 24°20' \text{ (Geo. Principle 16)}$$

$$\cot 24°20' = \frac{PT}{1.1925}$$

$$PT = 2.2113 (1.1925)$$

$$PT = 2.6370 \text{ in}$$

Compute ∠MTP. In right △MPT:

$$PT = 2.6370 \text{ in}$$

$$MP = \frac{0.9846 \text{ in}}{2} = 0.4923 \text{ in}$$

$$\tan \angle MTP = \frac{0.4923}{2.6370} = 0.18669$$

$$\angle MTP = 10°34'$$

$$\angle y = 2(\angle MTP) = 2(10°34') = 21°8'$$

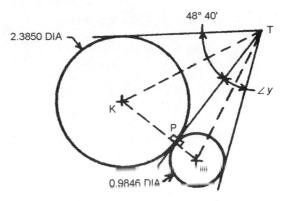

11. Analysis: In right △ABC compute AC. In right △CDE compute CD and DE.

$$x = 2DE + 2(0.668 \text{ in})$$

Compute AC. In right △ABC:

$$\angle BAC = 48°10'$$

$$BC = 0.668 \text{ in (Geo. Principle 15)}$$

$$\csc 48°10' = \frac{AC}{0.668}$$

$$AC = 1.3421(0.668)$$

$$AC = 0.8965 \text{ in}$$

Compute CD and DE. In right △CDE:

$$\angle DCE = 48°10' \text{ (Geo. Principle 3)}$$

$$CD = 2.980 \text{ in} - (0.8965 \text{ in} + 0.668 \text{ in}) = 1.4155 \text{ in}$$

$$\tan 48°10' = \frac{DE}{1.4155}$$

$$DE = 1.1171(1.4155)$$

$$DE = 1.5813 \text{ in}$$

$$x = 2(1.5813 \text{ in}) + 2(0.668 \text{ in}) = 4.499 \text{ in}$$

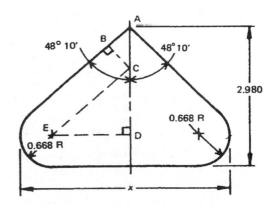

UNIT **62**   *(continued)*

12.   Analysis: In right △FGH compute ∠GFH and FH. In right △MPS compute ∠MSP and PS.

$$y = FH + 1.470\ in + PS$$

Compute ∠GFH and FH. In right △FGH:

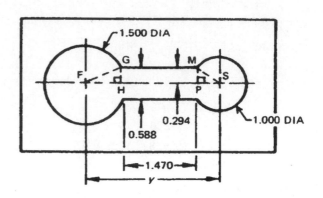

$$FG = \frac{1.500\ in}{2} = 0.750\ in$$

$$GH = 0.294\ in$$

$$\sin \angle GFH = \frac{0.294}{0.750} = 0.39200$$

$$\angle GFH = 23°5'$$

$$\cos 23°5' = \frac{FH}{0.750}$$

$$FH = 0.91993\ (0.750)$$

$$FH = 0.6899\ in$$

Compute ∠MSP and PS. In right △MPS:

$$MS = \frac{1.000\ in}{2} = 0.500\ in$$

$$MP = 0.294\ in$$

$$\sin \angle MSP = \frac{0.294}{0.500} = 0.58800$$

$$\angle MSP = 36°1'$$

$$\cos 36°1' = \frac{PS}{0.500}$$

$$PS = 0.80885\ (0.500)$$

$$PS = 0.4044\ in$$

$$y = 0.6899\ in + 1.470\ in + 0.4044\ in = 2.564\ in$$

13.   Analysis: In right △ABC compute AC. In right △CDE compute DE. In right △EFG compute EG.

$$y = AC + DE + EG + \frac{1.125\ in}{2}$$

Compute AC. In right △ABC:

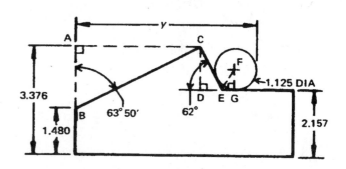

$$AB = 3.376\ in - 1.480\ in = 1.896\ in$$

$$\angle ABC = 63°50'$$

$$\tan 63°50' = \frac{AC}{1.896}$$

$$AC = 2.0353\ (1.896)$$

$$AC = 3.8589\ in$$

Compute DE. In right △CDE:

$$CD = 3.376\ in - 2.157\ in = 1.219\ in$$

$$\angle DCE = 62°$$

$$\cot 62° = \frac{DE}{1.219}$$

$$DE = 0.53171(1.219)$$

$$DE = 0.6482\ in$$

UNIT **62**   (*continued*)

13. Compute EG. In right △EFG:

$$FG = \frac{1.125 \text{ in}}{2} = 0.5625 \text{ in}$$

$$\angle FEG = \frac{180° - 62°}{2} = 59° \text{ (Geo. Principle 16)}$$

$$\cot 59° = \frac{EG}{0.5625}$$

$$EG = 0.60086 \ (0.5625)$$

$$EG = 0.3380 \text{ in}$$

$$y = 3.8589 \text{ in} + 0.6482 \text{ in} + 0.3380 \text{ in} + 0.5625 \text{ in} = 5.408 \text{ in}$$

14. Analysis: △HKP is isosceles, HM bisects ∠KHP. In right △HKM compute ∠KHM. In right △HPT compute ∠PHT.

$$x = 90° - (2\angle KHM + \angle PHT)$$

Compute ∠KHM. in right △HKM:

$$HK = 110.00 \text{ mm}$$

$$HM = \frac{101.30 \text{ mm}}{2} = 50.65 \text{ mm (Geo. Principle 8)}$$

$$\sin \angle KHM = \frac{50.65}{110.00} = 0.46045$$

$$\angle KHM = 27°24.97'$$

Compute ∠PHT. In right △HPT:

$$HP = 110.00 \text{ mm}$$

$$PT = 42.30 \text{ mm}$$

$$\sin \angle PHT = \frac{42.30}{110.00} = 0.38455$$

$$\angle PHT = 22°36.93'$$

$$\angle x = 90° - [2(27°24.97') + 22°36.93'] = 12°33.13' = 12.55°$$

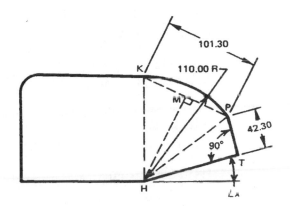

15. Analysis: In right △ABC compute ∠ABC and BC. In right △BCD compute ∠CBD. ∠ABD = ∠ABC − ∠CBD

$$\angle x = \angle ABD \text{ (Geo. Principle 4)}$$

Compute ∠ABC and BC. In right △ABC:

$$AB = 0.375 \text{ in} - \left(\frac{0.2343 \text{ in}}{2} + \frac{0.1407 \text{ in}}{2}\right) = 0.1875 \text{ in}$$

$$AC = 0.450 \text{ in} - \frac{0.1407 \text{ in}}{2} = 0.37965 \text{ in}$$

$$\tan \angle ABC = \frac{0.37965}{0.1875} = 2.0248$$

$$\angle ABC = 63°43'$$

$$\sec 63°43' = \frac{BC}{0.1875}$$

$$BC = 2.2583 \ (0.1875)$$

$$BC = 0.4234 \text{ in}$$

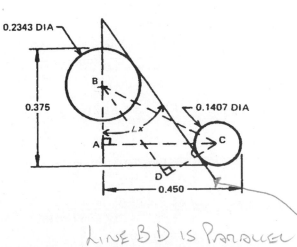

LINE BD IS PARALLEL TO

UNIT **62**   *(continued)*

15. Compute ∠CBD. In right △BCD:

$$BC = 0.4234 \text{ in}$$

$$DC = \frac{0.2343 \text{ in}}{2} + \frac{0.1407 \text{ in}}{2} = 0.1875 \text{ in (Geo. Principle 15)}$$

$$\sin \angle CBD = \frac{0.1875}{0.4234} = 0.44284$$

$$\angle CBD = 26°17'$$

$$\angle ABD = 63°43' - 26°17' = 37°26'$$

$$\angle x = 37°26'$$

16. Analysis: In right △EFG compute EG. In right △GHK compute GH.

$$y = GH$$

Compute EG. In right △EFG:

$$\angle F = 68°18'$$

$$EF = 1.636 \text{ in} - 1.340 \text{ in} = 0.296 \text{ in}$$

$$\tan 68°18' = \frac{EG}{0.296}$$

$$EG = 2.51289 (0.296)$$

$$EG = 0.7438 \text{ in}$$

Compute GH. In right △GHK:

$$\angle KGH = 90° - 68°18' = 21°42' \text{ (Geo. Principle 1)}$$

$$GK = (1.715 \text{ in} - 0.488 \text{ in}) - 0.7438 \text{ in} = 0.4832 \text{ in}$$

$$\sin 21°42' = \frac{GH}{0.4832}$$

$$GH = 0.36975 (0.4832)$$

$$GH = 0.1787 \text{ in}$$

$$y = GH = 0.179 \text{ in}$$

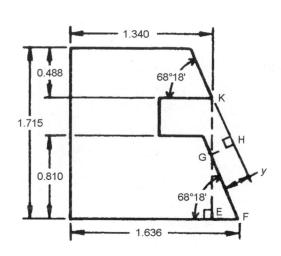

17. Analysis: In right △ABD compute AB. In right △CEF compute CF.

$$x = 8.500 \text{ in} - (0.750 \text{ in} + AB + CF + 0.750 \text{ in})$$

Compute AB: In right △ABD:

$$\angle D = 34°0'$$

$$AD = 2.100 \text{ in}$$

$$\tan 34°0' = \frac{AB}{2.100 \text{ in}}$$

$$AB = \tan 34°0' (2.100 \text{ in})$$

$$AB = 1.4165 \text{ in}$$

Compute CF: In right △CEF:

$$\angle E = 72°0'$$

$$EF = 1.070 \text{ in}$$

$$CF = \tan 72°0' (1.070 \text{ in})$$

$$CF = 3.2931 \text{ in}$$

$$x = 8.500 \text{ in} - (0.750 \text{ in} + AB + CF + 0.750 \text{ in})$$

$$x = 8.500 \text{ in} - (0.750 \text{ in} + 1.4165 \text{ in} + 3.2931 \text{ in} + 0.750 \text{ in})$$

$$x = 2.290 \text{ in}$$

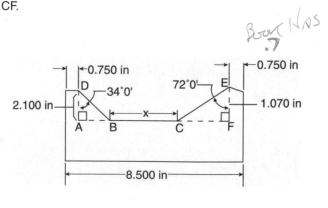

TEXT BOOK = 2.3404

UNIT **62**   *(continued)*

18. Analysis: In right $\triangle$ACO compute $\angle 1$, in right $\triangle$ABO compute $\angle 2$.

$$\angle y = 90° - (\angle 1 + \angle 2)$$

Compute $\angle 1$: In right $\triangle$ACO:

OC = 120.00 mm
AC = 135.00 mm

$$\tan \angle 1 = \frac{120.00 \text{ mm}}{135.00 \text{ mm}}$$
$$\tan \angle 1 = 0.88889$$
$$\angle 1 = 41.63354°$$

Compute OA: In right $\triangle$AOC:

$$OA^2 = OC^2 + AC^2$$
$$OA' = (120.00 \text{ m})^2 + (135.00 \text{ m})^2$$
$$OA^2 = \sqrt{(120.00 \text{ m})^2 + 135.00 \text{ mm})^2}$$

Compute $\angle 2$: In right $\triangle$ABO:

$$\sin \angle 2 = \frac{OB}{OA} = \frac{50.00 \text{ mm}}{180.6239 \text{ mm}}$$
$$\sin \angle 2 = 0.27682$$
$$\angle 2 = 16.0704°$$

$$\angle y = 90° - (\angle 1 + \angle 2)$$
$$\angle y = 90° - (41.63° + 16.07°)$$
$$\angle y = 32.30°$$

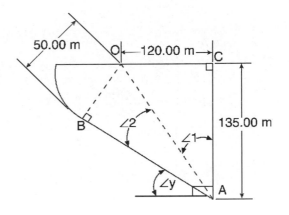

19. Analysis: In right $\triangle$ADB compute AD, in right $\triangle$ADC compute CD.

$$y = CD$$

Compute AD: In right $\triangle$ADB:

$$\angle A = 29°18'$$
$$AB = 5.370 \text{ in}$$

$$\cos 29°18' = \frac{5.370 \text{ in}}{AD}$$
$$AD = \frac{5.370 \text{ in}}{\cos 29°18'}$$
$$AD = 6.15777 \text{ in}$$

Compute CD: In right $\triangle$ADC:

$$\angle A = 29°18'$$
$$AD = 6.15777 \text{ in}$$

$$\tan 29°18' = \frac{CD}{6.15777 \text{ in}}$$

$$CD = 6.15777(\tan 29°18')$$
$$CD = 3.4555 \text{ in}$$
$$y = CD$$
$$y = 3.46 \text{ in}$$

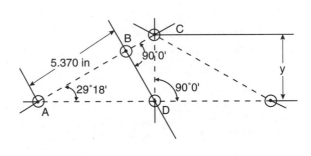

3.456

UNIT **62** *(continued)*

20. Analysis: In right △ACB: compute AC, in right △DFE compute DF.

$$x = 10.300 \text{ in} - (AC + DF)$$

. Compute AC: In right △ACB:

$\angle A = 35°48'$
BC = 2.200 in

$$\tan 35°48' = \frac{2.200 \text{ in}}{AC}$$

$$AC = \frac{2.200 \text{ in}}{\tan 35°48'}$$

AC = 3.0504 in

. Compute DF. In right △DFE:

$\angle F = 28°30'$
DE = 2.200 in

$$\tan 28°30' = \frac{2.200}{DF}$$

$$DF = \frac{2.200 \text{ in}}{\tan 28°30'}$$

DF = 4.0519 in

$$x = 10.300 - (AC + DF)$$

$$x = 10.300 - (3.0504 \text{ in} + 4.0519 \text{ in})$$

$$x = 3.1977 \text{ in, } 3.20 \text{ in} \quad 3.198$$

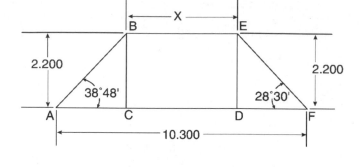

21. Analyze: In rt △ABO, AB = 1.200 in = 0.810 in

OB = 0.470 in

Compute $\angle$BAO and AO

In rt △ACO, AC is perpendicular to OC.

$\angle C = 90°$

AO has been computed.

OC = 0.450 in

Compute $\angle$CAO.

Computations:

Compute $\angle$BAO:

$$\tan \angle BAO = \frac{OB}{AB} = \frac{0.470}{0.810} = 0.58025$$

$\angle BAO = 30°7'$

Compute AO:

$$AO^2 = AB^2 + OB^2$$

$$AO^2 = (0.810 \text{ in})^2 + (0.470 \text{ in})^2$$

$$AO^2 = 0.8770 \text{ sq in}$$

AO = 0.9365 in

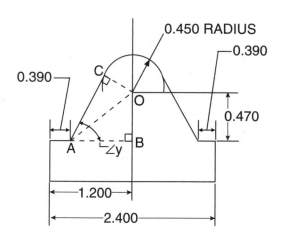

UNIT **62** *(continued)*

21. In rt △ACO, AO = 0.9365 in, OC = 0.450 in

Compute ∠CAO:

$$\sin \angle CAO = \frac{OC}{AO} = \frac{0.450}{0.9365} = 0.48051$$

∠CAO = 28°43′

∠y = 30°7′ = 58°50′

22. In rt △CEO, OE is perpendicular to CE at point E.

∠E = 90°

Radius OE = 80.0 mm

$$\angle ECO = \frac{1}{2}(58°) = 29°$$

Compute CE

In rt △CDB, ∠DCB = 90°−58° = 32°

DC = 80.0 mm + 115.0 mm = 195.0 mm

Compute DB

AB = 270.0 mm − CE + DB

Computations:

Compute CE:

$$\cot 29° = \frac{CE}{OE}$$

$$1.804\ 1 = \frac{CE}{80.0}$$

CE = 144.324 mm

Compute DB:

$$\tan 32° = \frac{DB}{DC}$$

$$0.624\ 87 = \frac{DB}{195.0}$$

DB = 121.850 mm

AB = 270.0 − 144.324 mm + 121.850 mm = 247.53 mm

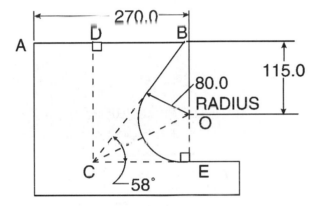

23: Analysis: In rt △ABC, AB = 320.0 mm, BC = 115.0 m

Compute ∠BAC and AC

In rt △ACD, DC = 196.0 mm. AC has been computed.

Compute ∠CAD

∠1 = ∠BAC + ∠CAD

Computations:

Compute ∠BAC:

$$\tan \angle BAC = \frac{115.0}{120.0} = 0.35938$$

∠BAC = 19.767°

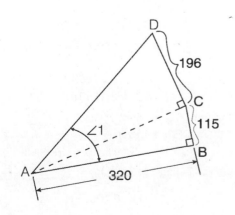

UNIT **62**   *(continued)*

23. Compute AC:

$$AC^2 = (320.0\,mm)^2 + (115.0\,mm)^2$$

$$AC^2 = 102,400\,m^2 + 13,225\,m^2$$

$$AC^2 = 115,625\,mm^2$$

$$AC = 340.0368\,mm$$

Compute ∠CAD:

$$\tan\angle CAD = \frac{196.0}{340.0368} = 0.57641$$

$$\angle CAD = 29.960°$$

$$\angle 1 = 19.767° + 29.960° = 49.73°$$

24. Analysis: In rt △ABO, AB = 3.650 in, OB = 4.000 in − 1.800 in = 2.200 in

Compute AO and ∠BAO:

In rt △ADO, OD = 1.800 in, AO has been computed.

Compute ∠DAO:

∠y = ∠BAO + ∠DAO

Computations:

Compute AO:

$$AO^2 = AB^2 + OB^2$$

$$AO^2 = (3.650\,in)^2 + (2.200\,in)^2$$

$$AO^2 = 13.3225\,sq\ in + 4.8400\,sq\ in$$

$$AO^2 = 18.1625\,sq\ in$$

$$AO = 4.26175\,in$$

Compute ∠BAO:

$$\tan\angle BAO = \frac{OB}{AB} = \frac{2.200}{3.650} = 0.60274$$

∠BAO = 31°5′

Compute ∠DAO:

$$\sin\angle DAO = \frac{OD}{AO} = \frac{1.800}{4.26175} = 0.42236$$

∠DAO = 24°59′

∠y = 31°5′ + 24°59′ = 56°4′

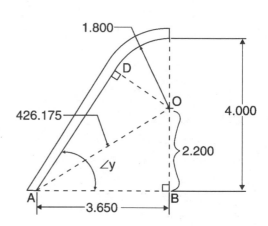

25. Analysis: In right △ABC compute AC. In right △CDE compute CD. in right △EFG compute GF.

y = 1.508 in + (AC − CD) + GF

Compute AC. In right △ABC:

∠ACB = 22°10′

BC = 2.337 in

$$\cos 22°10′ = \frac{AC}{2.337}$$

AC = 0.92609 (2.337)

AC = 2.1643 in

Compute CD. In right △CDE:

CE = 1.115 in

∠CDE = 22°10′ (Geo. Principle 5)

$$\sin 22°10′ = \frac{CD}{1.115}$$

CD = 0.4207 in

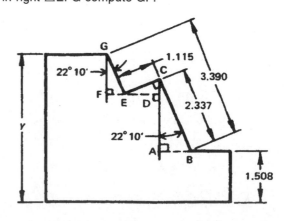

UNIT **62**   *(continued)*

25. Compute GF, In right △EFG:

$$\angle EGF = 22°10'$$

$$EG = 3.390 \text{ in} - 2.337 \text{ in} = 1.053 \text{ in}$$

$$\cos 22°10' = \frac{GF}{1.053}$$

$$GF = 0.92609(1.053)$$

$$GF = 0.9752 \text{ in}$$

$$y = 1.508 \text{ in} + (2.1643 \text{ in} - 0.4207 \text{ in}) + 0.9752 \text{ in} = 4.227 \text{ in}$$

26. Analysis: In right △MPS compute MP. In right △HKM compute HM.

$$x = \frac{2.000 \text{ in}}{2} + HM + MP$$

Compute MP. In right △MPS:

$$PS = 3.043 \text{ in} - 0.790 \text{ in} = 2.253 \text{ in}$$

$$\angle PMS = 59°20' \text{ (Geo. Principle 2)}$$

$$\cos 59°20' = \frac{MP}{2.253}$$

$$MP = 0.59297(2.253)$$

$$MP = 1.3360 \text{ in}$$

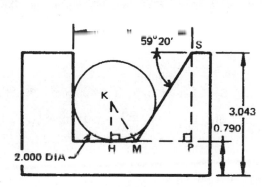

2.000 DIA

Compute HM. In right △HKM:

$$HK = \frac{2.000 \text{ in}}{2} = 1.000 \text{ in}$$

$$\angle KMH = \frac{180° - 59°20'}{2} = 60°20' \text{ (Geo. Principle 16)}$$

$$\cot 60°20' = \frac{HM}{1.000}$$

$$HM = 0.56962(1.000)$$

$$HM = 0.5696 \text{ in}$$

$$x = 1.000 \text{ in} + 0.5696 \text{ in} + 1.3360 \text{ in} = 2.906 \text{ in}$$

27. Analysis: In right △ABC compute BC. In right △CDE compute CD. In right △AFG compute AF.

$$x = (1.780 \text{ in} - 0.562 \text{ in}) + CD + BC - \sim AF$$

Compute BC. In right △ABC:

$$AB = 0.312 \text{ in}$$

$$\angle ABC = 54°30'$$

$$\cot 54°30' = \frac{BC}{0.312}$$

$$BC = 0.71329(0.312)$$

$$BC = 0.225 \text{ in}$$

Compute CD. In right △CDE:

$$CE = 0.157 \text{ in}$$

$$\angle CDE = 54°30'$$

$$\cot 54°30' = \frac{CD}{0.157}$$

$$CD = 1.2283(0.157)$$

$$CD = 0.1928 \text{ in}$$

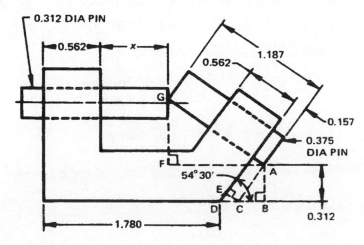

0.312 DIA PIN

0.375 DIA PIN

UNIT 62   (*continued*)

27. Compute AF. In right △AFG:

$$AG = 1.187 \text{ in}$$

$$\angle AGF = 54°30' \text{ (Geo. Principle 5)}$$

$$\sin 54°30' = \frac{AF}{1.187}$$

$$AF = 0.81412(1.187)$$

$$AF = 0.9664 \text{ in}$$

$$x = (1.780 \text{ in} - 0.562 \text{ in}) + 0.1928 \text{ in} + 0.2225 \text{ in} - 0.9664 \text{ in} = 0.667 \text{ in}$$

28. Analysis: In right △PST compute PS. In right △KMT side KM = (193.60 mm − 29.12 mm) − PS, compute ∠MKT.

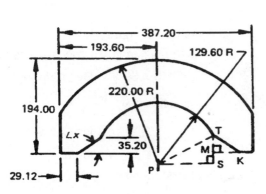

$$\angle x = \angle MKT$$

Compute PS. In right △PST:

$$PT = 129.60 \text{ mm}$$

$$ST = 220.00 \text{ mm} - (194.00 \text{ mm} - 35.20 \text{ mm}) = 61.20 \text{ mm}$$

$$\sin \angle TPS = \frac{61.20}{129.60} = 0.47222$$

$$\angle TPS = 28°11'$$

$$\cos 28°11' = \frac{PS}{129.60}$$

$$PS = 0.88144(129.60)$$

$$PS = 114.235 \text{ mm}$$

Compute ∠MKT. In right △KMT:

$$MT = 35.20 \text{ mm}$$

$$KM = (193.60 \text{ mm} - 29.12 \text{ mm}) - 114.235 \text{ mm} = 50.245 \text{ mm}$$

$$\tan \angle MKT = \frac{35.20}{50.245} = 0.70056$$

$$\angle MKT = 35°0.7' = 35.01°$$

$$\angle x = \angle MKT = 35.01 \text{ ρομαν } °$$

29. Analysis: Make CD ∥ AB. In right △CDE compute ∠DCE and CE. In right △CEF compute ∠ECF.

$$\angle x = \angle DCE + \angle ECF \text{ (Geo. Principle 5)}$$

Compute ∠DCE and CE. In right △CDE:

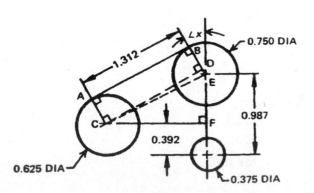

$$CD = 1.312 \text{ in}$$

$$DE = \frac{0.750 \text{ in}}{2} - \frac{0.625 \text{ in}}{2} = 0.625 \text{ in} \quad \text{·0625}$$

$$\tan \angle DCE = \frac{0.0625}{1.312} = 0.04764 \text{ in}$$

$$\angle DCE = 2°44'$$

$$\cos 2°44' = \frac{1.312}{CE}$$

$$CE = \frac{1.312}{0.99886}$$

$$CE = 1.3135 \text{ in}$$

UNIT **62** *(continued)*

29. Compute ∠ECF. In right △CEF:

        CE = 1.3135 in

        EF = 0.987 in − 0.392 in = 0.595 in

$$\sin \angle ECF = \frac{0.595}{1.3135} = 0.45299$$

$$\angle ECF = 26°56'$$

$$\angle x = 2°44' + 26°56' = 29°40'$$

30. Analysis: In right △ABC compute AB. In right △ADE compute AD.

$$y = 0.312\,in + 1.156\,in + (AB - AD) + \frac{0.375\,in}{2}$$

Compute AB. In right △ABC:

$$\angle BAC = 51°20'$$

$$BC = 0.625\,in + \left(0.686\,in - \frac{0.375\,in}{2}\right) = 1.1235\,in$$

$$\cot 51°20' = \frac{AB}{1.1235}$$

$$AB = 0.80020(1.1235)$$

$$AB = 0.8990\,in$$

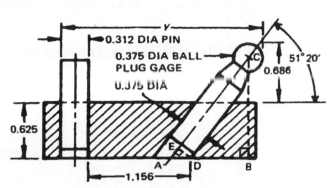

Compute AD. In right △ADE:

$$\angle DAE = 51°20'$$

$$ED = \frac{0.375\,in}{2} = 0.1875\,in$$

$$\csc 51°20' = \frac{AD}{0.1875}$$

$$AD = 1.2807(0.1875)$$

$$AD = 0.2401\,in$$

$$y = 0.312\,in + 1.156\,in + (0.8990\,in - 0.2401\,in) + \frac{0.375\,in}{2} = 2.314\,in$$

31. Analysis: In right △ABC compute AC. In right △BDF compute BD. In right △BDE compute BE.

$$y = (2.420\,in - AC) + BE + \frac{0.925}{2}$$

Compute AC. In right △ABC:

    ∠ABC = 69°17′ (Geo. Principle 2)

    AB = (3.120 in − 0.325 in) − 2.000 in − 0.795 in

$$\tan 69°17' = \frac{AC}{0.795}$$

$$AC = 2.6441(0.795)$$

$$AC = 2.1021$$

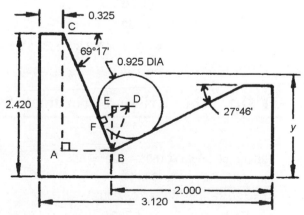

Compute BD. In right △BDF:

$$DF = \frac{0.925\,in}{2} = 0.4625$$

$$\angle DBF = \frac{180° - (69°17' + 27°46')}{2} = 41.475° \text{ or } 41°29' \text{ (Geo. Principle 16)}$$

$$\csc 41.475° = \frac{BD}{0.4625}$$

$$BD = 1.5099(0.4625)$$

$$BD = 0.6983\,in$$

UNIT **62**   (*continued*)

31   Compute BE. In right △BDE:

$$BD = 0.6983 \text{ in}$$

$$\angle DBE = 69°17' + 41°29' - 90° = 20°46'$$

$$\cos 20°46' = \frac{BE}{0.6983}$$

$$BE = 0.93503(0.6983)$$

$$BE = 0.6529$$

$$y = (2.420 \text{ in} - 2.1021 \text{ in}) + 0.6529 \text{ in} + 0.4625 \text{ in} = 1.433 \text{ in}$$

32   Analysis: In right △ABC compute ∠ABC and BC. In right △BCD use BC and BD to compute ∠CBD.

$$\angle x = 90° - (\angle ABC + \angle CBD) \text{ (Geo. Principle 5)}$$

Compute ∠ABC and BC. In right △ABC:

$$AC = 97.50 \text{ mm} - (81.25 \text{ mm} - 40.30 \text{ mm}) = 56.55 \text{ mm}$$

$$AB = 222.95 \text{ mm} - 97.50 \text{ mm} = 125.45 \text{ mm}$$

$$\tan \angle ABC = \frac{56.55}{125.45} = 0.45078$$

$$\angle ABC = 24°16'$$

$$\csc 24°16' = \frac{BC}{56.55}$$

$$BC = 2.4332(56.55)$$

$$BC = 137.60 \text{ mm}$$

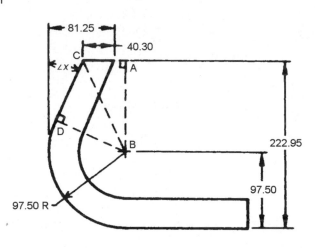

Compute ∠CBD. In right △BCD:

$$BC = 137.60 \text{ mm}$$

$$BC = 97.50 \text{ mm}$$

$$\cos \angle CBD = \frac{97.50}{137.60} = 0.70858$$

$$\angle CBD = 44°52.8'$$

$$\angle x = 90° (24°16' + 44°52.8') = 20°51.2' = 20.85°$$

UNIT **63**   The Cartesian Coordinate System

1.   Reference angle = 180° − 120° = 60°

sin 120° = sin 60° = 0.8660

cos 120° = −cos 60° = −0.5000

tan 120° = −tan 60° = −1.7321

cot 120° = −cot 60° = −0.5774

sec 120° = −sec 60° = −2.0000

csc 120° = csc 60° = 1.1547

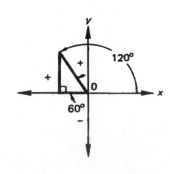

UNIT **63**   (*continued*)

2. Reference angle = 207° − 180° = 27°

   sin 207° = −sin 27° = −0.4540

   cos 207° = −cos 27° = −0.8910

   tan 207° = tan 27° = −0.5095

   cot 207° = cot 27° = 1.9626

   sec 207° = −sec 27° = −1.1223

   csc 207° = −csc 27° = −2.2027

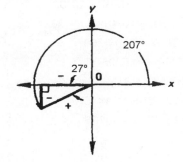

3. Reference angle = 260° − 180° = 80°

   sin 260° = −sin 80° = −0.9848

   cos 260° = −cos 80° = −0.1736

   tan 260° = tan 80° = 5.6713

   cot 260° = cot 80° = 0.1763

   sec 260° = −sec 80° = −5.7588

   csc 260° = −csc 80° = −1.0154

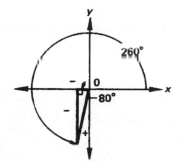

4. Reference angle = 180° − 172° = 8°

   sin 172° = sin 8° = 0.1392

   cos 172° = −cos 8° = −0.9903

   tan 172° = −tan 8° = −0.1405

   cot 172° = cot 8° = −7.1154

   sec 172° = −sec 8° = −1.0098

   csc 172° = csc 8° = 7.1853

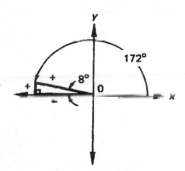

5. Reference angle = 360° − 300° = 60°

   sin 300° = −sin 60° = −0.8660

   cos 300° = cos 60° = 0.5000

   tan 300° = −tan 60° = −1.7321

   cot 300° = −cot 60° = −0.5774

   sec 300° = sec 60° = 2.0000

   csc 300° = −csc 60° = −1.1547

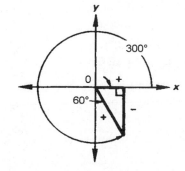

6. Reference angle = 360° − 350° = 10°

   sin 350° = −sin 10° = −0.1736

   cos 350° = cos 10° = 0.9848

   tan 350° = −tan 10° = −0.1763

   cot 350° = −cot 10° = −5.6713

   sec 350° = sec 10° = 1.0154

   csc 350° = −csc 10° = −5.7588

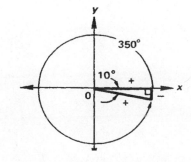

UNIT **63** (*continued*)

7. Reference angle = 208°50′ − 180° = 28°50′

   sin 208°50′ = −sin 28°50′ = −0.4823

   cos 208°50′ = −cos 28°50′ = −0.8760

   tan 208°50′ = tan 28°50′ = 0.5505

   cot 208°50′ = cot 28°50′ = 1.8165

   sec 208°50′ = −sec 28°50′ = −1.1415

   csc 208°50′ = −csc 28°50′ = −2.0735

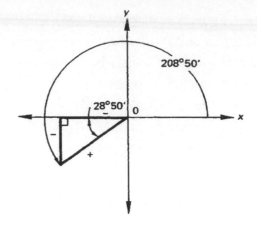

8. Reference angle = 180° − 96°42′ = 83°18′

   sin 96°42′ = sin 83°18′ = 0.9932

   cos 96°42′ = −cos 83°18′ = −0.1167

   tan 96°42′ = −tan 83°18′ = −8.5126

   cot 96°42′ = −cot 83°18′ = −0.1175

   sec 96°42′ = −sec 83°18′ = −8.5711

   csc 96°42′ = csc 83°18′ = 1.0069

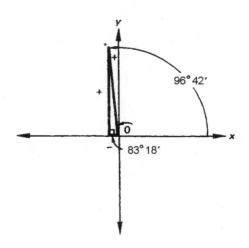

9. Reference angle = 180° − 146°10′ = 33°50′

   sin 146°10′ = sin 33°50′ = 0.5568

   cos 146°10′ = −cos 33°50′ = −0.8307

   tan 146°10′ = −tan 33°50′ = −0.67028

   cot 146°10′ = −cot 33°50′ = −1.4919

   sec 146°10′ = −sec 33°50′ = −1.2039

   csc 146°10′ = csc 33°50′ = −1.7960

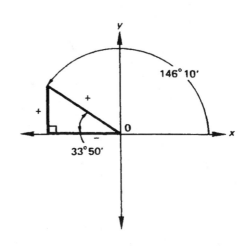

UNIT **63**   *(continued)*

10. Reference angle = 199.40° − 180° = 19.40°

    sin 199.40° = −sin 19.40° = −0.3322

    cos 199.40° = −cos 19.40° = −0.9432

    tan 199.40° = tan 19.40° = 0.3522

    cot 199.40° = cot 19.40° = 2.8397

    sec 199.40° = −sec 19.40° = −1.0602

    csc 199.40° = −csc 19.40° = −3.0106

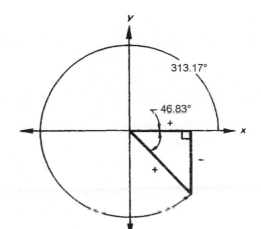

11. Reference angle = 360° − 313.17° = 46.83°

    sin 313.17° = −sin 46.83° = −0.7293

    cos 313.17° = cos 46.83° = 0.6842

    tan 313.17° = −tan 46.83° = −1.0660

    cot 313.17° = −cot 46.83° = −0.9381

    sec 313.17° = sec 46.83° = 1.4616

    csc 313.17° = −csc 46.83° = −1.3711

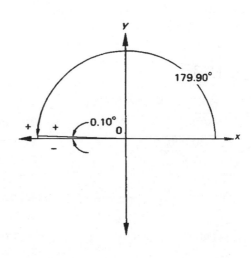

12. Reference angle = 180° − 179.90° = 0.10°

    sin 179.90° = sin 0.10° = 0.0017

    cos 179.90° = −cos 0.10° = −1.0000

    tan 179.90° = −tan 0.10° = −0.0017

    cot 179.90° = −cot 0.10° = −572.9572

    sec 179.90° = −sec 0.10° = −1.0000

    csc 179.90° = csc 0.10° = 572.9581

UNIT 64   Oblique Triangles: Law of Sines and Law of Cosines

1. $\dfrac{x}{\sin 32°} = \dfrac{8.820}{\sin 67°}$

$\dfrac{x}{0.52992} = \dfrac{6.300}{0.92050}$

$x = \dfrac{0.52992\,(8.820)}{0.92050}$

$x = 5.078 \text{ in}$

2. $\dfrac{x}{\sin 88°} = \dfrac{2.170}{\sin 35°20'}$

$\dfrac{x}{0.99939} = \dfrac{2.170}{0.57833}$

$x = \dfrac{0.99939\,(2.170)}{0.57833}$

$x = 3.750 \text{ in}$

3. $180° - (77° + 38°10') = 64°50'$

$\dfrac{x}{\sin 38°10'} = \dfrac{5.175}{\sin 64°50'}$

$\dfrac{x}{0.61795} = \dfrac{5.175}{0.90507}$

$x = \dfrac{0.61795\,(5.175)}{0.90507}$

$x = 3.533 \text{ in}$

4. $\sin 117° = \sin(180° - 117°) = \sin 63°$

$\dfrac{x}{\sin 22°} = \dfrac{64.10}{\sin 63°}$

$\dfrac{x}{0.37461} = \dfrac{64.10}{0.89101}$

$x = \dfrac{0.37461\,(64.10)}{0.89101}$

$x = 26.95 \text{ mm}$

5. $\dfrac{1.970}{\sin \angle x} = \dfrac{1.062}{\sin 17°30'}$

$\dfrac{1.970}{\sin \angle x} = \dfrac{1.062}{0.30071}$

$\sin \angle x = \dfrac{1.970\,(0.30071)}{1.062}$

$\sin \angle x = 0.55781$

$\angle x = 33°54'$

6. $\dfrac{82.50}{\sin \angle x} = \dfrac{87.00}{\sin 89°}$

$\dfrac{82.50}{\sin \angle x} = \dfrac{87.00}{0.99985}$

$\sin \angle x = \dfrac{82.50\,(0.99985)}{87.00}$

$\sin \angle x = 0.94813$

$\angle x = 71°28' = 71.47°$

7. $\sin 133° = \sin(180° - 133°) = \sin 47°$

$\dfrac{2.000}{\sin \angle x} = \dfrac{4.667}{\sin 47°}$

$\dfrac{2.000}{\sin \angle x} = \dfrac{4.667}{0.73135}$

$\sin \angle x = \dfrac{2.000\,(0.73135)}{4.667}$

$\sin \angle x = 0.31341$

$\angle x = 18°16'$

8. $\dfrac{1.440}{\sin \angle y} = \dfrac{0.820}{\sin 29°20'}$

$\dfrac{1.440}{\sin \angle y} = \dfrac{0.820}{0.48989}$

$\sin \angle y = \dfrac{1.440\,(0.48989)}{0.820}$

$\sin \angle y = 0.86029$

$\angle y = 59°21'$

$\angle x = 180° - (29°20' + 59°21') = 91°19'$

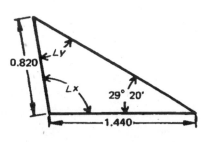

9. $\dfrac{310.00}{\sin \angle 1} = \dfrac{323.00}{\sin 84°}$

$\dfrac{310.00}{\sin \angle 1} = \dfrac{323.00}{0.99452}$

$\sin \angle 1 = \dfrac{310.00\,(0.99452)}{323.00}$

$\sin \angle 1 = 0.95449$

$\angle 1 = 72°39'$

$\angle 2 = 180° - (84° + 72°39') = 23°21'$

$\dfrac{x}{\sin 23°21'} = \dfrac{323.00}{\sin 84°}$

$\dfrac{x}{0.39635} = \dfrac{322.00}{0.99452}$

$x = \dfrac{0.39635\,(323.00)}{0.99452}$

$x = 128.73 \text{ mm}$

10. two solutions

11. two solutions

12. one solution

13. two solutions

14. one solution

15. one solution

16. two solutions

17. two solutions

18. $\cos 71°50' = 3.1178$

$x^2 = 3.900^2 + 5.000^2 - 2(3.900)(5.000)(0.31178)$

$x^2 = 15.2100 + 25.0000 - 12.1594$

$x^2 = 28.051$

$x = \sqrt{28.051} = 5.296 \text{ in}$

UNIT **64** (*continued*)

19. $\cos 80° = 0.17365$
$x^2 = 80.80^2 + 70.72^2 - 2(80.80)(70.72)(0.17365)$
$x^2 = 6528.64 + 5001.3184 - 1984.5333$
$x^2 = 9545.4251$
$x = \sqrt{9545.4251} = 97.70\,\text{mm}$

20. $\cos 127°40' - \cos(180° - 127°40') = -\cos 52°20'$
$= -0.61107$
$x^2 = 2.030^2 + 2.690^2 - 2(2.030)(2.690)(-0.61107)$
$x^2 = 4.121 + 7.236 - 6.674$
$x^2 = 18.031$
$x = \sqrt{18.031} - 4.246\,\text{in}$

21. $\cos \angle x = \dfrac{75.00^2 + 141.50^2 - 137.50^2}{2(75.00)(141.50)}$
$\cos \angle x = \dfrac{5625 + 20022.25 - 18906.25}{21225}$
$\cos \angle x = \dfrac{6741.00}{21225}$
$\cos \angle x = 0.31760$
$\angle x = 71°29' = 71.48°$

22. $\cos \angle x = \dfrac{2.250^2 + 2.601^2 - 4.059^2}{2(2.250)(2.601)}$
$\cos \angle x = \dfrac{5.0625 + 6.7652 - 16.4755}{11.7045}$
$\cos \angle x = \dfrac{-4.6478}{11.7045}$
$\cos \angle x = -0.39709$
$\cos 66°36' = 0.39709$
$\cos (180° - 66°36') = -0.39709$
$\cos 113°24' = -0.39709$
$\angle x = 113°24'$

23. $\cos \angle x = \dfrac{4.608^2 + 4.593^2 - 2.150^2}{2(4.608)(4.593)}$
$\cos \angle x = \dfrac{21.2337 + 21.0956 - 4.6225}{42.3291}$
$\cos \angle x = \dfrac{37.7068}{42.3291}$
$\cos \angle x = 0.89080$
$\angle x - 27°2'$

24. $\cos \angle x = \dfrac{1.368^2 + 1.005^2 - 2.322^2}{2(1.368)(1.005)}$
$\cos \angle x = \dfrac{1.8714 + 1.0100 - 5.3917}{2.7497}$
$\cos \angle x = \dfrac{-2.5103}{2.7497}$
$\cos \angle x = -0.91294$
$\cos 24°5' = 0.91294$
$\cos (180° - 24°5') = -0.91294$
$\cos 155°55' = -0.91294$
$\angle x = 155°55'$

25. $\cos 57° = 0.54464$
$x^2 = 38.73^2 + 38.73^2 - 2(38.73)(38.73)(0.54464)$
$x^2 = 1500.0129 + 1500.0129 - 1633.934$
$x^2 = 1366.0918$
$x = 36.96\,\text{mm}$

26. $\cos 157°20' = -\cos(180° - 157°20') = -\cos 22°40'$
$= -0.92276$
$x^2 = 1.7576^2 + 1.5314^2 - 2(1.7576)(1.5314)(-0.92276)$
$x^2 = 3.0892 + 2.3452 + 4.9674$
$x^2 = 10.4019$
$x = 3.225\,\text{in}$

27. a. $\cos 63°30' = 0.44620$
$x^2 = 0.875^2 + 1.250^2 - 2(0.875)(1.250)(0.44620)$
$x^2 = 0.7656 + 1.5625 - 0.9761$
$x^2 = 1.3520$
$x = 1.163\,\text{in}$

    b. $\dfrac{1.163}{\sin 63°30'} = \dfrac{0.875}{\sin \angle y}$
$\dfrac{1.163}{0.89493} = \dfrac{0.875}{\sin \angle y}$
$\sin \angle y = \dfrac{0.89493(0.875)}{1.163}$
$\sin \angle y = 0.67331$
$\angle y = 42°19'$

28. a. $\cos 89° = 0.01745$
$x^2 = 2.268^2 + 2.250^2 - 2(2.268)(2.250)(0.01745)$
$x^2 = 5.1438 + 5.0625 - 0.1781$
$x^2 = 10.0282$
$x = 3.167\,\text{in}$

UNIT **64** (*continued*)

28. b. $\dfrac{2.250}{\sin \angle y} = \dfrac{3.167}{\sin 89°}$

$\dfrac{2.250}{\sin \angle y} = \dfrac{3.167}{0.99985}$

$\sin \angle y = \dfrac{2.250\,(0.99985)}{3.167}$

$\sin \angle y = 0.71045$

$\angle y = 45°16'$

29. a. $\cos 147° = -\cos(180° - 147°) = -\cos 33° = -0.83867$

$x^2 = 167.76^2 + 212.00^2 - 2(167.76)(212.00)(-0.83867)$

$x^2 = 28143.418 + 44944 + 59654.798$

$x^2 = 132742.22$

$x = 364.34 \text{ mm}$

b. $\dfrac{167.76}{\sin \angle y} = \dfrac{364.34}{\sin 147°}$

$\sin 147° = \sin(180° - 147°) = \sin 33° = 0.54464$

$\dfrac{167.76}{\sin \angle y} = \dfrac{364.34}{0.54464}$

$\sin \angle y = \dfrac{167.76\,(0.54464)}{364.34}$

$\sin \angle y = 0.25078$

$\angle y = 14°31.4' = 14.52°$

30.

a. $\cos 28°40' = 0.87743$

$a^2 = 7.590^2 + 7.315^2 - 2(7.590)(7.315)(0.87743)$

$a^2 = 57.6081 + 53.5092 - 97.431$

$a^2 = 13.686$

$a = 3.700 \text{ in}$

$\dfrac{7.590}{\sin \angle x} = \dfrac{3.700}{\sin 28°40'}$

$\dfrac{7.590}{\sin \angle x} = \dfrac{3.700}{0.47971}$

$\sin \angle x = \dfrac{7.590\,(0.47971)}{3.700}$

$\sin \angle x = 0.98405$

$\angle x = 79°45'$

b. $\angle y = 180° - (28°40' + 79°45') = 71°35'$

31. a. $\cos \angle x = \dfrac{1.370^2 + 1.060^2 - 1.800^2}{2(1.370)(1.060)}$

$\cos \angle x = \dfrac{1.8769 + 1.1236 - 3.2400}{2.9044}$

$\cos \angle x = \dfrac{-0.2395}{2.9044}$

$\cos \angle x = -0.08246$

$\cos 85°16' = 0.08246$

$\cos (180° - 85°16') = -0.08246$

$\angle x = 94°44'$

b. $\dfrac{1.370}{\sin \angle y} = \dfrac{1.800}{\sin \angle x}$

$\sin \angle x = \sin (180° - 94°44') = 0.99659$

$\dfrac{1.370}{\sin \angle y} = \dfrac{1.800}{0.99659}$

$\sin \angle y = \dfrac{1.370\,(0.99659)}{1.800}$

$\sin \angle y = 0.75852$

$\angle y = 49°20'$

32. a. $\cos \angle x = \dfrac{169.50^2 + 151.00^2 - 78.00^2}{2(169.50)(151.00)}$

$\cos \angle x = \dfrac{28730.25 + 22801 - 6084}{51189}$

$\cos \angle x = \dfrac{45447.25}{51189}$

$\cos \angle x = 0.88783$

$\angle x = 27°23.86' = 27.40°$

b. $\dfrac{151.00}{\sin \angle y} = \dfrac{78.00}{\sin \angle x}$

$\dfrac{151.00}{\sin \angle y} = \dfrac{78.00}{0.46020}$

$\sin \angle y = \dfrac{151.00\,(0.46020)}{78.00}$

$\sin \angle y = 0.89090$

$\angle y = 62°59' - 62.98°$

33. a. $\cos \angle x = \dfrac{209.30^2 + 212.70^2 - 248.00^2}{2(209.30)(212.70)}$

$\cos \angle x = \dfrac{43806.49 + 45241.29 - 61504}{89036.22}$

$\cos \angle x = \dfrac{27543.78}{89036.22}$

$\cos \angle x = 0.30935$

$\angle x = 71°58.79' = 71.98°$

UNIT **64**   *(continued)*

34. In △ABC:

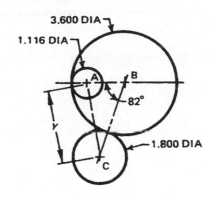

$$AB = \frac{3.600\,in}{2} - \frac{1.116\,in}{2} = 1.242\,in$$

$$BC = \frac{3.600\,in}{2} + \frac{1.800\,in}{2} = 2.700\,in$$

(Geo. Principle 21)

$$\cos 82° = 0.13917$$

$$y^2 = 1.242^2 + 2.700^2 - 2(1.242)(2.700)(0.13917)$$

$$y^2 = 1.5426 + 7.2900 - 0.9334$$

$$y^2 = 7.8992$$

$$y = 2.811\,in$$

35.

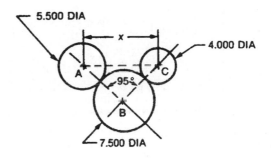

$$AB = \frac{5.500}{2} + \frac{7.500}{2} = 6.500$$

$$BC = \frac{7.500}{2} + \frac{4.000}{2} = 5.750$$

$$\cos 95° = -0.08716$$

$$x^2 = 6.500^2 + 5.750^2 - 2(6.500)(5.750)(-0.08716)$$

$$x^2 = 42.25 + 33.0625 + 6.5152$$

$$x^2 = 81.8277$$

$$x = 9.046\,in$$

36. Analysis: △EFG is isosceles, therefore,

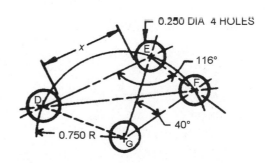

$$\angle FEG = \frac{180° - 40°}{2} = 70°$$

In isosceles △DEG: ∠DEG = 116° − 70° = 46°
and ∠DEG = 180° − 2(46°) = 88°
x = DE − 0.250 in

Compute DE:

$$\frac{0.750}{\sin 46°} = \frac{DE}{\sin 88°}$$

$$\frac{0.750}{0.71934} = \frac{DE}{0.99939}$$

$$DE = \frac{0.750(0.99939)}{0.71934}$$

$$DE = 1.0420\,in$$

$$x = 1.0420\,in - 0.250\,in = 0.792\,in$$

UNIT **64**   *(continued)*

37. Analysis: In isosceles △ABC compute ∠BAC. In right △ACD compute ∠CAD.

$$\angle x = \angle BAC + \angle CAD$$

Compute ∠BAC. In △ABC:

$$\cos \angle BAC = \frac{4.125^2 + 4.125^2 - 1.800^2}{2(4.125)(4.125)}$$

$$\cos \angle BAC = \frac{17.0156 + 17.0156 - 3.2400}{34.0312}$$

$$\cos \angle BAC = \frac{30.7912}{34.0312}$$

$$\cos \angle BAC = 0.90479$$

$$\angle BAC = 25°12'$$

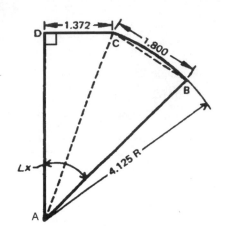

Compute ∠CAD. In right △ACD:

$$DC = 1.372 \text{ in}$$

$$AC = 4.125 \text{ in}$$

$$\sin \angle CAD = \frac{1.372}{4.125} = 0.33261$$

$$\angle CAD = 19°26'$$

$$x = 25°12' + 19°26' = 44°38'$$

38. Analysis: In △ABC compute AC. In △ACD compute ∠ACD, ∠CAD, and *y*.

Compute AC. In △ABC:

$$\cos 73° = 0.29237$$

$$AC^2 = 75.60^2 + 112.00^2 - 2(75.60)(112.00)(0.29237)$$

$$AC^2 = 5715.36 + 12544 - 4951.1105$$

$$AC^2 = 13308.25$$

$$AC = 115.361 \text{ mm}$$

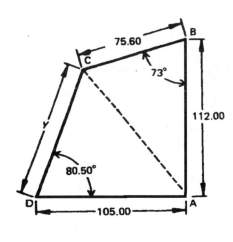

Compute ∠ACD, ∠CAD, and *y*. In △ACD:

$$\frac{105.00}{\sin \angle ACD} = \frac{AC}{\sin 80.50°}$$

$$\frac{105.00}{\sin \angle ACD} = \frac{115.361}{0.98628}$$

$$\sin \angle ACD = \frac{105.00(0.98628)}{115.361}$$

$$\sin \angle ACD = 0.89770$$

$$\angle ACD = 63°51.54'$$

$$\angle CAD = 180° - (80°30' + 63°51.54') = 35°38.46'$$

$$\frac{y}{\sin 35°38.46'} = \frac{115.361}{\sin 80°30'}$$

$$\frac{y}{0.58270} = \frac{115.361}{0.98629}$$

$$y = \frac{0.58270(115.361)}{0.98629}$$

$$y = 68.16 \text{ mm}$$

UNIT **64**   (*continued*)

39. Analysis: In △EFG compute ∠EFG, ∠FEG, and FG. In right △GFH compute ∠H and *y*.

Compute ∠EFG, ∠FEG, and FG. In △EFG:

$$EF = \frac{3.140\,in}{2} = 1.570\,in$$

$$\frac{EF}{\sin 72°40'} = \frac{1.000}{\sin \angle EFG}$$

$$\frac{1.570}{0.95459} = \frac{1.000}{\sin \angle EFG}$$

$$\sin \angle EFG = \frac{0.95459(1.000)}{1.570}$$

$$\sin \angle EFG = 0.60802$$

∠EFG   37°27′

∠FEG = 180° − (72°40′ + 37°27′) = 69°53′

$$\frac{EF}{\sin 72°40'} = \frac{FG}{\sin \angle FEG}$$

$$\frac{1.570}{0.95459} = \frac{FG}{0.93899}$$

$$FG = \frac{1.570(0.93899)}{0.95459}$$

$$FG = 1.5443\,in$$

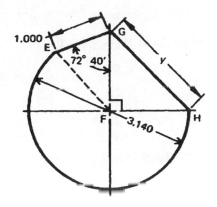

Compute ∠H and *y*. In right △GFH:

FG = 1.5443 in

$$FH = \frac{3.140\,in}{2} = 1.570\,in$$

$$\tan \angle H = \frac{1.5443}{1.570} = 0.98363$$

∠H = 44°32′

$$\sec 44°32' = \frac{y}{1.570}$$

$$y = 1.4028(1.570)$$

$$y = 2.202\,in$$

40. Analysis: In △ABC compute BC. In right △BCD compute ∠BCD and BD.

y = BD

Compute BC. In △ABC:

AB = 2.800 in − 0.664 in = 2.136 in   (Geo. Principle 21)

AC = 2.800 in − 0.400 in = 2.400 in

cos 58°50′ = 0.51753

$BC^2 = 2.136^2 + 2.400^2 − 2(2.136)(2.400)(0.51753)$

$BC^2 = 4.5625 + 5.7600 − 5.3061$

$BC^2 = 5.0164$

BC = 2.2397 in

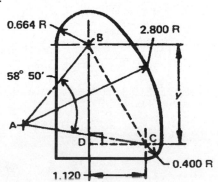

UNIT **64** *(continued)*

40. Compute ∠BCD and BD. In △BCD:

$$CD = 1.120 \text{ in}$$

$$BC = 2.2397 \text{ in}$$

$$\cos \angle BCD = \frac{1.120}{2.2397} = 0.50007$$

$$\angle BCD = 60°$$

$$\tan 60° = \frac{BD}{1.120}$$

$$BD = 1.7321(1.120)$$

$$BD = 1.940 \text{ in}$$

$$y = 1.940$$

41. Analysis: In △EGK compute EG, ∠GEK, and ∠EGK. In △EFG compute FG, ∠EFG, and ∠EGF. In △FGH compute ∠FHG and ∠GFH.

$$\angle x = \angle EFG + \angle GFH$$

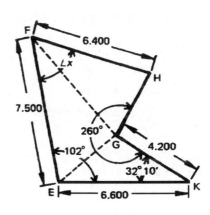

Compute EG, ∠GEK, and ∠EGK. In △EGK:

$$\cos 32°10' = 0.84650$$

$$EG^2 = 6.600^2 + 4.200^2 - 2(6.600)(4.200)(0.84650)$$

$$EG^2 = 43.5600 + 17.6400 - 46.9300$$

$$EG^2 = 14.2700$$

$$EG = 3.778 \text{ in}$$

$$\frac{4.200}{\sin \angle GEK} = \frac{3.778}{\sin 32°10'}$$

$$\frac{4.200}{\sin \angle GEK} = \frac{3.778}{0.53238}$$

$$\sin \angle GEK = \frac{4.200(0.53238)}{3.778}$$

$$\sin \angle GEK = 0.59185$$

$$\angle GEK = 36°17'$$

$$\angle EGK = 180° - (32°10' + 36°17') = 111°33'$$

Compute FG, ∠EFG, and ∠EGF. In △EFG:

$$\angle FEG = 102° - 36°17' = 65°43'$$

$$FG^2 = 7.500^2 + EG^2 - 2(7.500)(EG)(\cos \angle FEG)$$

$$FG^2 = 7.500^2 + 3.778^2 - 2(7.500)(3.778)(0.41125)$$

$$FG^2 = 56.2500 + 14.2733 - 23.3055$$

$$FG^2 = 47.2178$$

$$FG = 6.872 \text{ in}$$

$$\frac{EG}{\sin \angle EFG} = \frac{FG}{\sin \angle FEG}$$

$$\frac{3.778}{\sin \angle EFG} = \frac{6.872}{0.91152}$$

$$\sin \angle EFG = \frac{3.778(0.91152)}{6.872}$$

$$\sin \angle EFG = 0.50112$$

$$\angle EFG = 30°4'$$

$$\angle EGF = 180° - (65°43' + 30°4') = 84°13'$$

UNIT **64**   (*continued*)

41. Compute ∠FHG and ∠GFH. In △FGH:

$$\angle FGH = 260° - (84°13' + 111°33') = 64°14'$$

$$\frac{FG}{\sin \angle FHG} = \frac{6.400}{\sin \angle FGH}$$

$$\frac{6.872}{\sin \angle FHG} = \frac{6.400}{0.90057}$$

$$\sin \angle FHG = \frac{6.872\,(0.90057)}{6.400}$$

$$\angle FHG = 0.96699$$
$$\angle FHG = 75°14'$$

$$\angle GFH = 180° - (64°14' + 75°14') = 40°32'$$

$$\angle x = 30°4' + 40°32' = 70°30'$$

42. Analysis: In △ABC compute ∠ABC. In △AED compute ∠AED. In △EBD compute ∠EBD.

$$\angle y = \angle EBD - \angle ABC$$

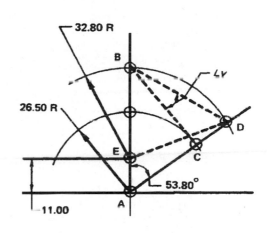

Compute ∠ABC. In △ABC:

$$AB = 11.00\,mm + 32.80\,mm = 43.80\,mm$$
$$AC = 26.50\,mm$$
$$\angle BAC = 53.80°$$
$$BC^2 = 43.80^2 + 26.50^2 - 2(43.80)(26.50)(\cos 53.80°)$$
$$BC^2 = 1918.44 + 702.25 - 2(43.80)(26.50)(0.59060)$$
$$BC^2 = 1918.44 + 702.25 - 1371.0188$$
$$BC^2 = 1249.6712$$
$$BC = 35.3507\,mm$$

$$\frac{AC}{\sin \angle ABC} = \frac{BC}{\sin 53.80°}$$

$$\frac{26.50}{\sin \angle ABC} = \frac{35.3507}{0.80696}$$

$$\sin \angle ABC = \frac{26.50\,(0.80696)}{35.3507}$$

$$\sin \angle ABC = 0.60492$$
$$\angle ABC = 37.22°$$

Compute ∠AED. In △AED:

$$AE = 11.00\,mm$$
$$ED = 32.80\,mm$$
$$\angle EAD = 53.80°$$

$$\frac{11.00}{\sin \angle EDA} = \frac{32.80}{\sin 53.80°}$$

$$\frac{11.00}{\sin \angle EDA} = \frac{32.80}{0.80696}$$

$$\sin \angle EDA = \frac{11.00\,(0.80696)}{32.80}$$

$$\sin \angle EDA = 0.27063$$

$$\angle EDA = 15.70°$$

$$\angle AED = 180° - (53.80° + 15.70°) = 110.50°$$

Compute ∠EBD. In △EBD:

$$\angle BED = 180° - 110.50° = 69.50°$$

$$BE = 32.80\,mm$$

$$ED = 32.80\,mm$$

△EBD is isosceles, $\angle EBD = \dfrac{180° - 69.50°}{2} = 55.25°$

$$\angle y = 55.25° - 37.22° = 18.03°$$

UNIT **65** Achievement Review—Section Six

1.   *a* is opp
    b is adj
    c is hyp

2.   *a* is adj
    b is opp
    c is hyp

3.   *m* is hyp
    s is adj
    p is opp

4.   *r* is hyp
    x is adj
    y is opp

5. a. 0.3746
8. 0.0061
11. 0.1293

6. 0.9545
9. 0.4493
12. 1.1815

7. 1.2661
10. 0.2568

13. 45°50′
14. 26°50′
15. 80°10′

16. 41°24′
17. 50°36′
18. 80°51′

19. 46.76°
20. 54.32°
21. 70.10°

22. cos 54°
24. sin 73°7′

23. cot 41°41′
25. tan 9.53°

26. $\tan \angle A = \dfrac{5.920}{6.350} = 0.93228$

$\angle A = 43°0′$

27. $\cos 32° = \dfrac{a}{22.200}$

$0.84805 = \dfrac{a}{22.200}$

$a = 0.84805(22.200)$

$a = 18.827 \text{ in}$

28. $\cos \angle D = \dfrac{88.000}{123.000} = 0.1754$

$\angle D = 43.33°$

32. (1) $CB = 12.750 \text{ in} - 8.080 \text{ in} = 4.670 \text{ in}$

$\cos 32°30′ = \dfrac{4.670}{c}$

$0.84339 = \dfrac{4.670}{c}$

$c = \dfrac{4.670}{0.84339}$

$c = 5.537 \text{ in}$

(2) $\tan 32°30′ = \dfrac{AC}{4.670}$

$0.63707 = \dfrac{AC}{4.670}$

$AC = 2.9751 \text{ in}$

$d = 6.050 \text{ in} - 2.9751 \text{ in} = 3.075 \text{ in}$

33. $BC = \dfrac{25.700 \text{ mm} - 16.700 \text{ mm}}{2} = 4.500 \text{ mm}$

$\tan \angle BAC = \dfrac{4.500}{78.000} = 0.05769$

$\angle BAC = 3°18.1′ = 3.30°$

$\angle T = 2(3.30°) = 6.60°$

29. $\tan \angle 1 = \dfrac{120.000}{87.000} - 1.3703$

$\angle 1 = 54°3.5′ = 54.06°$

30. a. $\sin 21.15° = \dfrac{g}{25.200}$

$0.36081 = \dfrac{g}{25.200}$

$g = 0.36081(25.200)$

$g = 9.092 \text{ mm}$

b. $\cos 21.15° = \dfrac{h}{25.200}$

$0.93264 = \dfrac{h}{25.200}$

$h = 0.93264(25.200)$

$h = 23.503 \text{ mm}$

c. $\angle H = 90° - 21.15° = 68.85°$

31. a. $\tan \angle A = \dfrac{15.000}{9.370} = 1.60085$

$\angle A = 58°1′$

b. $\angle B = 90° - 58°1′ = 31°59′$

c. $\sin \angle A = \dfrac{15.000}{c}$

$\sin 58°1′ = \dfrac{15.000}{c}$

$c = \dfrac{15.000}{0.84820}$

$c = 17.685 \text{ in}$

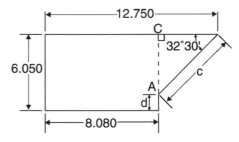

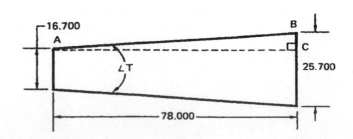

UNIT **65** (*continued*)

34. $AO = \dfrac{168.200\,\text{mm}}{2} = 84.100\,\text{mm}$

$\angle AOC = \dfrac{360°}{4} = 90°$

$\angle AOB = \dfrac{90°}{2} = 45°$

In right $\triangle AOB$:

$\sin \angle AOB = \dfrac{AB}{AO}$

$\sin 45° = \dfrac{AB}{84.100}$

$0.70711 = \dfrac{AB}{84.100}$

$AB = 59.46795\,\text{mm}$

$x = 2(59.46795) = 118.936\,\text{mm}$

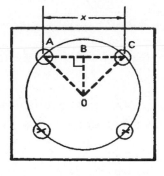

35. $OC = \dfrac{1.000\,\text{in}}{2} = 0.500\,\text{in}$

$\angle CAO = \dfrac{70°50'}{2} = 35°25'$

In right $\triangle ACO$:

$\cot \angle CAO = \dfrac{AC}{OC}$

$\cot 35°25' = \dfrac{AC}{0.500}$

$1.4063 = \dfrac{AC}{0.500}$

$AC = 0.70315\,\text{in}$

$d = 3.900\,\text{in} - [2(0.450\,\text{in}) + 2(0.70315\,\text{in}) + 2(0.500\,\text{in})] = 0.594\,\text{in}$

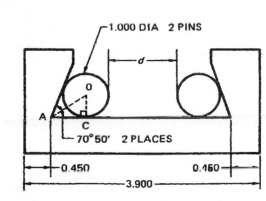

36. Analysis: In right $\triangle BCD$ compute BD. In right $\triangle AEB$ compute $\angle A$ and AB.

$x = AB$

(1) Compute BD. In right $\triangle BCD$:

$DC = 231.000\,\text{mm} - 176.000\,\text{mm} = 55.000\,\text{mm}$

$\tan 64° = \dfrac{BD}{DC}$

$2.0503 = \dfrac{BD}{55.000}$

$BD = 112.7665\,\text{mm}$

Compute $\angle A$ and AB. In right $\triangle AEB$:

$EB = 176.000\,\text{mm}$

$AE = 198.000\,\text{mm} - 112.7665\,\text{mm} = 85.2335\,\text{mm}$

$\tan \angle A = \dfrac{EB}{AE} = \dfrac{176.000}{85.2335} = 2.0649$

$\angle A = 64°9.6' = 64.16°$

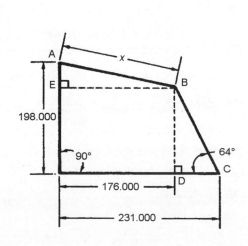

UNIT **65** *(continued)*

36. e. (2) $\sin 64°9.6' = \dfrac{EB}{AB}$

$0.90001 = \dfrac{176.000}{AB}$

$AB = 195.553\,mm$

$x = 195.553\ mm$

37. Analysis: In right $\triangle ABC$ compute AC. In right $\triangle ADO$ compute AO.

$y = (AO + OE) - AC$

Compute AC. In right $\triangle ABC$:

$\angle BAC = \dfrac{62°50'}{2} = 31°25'$

$BC = 1.850\ in - 0.950\ in = 0.900\ in$

$\cot 31°25' = \dfrac{AC}{0.900}$

$1.6372 = \dfrac{AC}{0.900}$

$AC = 1.47348$

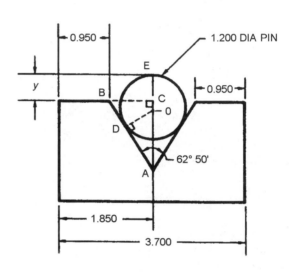

Compute AO. In right $\triangle ADO$:

$\angle DAO = 31°25'$

$DO = \dfrac{1.200\ in}{2} = 0.600\ in$

$\sin 31°25' = \dfrac{DO}{AO}$

$0.52126 = \dfrac{0.600}{AO}$

$AO = 1.15106\,in$

$y = (1.15106\ in + 0.600\ in) - 1.47348\ in = 0.278\ in$

38. Analysis: In right $\triangle OAB$ compute $\angle ABO$ and OB. In right $\triangle OCB$ compute $\angle OBC$.

$\angle x = 90° - (\angle ABO + \angle OBC)$

Compute $\angle ABO$ and OB. In right $\triangle OAB$:

$AB = 7.900\ in - 4.300\ in = 3.600\ in$

$OA = 4.800\ in - (1.300\ in + 1.500\ in) = 2.000\ in$

$\tan \angle ABO = \dfrac{OA}{AB} = \dfrac{2.000}{3.600} = 0.55556$

$\angle ABO = 29°3'$

$OB^2 = 2.000^2 + 3.600^2$

$OB^2 = 4.000 + 12.960$

$OB^2 = 16.960$

$OB = 4.11825\,in$

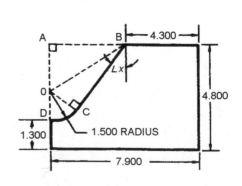

UNIT **65** *(continued)*

38. g. Compute ∠OBC. In right △OCB:

OC = 1.500 in

OB = 4.11825 in

$$\sin \angle OBC = \frac{1.500}{4.11825} = 0.36423$$

∠OBC = 21°22′

∠*x* = 90° − (29°3′ + 21°22′) = 39 ρομαν °35′

39. Analysis: In right △ABC compute ∠BAC and AC. In right △ADC compute CD and ∠DAC. In right △ABE compute ∠BAE.

∠*y* = ∠BEA = 90° − ∠BAE

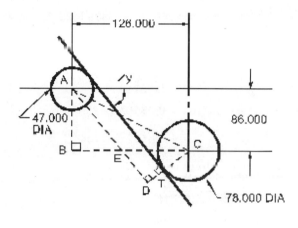

Compute ∠BAC and AC. In right △ABC:

$$\tan \angle BAC = \frac{128.000}{86.000} - 1.4651$$

∠BAC = 55.69°

AC² = 86.000² + 126.000²

AC² = 7396 + 15876

AC² = 23272

AC = 152.55163 mm

Compute CD and ∠DAC. In right △ADC:

AC = 152.55163 mm

$$DC = \frac{47.000\,mm}{2} + \frac{78.000\,mm}{2} = 62.500\,mm$$

$$\sin \angle DAC = \frac{DC}{AC} = \frac{62.500}{152.55163} - 0.40070$$

∠DAC = 24.19°

Compute ∠BAE. In right △ABE:

∠BAE = ∠BAC − ∠DAC = 55.69° − 24.19° = 31.50°

∠*y* = ∠BEA = 90° − ∠BAE = 90° − 31.50° = 58.50°

40. Reference angle = 180° − 115° = 65°

sin 115° = sin 65° = 0.9063

cos 115° = −cos 65° = −0.4226

tan 115° = −tan 65° = −2.1445

cot 115° = −cot 65° = −0.4663

sec 115° = −sec 65° = −2.3662

csc 115° = csc 65° = 1.1034

41. Reference angle = 223° − 180° = 43°

sin 223° = −sin 43° = −0.6820

cos 223° = −cos 43° = −0.7314

tan 223° = tan 43° = 0.9325

cot 223° = cot 43° = 1.0724

sec 223° = −sec 43° = −1.3673

csc 223° = −csc 43° = −1.4663

42. Reference angle = 360° − 310°30′ = 49°30′

sin 310°30′ = −sin 49°30′ = −0.7604

cos 310°30′ = cos 49°30′ = 0.6494

tan 310°30′ = −tan 49°30′ = −1.1709

cot 310°30′ = −cot 49°30′ = −0.8541

sec 310°30′ = sec 49°30′ = 1.5398

csc 310°30′ = −csc 49°30′ = −1.3151

43. $$\frac{a}{\sin 72°} = \frac{192.600}{\sin 80°}$$

$$\frac{a}{0.951\,06} = \frac{192.600}{0.984\,81}$$

a = 185.999 mm

UNIT 65   *(continued)*

44   $\sin 109° = \sin(180° - 109°) = \sin 71° = 0.94552$

$$\frac{17.000}{\sin \angle D} = \frac{21.000}{\sin 109°}$$

$$\frac{17.000}{\sin \angle D} = \frac{21.000}{0.94552}$$

$$21.000(\sin \angle D) = 17.000(0.94552)$$

$$\sin \angle D = 0.76542$$

$$\angle D = 49°57'$$

45. a. $\angle A = 180° - (36°40' + 32°50') = 180° - 69°30' = 110°30'$

b. $\sin 110°30' = \sin (180° - 110°30') = 69°30' = 0.93667$

$$\frac{a}{\sin 110°30'} = \frac{9.425}{\sin 36°40'}$$

$$\frac{a}{0.93667} = \frac{9.425}{0.59716}$$

$$0.59716a = 0.93667(9.425)$$

$$a = 14.784 \, in$$

c. $\dfrac{b}{\sin 32°50'} = \dfrac{9.425}{\sin 36°40'}$

$$\frac{b}{0.54220} = \frac{9.425}{0.59716}$$

$$0.59716b = 0.54220(9.425)$$

$$b = 8.558 \, in$$

46. $d^2 = 70.000^2 + 119.000^2 - 2(70.000)(119.000)(\cos 80°)$

$d^2 = 4900 + 14161 - 2(70.000)(119.000)(0.17365)$

$d^2 = 19061 - 2893.009$

$d^2 = 16167.991$

$d = 127.153 \, mm$

47. $\cos \angle E = \dfrac{100.000^2 + 80.000^2 - 160.000^2}{2(100.000)(80.000)}$

$$\cos \angle E = \frac{10000 + 6400 - 25600}{16000}$$

$$\cos \angle E = -0.575$$

$$\cos 54.90° = 0.575$$

$$\cos (180° - 54.90°) = -0.575$$

$$\cos 125.10° = -0.575$$

$$\angle E = 125.10°$$

48. a $m^2 = 13.900^2 + 14.400^2 - 2(13.900)(14.400)(\cos 34°50')$

$m^2 = 193.21 + 207.36 - 2(13.900)(14.400)(0.82082)$

$m^2 = 400.57 - 328.59066$

$m^2 = 71.97934$

$m = 8.484 \, in$

UNIT **65**   *(continued)*

48. b $\dfrac{13.900}{\sin \angle N} = \dfrac{8.484064}{\sin 34°50'}$

$\dfrac{13.900}{\sin \angle N} = \dfrac{8.484064}{0.57119}$

$\sin \angle N = 0.93582$

$\angle N = 60°22'$

c $\angle P = 180° - (34°50' + 69°22') = 75°48'$

49. $\angle CDB = 180° - (97°30' + 29°10') = 53°20'$

In $\triangle ABD$:

$\angle ADB = 108° - 53°20' = 54°40'$

$\angle ADB = 108° - (54°40' + 42°40') = 82°40'$

$\dfrac{d}{\sin 54°40'} = \dfrac{9.555}{\sin 82°40'}$

$\dfrac{d}{0.81580} = \dfrac{9.555}{0.99182}$

$d = 7.859 \text{ in}$

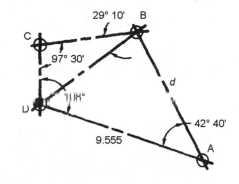

50.   Analysis: In right $\triangle ABC$ compute AC. In $\triangle ACD$ compute $\angle x$.

Compute AC. In right $\triangle ABC$:

BC = 20.000 mm − 17.000 mm = 3.000 mm

$AC^2 = 27.500^2 + 3.000^2$

$AC^2 = 756.25 + 9$

$AC^2 = 765.25$

$AC = 27.66315 \text{ mm}$

Compute $\angle x$. In $\triangle ACD$:

$\cos \angle x = \dfrac{32.000^2 + 15.000^2 - 27.66315^2}{2(32.000)(15.000)}$

$\cos \angle x = \dfrac{1024 + 225 - 765.25}{960}$

$\cos \angle x = 0.50391$

$\angle x = 59.74°$

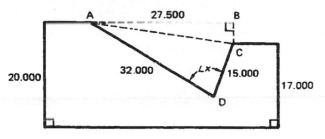

51. $\cos 129°10' = -\cos(180° - 129°10') = -\cos 50°50' = -0.63135784$

In $\triangle ABC$, $AB^2 = 8.293^2 + 5.065^2 - 2(8.293)(5.065)\cos 129°10'$

$AB^2 = 68.773849 + 25.654225 + 53.05769$

$AB^2 = 147.48576$

$AB = 12.144372$

$\cos \angle BAC = \dfrac{12.144372^2 + 8.293^2 - 5.065^2}{2(12.144372)(8.293)}$

$\cos \angle BAC = \dfrac{147.48577 + 68.773849 - 25.654225}{201.426554}$

$\cos \angle BAC = \dfrac{190.605394}{201.426554} = 0.94628$

$\angle BAC = 18°52'$

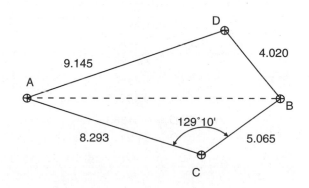

UNIT 65 (continued)

51.

In $\triangle$ABD, $\cos \angle DAB = \dfrac{12.144372^2 + 9.145^2 - 4.020^2}{2(12.144372)(9.145)}$

$\cos \angle DAB = \dfrac{147.48577 + 83.631025 - 16.1604}{222.12056}$

$\cos \angle DAB = \dfrac{214.956395}{222.12056} = 0.9677465$

$\angle DAB = 14°35'$

$\angle A = \angle BAC + \angle DAB = 18°52' + 14°35' = 33°27'$

52. In rt $\triangle$ABC, CB = 16.70 mm $\div$ 2 = 8.35 mm

$AC^2 = CB^2 + AB^2$

$10.200^2 = 8.35^2 + AB^2$

$104.04 = 69.7225 + AB^2$

$AB^2 = 34.3175$

$AB = 5.8581$

$\sin \angle CAB = \dfrac{CB}{AC} = \dfrac{8.35}{10.20} = 0.8186$

$\angle CAB = 54.95°$

In $\triangle$ABD, AB = 5.858 1 mm, AD = 6.100 mm, BD = 16.700 mm $\div$ 2 = 8.35 mm

$\cos \angle BAD = \dfrac{5.8581^2 + 6.100^2 - 8.35^2}{2(5.8581)(6.100)} = \dfrac{34.3173 + 37.21 - 69.7225}{71.4688} = \dfrac{1.8048}{71.4688} = 0.02525$

$\angle BAD = 88.55°$

$\angle A = \angle CAB + \angle BAD = 54.95° + 88.555° = 143.50°$

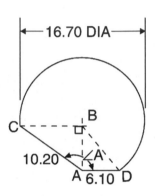

53. Analysis: In $\triangle$BCD compute BD, $\angle$CBD and $\angle$BDC. In #ABD compute AD, $\angle$BDA, and $\angle$BAD. In $\triangle$ADE compute $\angle$DAE.

$\angle x = \angle BAD + \angle DAB$

Compute BD, $\angle$CBD and $\angle$BDC. In $\triangle$BCD:

$BD^2 = 8.300^2 + 5.200^2 - 2(8.300)(5.200)(\cos 28°)$

$BD^2 = 68.89 + 27.04 - 2(8.300)(5.200)(0.88295)$

$BD^2 = 68.89 + 27.04 - 76.21624$

$BD^2 = 19.71376$

$BD = 4.44002 \text{ in}$

$\dfrac{5.200}{\sin \angle CBD} = \dfrac{4.44002}{\sin 28°}$

$\dfrac{5.200}{\sin \angle CBD} = \dfrac{4.44002}{0.46947}$

$\sin \angle CBD = 0.54983$

$\angle CBD = 33°21'$

$\angle BDC = 180° - (28° + 33°21') = 118°39'$

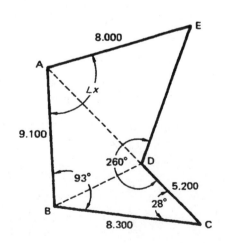

UNIT **65**   (*continued*)

53. Compute AD, ∠BDA, and ∠BAD. In △ABD:

BD = 4.44002 in

∠ABD = 93° − ∠CBD = 93° − 33°21′ = 59°39′

$AD^2 = AB^2 + BD^2 − 2(AB)(BD)(\cos ∠ABD)$

$AD^2 = 9.100^2 + 4.44002^2 − 2(9.100)(4.44002)(\cos 59°39′)$

$AD^2 = 82.81 + 19.7138 − 2(9.100)(4.44002)(0.50528)$

$AD^2 = 82.81 + 19.7138 − 40.8309$

AD = 7.85448 in

$$\frac{AB}{\sin ∠BDA} = \frac{AD}{\sin ∠ABD}$$

$$\frac{9.100}{\sin ∠BDA} = \frac{7.85448}{\sin 59°39′}$$

$$\frac{9.100}{\sin ∠BDA} = \frac{7.85448}{0.86295}$$

sin ∠BDA = 0.999792

∠BDA = 88°50′

∠BAD = 180° − (88°50′ + 59°39′) = 31°31′

Compute ∠DAE. In △ADE:

AD = 7.85448 in

∠ADE = 260° − (118°39′ + 88°50′)
       = 52°31′

$$\frac{AD}{\sin ∠AED} = \frac{AE}{\sin ∠ADE}$$

$$\frac{7.85448}{\sin ∠AED} = \frac{8.000}{\sin 52°31′}$$

$$\frac{7.85448}{\sin ∠AED} = \frac{8.000}{0.79353}$$

sin ∠AED = 0.77910

∠AED = 51°11′

∠DAE = 180° − (52°31′ + 51°11′) = 76°18′

∠x = 31°31′ + 76°18′ = 107°40′

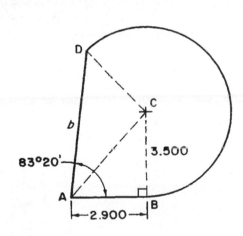

54. In right △ABC:

$AC^2 = 2.900^2 + 3.500^2$

$AC^2 = 8.41 + 12.25$

$AC^2 = 20.66$

AC = 4.5453 in

$\tan ∠BAC = \dfrac{3.500}{2.900} = 1.2069$

∠BAC = 50°21′

In △ACD, AC = 4.5453 in, DC = 3.500 in, ∠CAD = 32°59′

$$\frac{4.5453}{\sin ∠ADC} = \frac{3.500}{\sin 32°59′}$$

$$\frac{4.5453}{\sin ∠ADC} = \frac{3.500}{0.54439}$$

3.500 sin ∠ADC = 2.47442

sin ∠ADC = 0.70698

∠ADC = 44°59′

∠ACD = 180° − (32°59′ + 44°59′) = 102°2′

sin 102°2′ = sin(180° − 102°2′) = sin 77°58′

$$\frac{b}{\sin 102°2′} = \frac{3.500}{\sin 32°59′}$$

$$\frac{b}{0.97803} = \frac{3.500}{0.54439}$$

0.54439b = 3.4231

b = 6.288 in

UNIT **65**   *(continued)*

55.

In rt △ADC, $AC^2 = 16.80^2 + 20.50^2$

$$AC^2 = 282.24 + 420.25$$

$$AC^2 = 702.49$$

$$AC = 26.5045$$

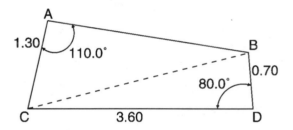

In △ABC, $\cos \angle B = \dfrac{18.00^2 + 11.60^2 - 26.5045^2}{2(18.00)(11.60)} = \dfrac{324 + 1334.56 - 702.49}{417.6} = \dfrac{-243.93}{417.6} = 0.58412$

$\angle B = 180° - 54°16' = 125°44'$

56.

In △CBD, $CB^2 = 3.60^2 + 0.70^2 - 2(3.60)(0.70)(\cos 80°)$

$$CB^2 = 12.96 + 0.49 - 2(3.60)(0.70)(0.1736)$$

$$CB^2 = 12.96 + 0.49 - 0.8749$$

$$CB^2 = 12.5751$$

$$CB^2 = 3.5461 \text{ in}$$

In △CBA, $\sin 110° = \sin(180° - 110°) = \sin 70°$

$$\frac{1.300}{\sin \angle ABC} = \frac{CB}{\sin 70°}$$

$$\frac{1.30}{\sin \angle ABC} = \frac{3.5461}{0.9397}$$

$$3.5461 \sin \angle ABC = 1.2216$$

$$\sin \angle ABC = 0.3445$$

$$\angle ABC = 20.15°$$

$$\angle ACB = 180° - (110° + 20.15°) = 49.85°$$

$$\frac{AB}{\sin 49385°} = \frac{3.5461}{\sin 70°}$$

$$\frac{AB}{0.7644} = \frac{3.5461}{0.9397}$$

$$0.9397 \, AB = 2.7106$$

$$AB = 2.8845$$

$$a = AB = 2.885 \text{ in}$$

Section Seven
Compound Angles

UNIT 66 Introduction to Compound Angles

1. a. $CB^2 = L^2 + W^2$
    $CB^2 = 2.700^2 + 2.000^2$
    $CB^2 = 7.290 + 4.000$
    $CB^2 = 11.290$
    $CB = 3.36006$ in
    $AB^2 = AC^2 + CB^2$
    $AB^2 = 1.500^2 + 3.36006^2$
    $AB^2 = 2.250 + 11.290$
    $AB^2 = 13.5400$
    $AB = 3.680$ in

    b. $\tan \angle CAB = \dfrac{CB}{AC} = \dfrac{3.36006}{1.500} = 2.2400$
    $\angle CAB = 65°57'$

2. a. $CB^2 = L^2 + W^2$
    $CB^2 = 100.00^2 + 80.00^2$
    $CB^2 = 10000 + 6400$
    $CB^2 = 16400$
    $CB = 128.06248$ mm
    $AB^2 = AC^2 + CB^2$
    $AB^2 = 50.00^2 + 128.06248^2$
    $AB^2 = 2500 + 16400$
    $AB^2 = 18900$
    $AB = 137.48$ mm

    b. $\tan \angle CAB = \dfrac{CB}{AC} = \dfrac{128.06248}{50.00} = 2.5612$
    $\angle CAB = 68°40.3' = 68.67°$

3. a. $CB^2 = L^2 + W^2$
    $CB^2 = 4.900^2 + 4.200^2$
    $CB^2 = 24.010 + 17.640$
    $CB^2 = 41.650$
    $CB = 6.45368$ in
    $AB^2 = AC^2 + CB^2$
    $AB^2 = 4.340^2 + 6.45368^2$
    $AB^2 = 18.8356 + 41.6500$
    $AB^2 = 60.4856$
    $AB = 7.777$ in

    b. $\tan \angle CAB = \dfrac{CB}{AC} = \dfrac{6.45368}{4.340} = 1.4870$
    $\angle CAB = 56°5'$

4. a. $CB^2 = L^2 + W^2$
    $CB^2 = 90.00^2 + 70.00^2$
    $CB^2 = 8100 + 4900$
    $CB^2 = 13000$
    $CB = 114.01754$ mm
    $AB^2 = AC^2 + CB^2$
    $AB^2 = 75.00^2 + 114.01754^2$
    $AB^2 = 5625 + 13000$
    $AB^2 = 18625$
    $AB = 136.47$ mm

    b. $\tan \angle CAB = \dfrac{CB}{AC} = \dfrac{114.01754}{75.00} = 1.5202$
    $\angle CAB = 56°39.8' = 56.66°$

5. a. $CB^2 = L^2 + W^2$
    $CB^2 = 1.400^2 + 1.000^2$
    $CB^2 = 1.960 + 1.000$
    $CB^2 = 2.960$
    $CB = 1.720465$ in
    $AB^2 = AC^2 + CB^2$
    $AB^2 = 0.800^2 + 1.720465^2$
    $AB^2 = 0.640 + 2.960$
    $AB^2 = 3.600$
    $AB = 1.897$ in

    b. $\tan \angle CAB = \dfrac{CB}{AC} = \dfrac{1.720465}{0.800} = 2.1506$
    $\angle CAB = 65°4'$

6. a. $CB^2 = L^2 + W^2$
    $CB^2 = 32.40^2 + 25.20^2$
    $CB^2 = 1049.76 + 635.04$
    $CB^2 = 1684.80$
    $CB = 41.046315$ mm
    $AB^2 = AC^2 + CB^2$
    $AB^2 = 18.00^2 + 41.046315^2$
    $AB^2 = 324.00 + 1684.80$
    $AB^2 = 2008.80$
    $AB = 44.82$ mm

    b. $\tan \angle CAB = \dfrac{CB}{AC} = \dfrac{41.046315}{18.00} = 2.2804$
    $\angle CAB = 66°19.3' = 66.32°$

UNIT 67   Drilling and Boring Compound-Angular Holes: Computing Angles of Rotation and Tilt Using Given Lengths

1. a. $\tan \angle R = \dfrac{1.900}{2.400} = 0.79167$

    $\angle R = 38°22'$

    b. $\sin \angle R = \dfrac{1.900}{CB}$

    $\sin 38°22' = \dfrac{1.900}{CB}$

    $0.62069 = \dfrac{1900}{CB}$

    $CB = 3.06111$ in

    $\tan \angle T = \dfrac{CB}{2.600} = \dfrac{3.06111}{2.600} = 1.1774$

    $\angle T = 49°39'$

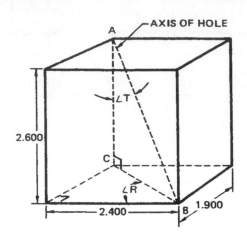

2. a. $\tan \angle R = \dfrac{30.00}{48.00} = 0.62500$

    $\angle R = 32°0.3' = 32.01°$

    b. $\sin \angle R = \dfrac{30.00}{CB}$

    $\sin 32°0.3' = \dfrac{30.00}{CB}$

    $0.52999 = \dfrac{30.00}{CB}$

    $CB = 56.60484$ mm

    $\tan \angle T = \dfrac{56.60484}{55.00} = 1.0292$

    $\angle T = 45°49.5' = 45.83°$

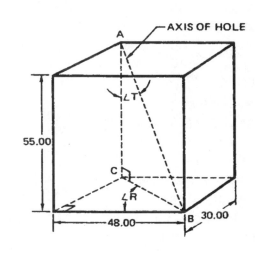

3. a. $\tan \angle R = \dfrac{3.750}{4.000} = 0.9375$

    $\angle R = 43°9'$

    b. $\sin \angle R = \dfrac{3.750}{CB}$

    $\sin 43°9' = \dfrac{3.750}{CB}$

    $0.68391 = \dfrac{3.750}{CB}$

    $CB = 5.48318$

    $\tan \angle T = \dfrac{CB}{4.750} = \dfrac{5.48318}{4.750} = 1.1544$

    $\angle T = 49°6'$

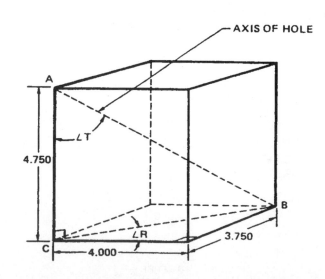

UNIT **67**   *(continued)*

4. a. $\tan \angle R = \dfrac{32.00}{37.00} = 0.86486$

$\angle R = 40°51.3' = \cancel{40.286°}$ 40.86° ✓

b. $\sin \angle R = \dfrac{32.00}{CB}$

$\sin 40°51.3' = \dfrac{32.00}{CB}$

$0.65415 = \dfrac{32.00}{CB}$

$CB = 48.91844 \text{ mm}$

$\tan \angle T = \dfrac{CB}{42.00} = \dfrac{48.91844}{42.00} = 1.1647$

$\angle T = 49°21' = 49.35°$

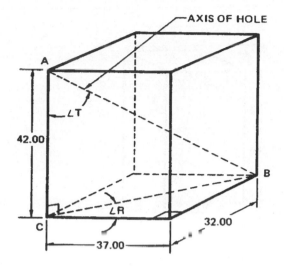

5. a. $\tan \angle R = \dfrac{0.750}{0.860} = 0.87209$

$\angle R = 41°5'$

b. $\sin \angle R = \dfrac{0.750}{CB}$

$\sin 41°5' = \dfrac{0.750}{CB}$

$0.65716 = \dfrac{0.750}{CB}$

$CB = 1.14127 \text{ in}$

$\tan \angle T = \dfrac{CB}{0.970} = \dfrac{1.14127}{0.970} = 1.1766$

$\angle T = 49°38'$

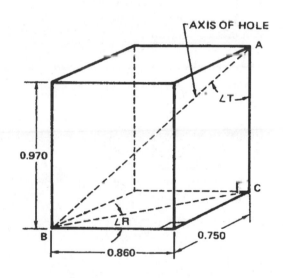

6. a. $\tan \angle R = \dfrac{15.00}{18.00} = 0.83333$

$\angle R = 39°48.3' = 39.805° = 39.81°$

b. $\sin \angle R = \dfrac{15.00}{CB}$

$\sin 39°48.3' = \dfrac{15.00}{CB}$

$0.64018 = \dfrac{15.00}{CB}$

$CB = 23.43091 \text{ mm}$

$\tan \angle T = \dfrac{CB}{22.00} = \dfrac{23.43091}{22.00} = 1.0650$

$\angle T = 46°48.2' = \cancel{48.80°}$

46.80°

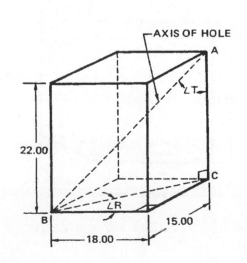

UNIT **67**   (*continued*)

7. a.

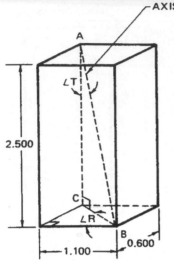

b. $\tan \angle R = \dfrac{0.600}{1.100} = 0.54545$

$\angle R = 28°37'$

c. $\sin \angle R = \dfrac{0.600}{CB}$

$\sin 28°37' = \dfrac{0.600}{CB}$

$0.47895 = \dfrac{0.600}{CB}$

$CB = 1.25274 \text{ in}$

$\tan \angle T = \dfrac{CB}{2.500} = \dfrac{1.25274}{2.500} = 0.50110$

$\angle T = 26°37'$

8. a.

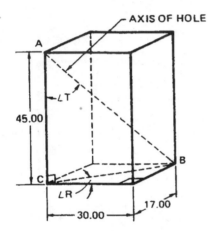

b. $\tan \angle R = \dfrac{17.00}{30.00} = 0.56667$

$\angle R = 29°32.3' = 29.54°$

c. $\sin \angle R = \dfrac{17.00}{CB}$

$\sin 29°32.3' = \dfrac{17.00}{CB}$

$0.49301 = \dfrac{17.00}{CB}$

$CB = 34.48206 \text{ mm}$

$\tan \angle T = \dfrac{CB}{45.00} = \dfrac{34.48206}{45} = 0.76639$

$\angle T = 37°28' = 37.47°$

9. a.

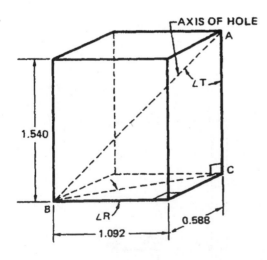

b. $\tan \angle R = \dfrac{0.588}{1.092} = 0.53846$

$\angle R = 28°18'$

c. $\sin \angle R = \dfrac{0.588}{CB}$

$\sin 28°18' = \dfrac{0.588}{CB}$

$0.47409 = \dfrac{0.588}{CB}$

$CB = 1.24027 \text{ in}$

$\tan \angle T = \dfrac{CB}{1.540} = \dfrac{1.24027}{1.540} = 0.80537$

$\angle T = 38°51'$

UNIT **67**   *(continued)*

10. a.

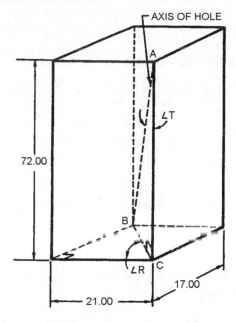

b. $\tan \angle R = \dfrac{17.00}{21.00} = 0.80952$

$\angle R = 38°59.5' = 38.99°$

c. $\sin \angle R = \dfrac{17.00}{CB}$

$\sin 38°59.5' = \dfrac{17.00}{CB}$

$0.62920 = \dfrac{17.00}{CB}$

$CB = 27.01844$

$\tan \angle T = \dfrac{CB}{72.00} = \dfrac{27.01844}{72.00} = 0.37526$

$\angle T = 20°34.2' = 20.57°$

UNIT **68**   Drilling and Boring Compound-Angular Holes: Computing Angles of Rotation and Tilt Using Given Angles

1. Make BC = 1

a. In right △BCD, BC = 1, ∠BDC = 35°.
Compute DC:

$\cot 35° = \dfrac{DC}{BC}$

$1.4282 = \dfrac{DC}{1}$

$DC = 1.4282$

In right △AEC, AE = DC = 1.4282, ∠CAE = 42°.
Compute CE:

$\tan 42° = \dfrac{CE}{AE}$

$0.90040 = \dfrac{CE}{1.4282}$

$CE = 1.2860$

In right △BCE, BC = 1, CE = 1.2860.
Compute ∠R:

$\cot \angle R = \dfrac{CE}{BC} = \dfrac{1.2860}{1} = 1.2860$

$\angle R = 37°52'$

1. b. In right △BCE, ∠R = 37°52', BC – 1.
Compute BE:

$\csc 37°52' = \dfrac{BE}{BC}$

$1.6291 = \dfrac{BE}{1}$

$BE = 1.6291$

In right △AEB, AE = 1.4281, BE = 1.6291.
Compute ∠T:

$\tan \angle T = \dfrac{BE}{AE} = \dfrac{1.6291}{1.4281} = 1.1407$

$\angle T = 48°46'$

2. Make BC = 1

a. In right △BCD, BC = 1, ∠BDC = 27°.
Compute DC:

$\cot 27° = \dfrac{DC}{BC}$

$1.9626 = \dfrac{DC}{1}$

$DC = 1.9626$

UNIT **68** (*continued*)

2. a. In right △AEC, AE = DC = 1.9626, ∠CAE = 33°50′.
   Compute CE:

   $$\tan 33°50' = \frac{CE}{AE}$$

   $$0.67028 = \frac{CE}{1.9626}$$

   $$CE = 1.3155$$

   In right △BCE, BC = 1, CE = 1.3155.
   Compute ∠R:

   $$\cot \angle R = \frac{CE}{BC}$$

   $$\cot \angle R = \frac{1.3155}{1}$$

   $$\angle R = 37°14'$$

   b. In right △BCE, ∠R = 37°14′, BC = 1.
   Compute BE:

   $$\csc 37°14' = \frac{BE}{BC}$$

   $$1.6527 = \frac{BE}{1}$$

   $$BE = 1.6527$$

   In right △AEB, AE = 1.9626, BE = 1.6527.
   Compute ∠T:

   $$\tan \angle T = \frac{BE}{AE} = \frac{1.6527}{1.9626} = 0.84210$$

   $$\angle T = 40°6'$$

3. Make EC = 1

   a. In right △AEC, EC = 1, ∠EAC = 18.25° = 18°15′.
   Compute AE:

   $$\cot 18°15' = \frac{AE}{EC}$$

   $$3.0326 = \frac{AE}{1}$$

   $$AE = 3.0326$$

   In right △DCB, DC = AE = 3.0326, ∠CDB = 31°.
   Compute CB:

   $$\tan 31° = \frac{CB}{DC}$$

   $$0.60086 = \frac{CB}{3.0326}$$

   $$CB = 1.8222$$

3. a. In right △ECB, EC = 1, CB = 1.8222.
   Compute ∠R:

   $$\cot \angle R = \frac{CB}{EC}$$

   $$\cot \angle R = \frac{1.8222}{1}$$

   $$\angle R = 28°45.4' = 28.76°$$

   b. In right △ECB, ∠R = 28°45.4′, EC = 1.
   Compute EB:

   $$\csc 28°45.4' = \frac{EB}{EC}$$

   $$2.0786 = \frac{EB}{1}$$

   $$EB = 2.0786$$

   In right △AEB, EB = 2.0786, AE = 3.0326.
   Compute ∠T:

   $$\tan \angle T = \frac{EB}{AE} = \frac{2.0786}{3.0326} = 0.68542$$

   $$\angle T = 34°25.7' = 34.43°$$

4. Make EC = 1

   a. In right △AEC, EC = 1, ∠EAC = 21°50′.
   Compute AE:

   $$\cot 21°50' = \frac{AE}{EC}$$

   $$2.4960 = \frac{AE}{1}$$

   $$AE = 2.4960$$

   In right △DCB, DC = AE = 2.4960, ∠CDB = 33°.
   Compute CB:

   $$\tan 33° = \frac{CB}{DC}$$

   $$0.64941 = \frac{CB}{2.4960}$$

   $$CB = 1.6209$$

   In right △ECB, EC = 1, CB = 1.6209.
   Compute ∠R:

   $$\cot \angle R = \frac{CB}{EC}$$

   $$\cot \angle R = \frac{1.6209}{1}$$

   $$\angle R = 31°40'$$

UNIT **68** (*continued*)

4. b. In right △ECB, ∠R = 31°40′, EC = 1.
   Compute EB:

   $$\csc 31°40' = \frac{EB}{EC}$$

   $$1.9048 = \frac{EB}{1}$$

   $$EB = 1.9048$$

   In right △AEB, EB = 1.9048, AE = 2.4960.
   Compute ∠T:

   $$\tan \angle T = \frac{EB}{AE} = \frac{1.9048}{2.4960} = 0.76314$$

   $$\angle T = 37°21'$$

5. Make DE = 1, BC = DE = 1

   a. In right △AED, DE = 1, ∠DAE = 30°.
   Compute AE:

   $$\cot 30° = \frac{AE}{DE}$$

   $$1.7321 = \frac{AE}{1}$$

   $$E = 1.7321$$

   In right △AEC, AE = 1.7321, ∠CAE = 42°10′.
   Compute EC:

   $$\tan 42°10' = \frac{EC}{AE}$$

   $$0.90560 = \frac{EC}{1.7321}$$

   $$EC = 1.5687$$

   In right △ECB, BC = 1, EC = 1.5687.
   Compute ∠R:

   $$\cot \angle R = \frac{EC}{BC} = \frac{1.5687}{1} = 1.5687$$

   $$\angle R = 32°31'$$

   b. In right △ECB, ∠R = 32°31′, BC = 1.
   Compute EB:

   $$\csc 32°31' = \frac{EB}{BC}$$

   $$1.8603 = \frac{EB}{1}$$

   $$EB = 1.8603$$

5. b. In right △AEB, EB = 1.8603, AE = 1.7321.
   Compute ∠T:

   $$\tan \angle T = \frac{EB}{AE} = \frac{1.8603}{1.7321} = 1.0741$$

   $$\angle T = 47°3'$$

6. Make DE = 1, BC = DE = 1

   a. In right △AED, DE = 1, ∠DAE = 27.40° = 27°24′.
   Compute AE:

   $$\cot 27°24' = \frac{AE}{DE}$$

   $$1.9292 = \frac{AE}{1}$$

   $$AE = 1.9292$$

   In right △AEC, AE = 1.9292, ∠CAE = 41°.
   Compute EC:

   $$\tan 41° = \frac{EC}{AE}$$

   $$0.86929 = \frac{EC}{1.9292}$$

   $$EC = 1.6770$$

   In right △ECB, BC = 1, EC = 1.6770.
   Compute ∠R:

   $$\cot \angle R = \frac{EC}{BC} = \frac{1.6770}{1} = 1.6770$$

   $$\angle R = 30°48.5' = 30.81°$$

   b. In right △ECB, ∠R = 30°48.5′, BC = 1.
   Compute EB:

   $$\csc 30°48.5' = \frac{EB}{BC}$$

   $$1.9525 = \frac{EB}{1}$$

   $$EB = 1.9525$$

   In right △AEB, EB = 1.9525, AE = 1.9292.
   Compute ∠T:

   $$\tan \angle T = \frac{EB}{AE} = \frac{1.9525}{1.9292} = 1.0121$$

   $$\angle T = 45°20.6' = 45.34°$$

UNIT **68**   (*continued*)

7. a.

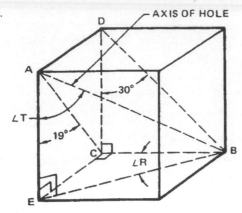

Make EC = 1

b. In right △AEC, EC = 1, ∠EAC = 19°.
Compute AE:

$$\cot 19° = \frac{AE}{EC}$$

$$2.9042 = \frac{AE}{1}$$

$$AE = 2.9042$$

In right △DCB, DC = AE = 2.9042, ∠CDB = 30°.
Compute CB:

$$\tan 30° = \frac{CB}{DC}$$

$$0.57735 = \frac{CB}{2.9042}$$

$$CB = 1.6767$$

In right △ECB, EC = 1, CB = 1.6767.
Compute ∠R:

$$\cot ∠R = \frac{CB}{EC} = \frac{1.6767}{1} = 1.6767$$

$$∠R = 30°49'$$

c. In right △ECB, ∠R = 30°49', EC = 1.
Compute EB:

$$\csc 30°49' = \frac{EB}{EC}$$

$$1.9520 = \frac{EB}{1}$$

$$EB = 1.9520$$

In right △AEB, EB = 1.9520, AE = 2.9042.
Compute ∠T:

$$\tan ∠T = \frac{EB}{AE} = \frac{1.9520}{2.9042} = 0.67213$$

$$∠T = 33°54'$$

8. a.

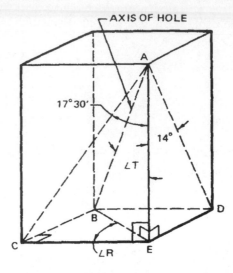

Make ED = 1, CB = ED = 1

b. In right △AED, ED = 1, ∠DAE = 14°.
Compute AE:

$$\tan 14° = \frac{ED}{AE}$$

$$0.24933 = \frac{1}{AE}$$

$$AE = \frac{1}{0.24933}$$

AE = 4.01075

In right △AEC, AE = 4.01075, ∠CAE = 17°30'.
Compute CE:

$$\tan 17°30' = \frac{CE}{AE}$$

$$0.31530 = \frac{CE}{4.01075}$$

CE = 1.2646

In right △ECB, CB = ED = 1, CE = 1.2646.
Compute ∠R:

$$\cot ∠R = \frac{CE}{CB}$$

$$\cot ∠R = \frac{1.2646}{1}$$

$$∠R = 38°20'$$

c. In right △ECB, ∠R = 38°20', CB = 1.
Compute BE:

$$\csc 38°20' = \frac{BE}{CB}$$

$$1.6123 = \frac{BE}{1}$$

$$BE = 1.6123$$

UNIT **68**   *(continued)*

8. c. In right △AEB, BE = 1.6123, AE = 4.01075.

Compute ∠T:

$$\tan \angle T = \frac{BE}{AE} = \frac{1.6123}{4.01075} = 0.40199$$

$$\angle T = 21°54'$$

9. a.

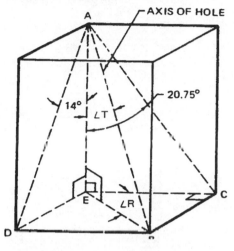

Make DE = 1, BC = DE = 1

b. In right △AED, DE = 1, ∠DAE = 16°.

Compute AE:

$$\cot 14° = \frac{AE}{DE}$$

$$4.0108 = \frac{AE}{1}$$

$$AE = 4.0108$$

In right △AEC, AE = 4.0108, ∠CAE = 20.75° = 20°45'.

Compute EC:

$$\tan 20°45' = \frac{EC}{AE}$$

$$0.37887 = \frac{EC}{4.0108}$$

$$EC = 1.5196$$

In right △ECB, BC = 1, EC = 1.5196.

Compute ∠R:

$$\cot \angle R = \frac{EC}{BC} = \frac{1.5196}{1} = 1.5196$$

$$\angle R = 32°21' = 33.35°$$

c. In right △ECB, ∠R = 33°21', BC = 1.

Compute EB:

$$\csc 33°21' = \frac{EB}{BC}$$

$$1.8190 = \frac{EB}{1}$$

$$EB = 1.8190$$

9. c. In right △AEB, EB = 1.8190, AE = 4.0108.

Compute ∠T:

$$\tan \angle T = \frac{EB}{AE} = \frac{1.8190}{4.0108} = 0.45353$$

$$\angle T = 24°23.7' = 24.40°$$

10. a.

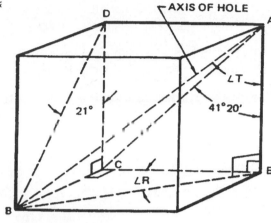

Make BC = 1

b. In right △BCD, BC = 1, ∠BDC = 21°.

Compute DC:

$$\cot 21° = \frac{DC}{BC}$$

$$2.6051 = \frac{DC}{1}$$

$$DC = 2.6051$$

In right △AEC, AE = DC = 2.6051, ∠CAE = 41°20'.

Compute CE:

$$\tan 41°20' = \frac{CE}{AE}$$

$$0.87955 = \frac{CE}{2.6051}$$

$$CE = 2.2913$$

In right △BCE, BC = 1, CE = 2.2913.

Compute ∠R:

$$\cot \angle R = \frac{CE}{BC} = \frac{2.2913}{1} = 2.2913$$

$$\angle R = 23°35'$$

c. In right △BCE, ∠R = 23°35', BC = 1.

Compute BE:

$$\csc 23°35' = \frac{BE}{BC}$$

$$2.4995 = \frac{BE}{1}$$

$$BE = 2.4995$$

UNIT **68** (*continued*)

10. c. In right $\triangle AEB$, $AE = DC = 2.6051$, $BE = 2.4995$.
Compute $\angle T$:

$$\tan \angle T = \frac{BE}{AE} = \frac{2.4995}{2.6051} = 0.95946$$

$$\angle T = 43°49'$$

11. a. $\tan \angle R = \dfrac{\tan \angle B}{\tan \angle A} = \dfrac{\tan 18°}{\tan 41°} = \dfrac{0.32492}{0.86929} = 0.37378$

$$\angle R = 20°30'$$

b. $\tan \angle T = \sqrt{\tan^2 \angle A + \tan^2 \angle B}$

$\tan \angle T = \sqrt{\tan^2 41° + \tan^2 18°}$

$\tan \angle T = \sqrt{(0.86929)^2 + (0.32492)^2}$

$\tan \angle T = \sqrt{0.7556651 + 0.105573}$

$\tan \angle T = \sqrt{0.8612381}$

$\tan \angle T = 0.92803$

$$\angle T = 42°52'$$

12. a. $\tan \angle R = \dfrac{\tan \angle B}{\tan \angle A}$

$\tan 33°10' = \dfrac{\tan 23°}{\tan \angle A}$

$0.65355 = \dfrac{0.42447}{\tan \angle A}$

$\tan \angle A = \dfrac{0.42447}{0.65355}$

$\tan \angle A = 0.64948$

$$\angle A = 33°0'$$

b. $\tan \angle T = \sqrt{\tan^2 \angle A + \tan^2 \angle B}$

$\tan \angle T = \sqrt{\tan^2 33°0' + \tan^2 23°}$

$\tan \angle T = \sqrt{0.64948^2 + 0.42447^2}$

$\tan \angle T = \sqrt{0.4218243 + 0.1801748}$

$\tan \angle T = \sqrt{0.6019991}$

$\tan \angle T = 0.77589$

$$\angle T = 37°48'$$

13. a. $\tan \angle T = \sqrt{\tan^2 \angle A + \tan^2 \angle B}$

$\tan 41.30° = \sqrt{\tan^2 38° + \tan^2 \angle B}$

$0.87852 = \sqrt{0.78129^2 + \tan^2 \angle B}$

$0.87852^2 = 0.78129^2 + \tan^2 \angle B$

$0.7717973 = 0.610414 + \tan^2 \angle B$

$\tan^2 \angle B = 0.1613833$

$\tan \angle B = 0.40173$

$\angle B = 21°53.2'$

$$\angle B = 21.89°$$

13. b. $\tan \angle R = \dfrac{\tan \angle B}{\tan \angle A} = \dfrac{0.40174}{0.78128} = 0.51421$

$$\angle R = 27°12.8' = 27.21°$$

14. a. $\tan \angle R = \dfrac{\tan \angle B}{\tan \angle A} = \dfrac{\tan 19°10'}{\tan 25°} = \dfrac{0.34758}{0.46631} = 0.74539$

$$\angle R = 36°42'$$

b. $\tan \angle T = \sqrt{\tan^2 \angle A + \tan^2 \angle B}$

$\tan \angle T = \sqrt{0.46631^2 + 0.34758^2}$

$\tan \angle T = \sqrt{0.217445 + 0.1208118}$

$\tan \angle T = \sqrt{0.3382568}$

$\tan \angle T = 0.58160$

$$\angle T = 30°11'$$

15. a. $\tan \angle R = \dfrac{\tan \angle B}{\tan \angle A}$

$\tan 32°10' = \dfrac{\tan 19°}{\tan \angle A}$

$0.62730 = \dfrac{0.34433}{\tan \angle A}$

$\tan \angle A = 0.54890$

$$\angle A = 28°45.8' = 28.76'$$

b. $\tan \angle T = \sqrt{\tan^2 \angle A + \tan^2 \angle B}$

$\tan \angle T = \sqrt{\tan^2 28°45.8' + \tan^2 19°}$

$\tan \angle T = \sqrt{0.54890^2 + 0.34433^2}$

$\tan \angle T = \sqrt{0.3012912 + 0.1185631}$

$\tan \angle T = \sqrt{0.4198543}$

$\tan \angle T = 0.64796$

$$\angle T = 32°56.5' = 32.94°$$

16. a. $\tan \angle T = \sqrt{\tan^2 \angle A + \tan^2 \angle B}$

$\tan 29°30' = \sqrt{\tan^2 23°20' + \tan^2 \angle B}$

$0.56577 = \sqrt{0.43136^2 + \tan^2 \angle B}$

$0.56577^2 = 0.43136^2 + \tan^2 \angle B$

$0.3200956 = 0.1860714 + \tan^2 \angle B$

$\tan^2 \angle B = 0.1340242$

$\tan \angle B = 0.36609$

$$\angle B = 20°6'$$

b. $\tan \angle R = \dfrac{\tan \angle B}{\tan \angle A} = \dfrac{0.36609}{0.43136} = 0.84869$

$$\angle R = 40°19'$$

1. Make DC = 1

    a. In right $\triangle$BDC, DC = 1, $\angle$B = 44°.
        Compute DB:

        $$\cot 44° = \frac{DB}{DC}$$

        $$1.0355 = \frac{DB}{1}$$

        $$DB = 1.0355$$

        In right $\triangle$ADC, DC = 1, $\angle$A = 32°.
        Compute AD:

        $$\cot 32° = \frac{AD}{DC}$$

        $$1.6003 = \frac{AD}{1}$$

        $$AD = 1.6003$$

        In right $\triangle$ADB, DB = 1.0355, AD = 1.6003.
        Compute $\angle$A:

        $$\tan \angle A = \frac{DB}{AD} = \frac{1.0355}{1.6003} = 0.64707$$

        $$\angle A = 32°54'$$

        In right $\triangle$AED, $\angle$R = 90° − 32°54' = 57°6'

    b. In right $\triangle$AEB, $\angle$A = 32°54', AD = 1.6003.
        Compute DE:

        $$\sin 32°54' = \frac{DE}{AD}$$

        $$0.54317 = \frac{DE}{1.6003}$$

        $$DE = 0.86923$$

        In right $\triangle$CDE, DC = 1, DE = 0.86923.
        Compute $\angle$T:

        $$\cot \angle T = \frac{DE}{DC} = \frac{0.86923}{1} = 0.86923$$

        $$\angle T = 49°0'$$

2. Make DC = 1

    a. In right $\triangle$BDC, DC = 1, $\angle$B = 39°.
        Compute DB:

        $$\cot 39° = \frac{DB}{DC}$$

        $$1.2349 = \frac{DB}{1}$$

        $$DB = 1.2349$$

2. a. In right $\triangle$ADC, DC = 1, $\angle$A = 27°.
        Compute AD:

        $$\cot 27° = \frac{AD}{DC}$$

        $$1.9626 = \frac{AD}{1}$$

        $$AD = 1.9626$$

        In right $\triangle$ADB, DB = 1.2349, AD = 1.9626.
        Compute $\angle$A:

        $$\tan \angle A = \frac{DB}{AD} = \frac{1.2349}{1.9626} = 0.62922$$

        $$\angle A = 32°11'$$

        In right $\triangle$AED, $\angle$R = 90° − 32°11' = 57°49'

    b. In right $\triangle$AED, $\angle$A = 32°11', AD = 1.9626.
        Compute DE:

        $$\sin 32°11' = \frac{DE}{AD}$$

        $$0.53263 = \frac{DE}{1.9626}$$

        $$DE = 1.0453$$

        In right $\triangle$CDE, DC = 1, DE = 1.0453.
        Compute $\angle$T:

        $$\cot \angle T = \frac{DE}{DC} = \frac{1.0453}{1} = 1.0453$$

        $$\angle T = 43°44'$$

3. Make DC = 1

    a. In right $\triangle$BDC, DC = 1, $\angle$B = 27°50'.
        Compute DB:

        $$\cot 27°50' = \frac{DB}{DC}$$

        $$1.8940 = \frac{DB}{1}$$

        $$DB = 1.8940$$

        In right $\triangle$ADC, DC = 1, $\angle$A = 18°10'.
        Compute AD:

        $$\cot 18°10' = \frac{AD}{DC}$$

        $$3.0475 = \frac{AD}{1}$$

        $$AD = 3.0475$$

UNIT **69** (*continued*)

3. a. In right △ADB, DB = 1.8940, AD = 3.0475.

Compute ∠A:

$$\tan \angle A = \frac{DB}{AD} = \frac{1.8940}{3.0475} = 0.62149$$

$$\angle A = 31°52'$$

In right △AED, ∠R = 90° − 31°52' = 58°8'

b. In right △AED, ∠A = 31°52', AD = 3.0475.

Compute DE:

$$\sin 31°52' = \frac{DE}{AD}$$

$$0.52794 = \frac{DE}{3.0475}$$

$$DE = 1.6089$$

In right △CDE, DC = 1, DE = 1.6089.

Compute ∠T:

$$\cot \angle T = \frac{DE}{DC} = \frac{1.6089}{1} = 1.6089$$

$$\angle T = 31°52'$$

4. Make DC = 1

a. In right △BCD, DC = 1, ∠B = 37.10°
= 37°06'.

Compute DB:

$$\cot 37°06' = \frac{DB}{DC}$$

$$1.3222 = \frac{DB}{1}$$

$$DB = 1.3222$$

In right △ADC, DC = 1, ∠A = 23°20' =
23°12'.

Compute AD:

$$\cot 23°12' = \frac{AD}{DC}$$

$$2.3332 = \frac{AD}{1}$$

$$AD = 2.3332$$

In right △ADB, DB = 1.3222, AD = 2.3332.

Compute ∠A:

$$\tan \angle A = \frac{DB}{AD} = \frac{1.3222}{2.3332} = 0.56669$$

$$\angle A = 29°32.4'$$

In right △AED:

∠R = 90° − 29°32.4' = 60°27.6' = 60.46°

4. b. In right △AED, ∠A = 29°32.4', AD = 2.3332.

Compute DE:

$$\sin 29°32.4' = \frac{DE}{AD}$$

$$0.49303 = \frac{DE}{2.3332}$$

$$DE = 1.1503$$

In right △CDE, DC = 1, DE = 1.1503.

Compute ∠T:

$$\cot \angle T = \frac{DE}{DC} = \frac{1.1503}{1} = 1.1503$$

$$\angle T = 41°0' = 41.00°$$

5. a.

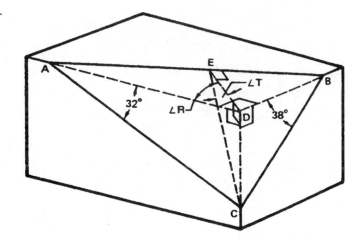

Make DC = 1

b. In right △DBC, DC = 1, ∠B = 38°.

Compute DB:

$$\cot 38° = \frac{DB}{DC}$$

$$1.2799 = \frac{DB}{1}$$

$$DB = 1.2799$$

In right △ADC, DC = 1, ∠A = 32°.

Compute AD:

$$\cot 32° = \frac{AD}{DC}$$

$$1.6003 = \frac{AD}{1}$$

$$AD = 1.6003$$

In right △ADB, DB = 1.2799, AD = 1.6003.

Compute ∠A:

$$\tan \angle A = \frac{DB}{AD} = \frac{1.2799}{1.6003} = 0.79979$$

$$\angle A = 38°39'$$

UNIT **69** (*continued*)

5. b. In right △AED:

    ∠R = 90° − 38°39′ = 51°21′

  c. In right △AED, ∠A = 38°39′, AD = 1.6003.
Compute DE:

$$\sin 38°39′ = \frac{DE}{AD}$$

$$0.62456 = \frac{DE}{1.6003}$$

DE = 0.99948

6. a.

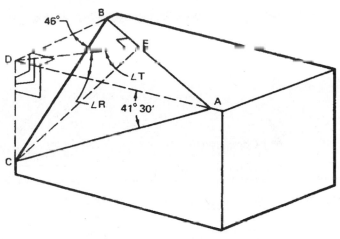

Make DC = 1

  b. In right △BDC, DC = 1, ∠B = 46°.
Compute DB:

$$\cot 46° = \frac{DB}{DC}$$

$$0.96569 = \frac{DB}{1}$$

DB = 0.96569

In right △ADC, DC = 1, ∠A = 41°30′.
Compute AD:

$$\cot 41°30′ = \frac{AD}{DC}$$

$$1.1303 = \frac{AD}{1}$$

AD = 1.1303

5. c. In right △CDE, CD = 1, DE = 0.99948.
Compute ∠T:

$$\cot ∠T = \frac{DE}{DC} = \frac{0.99948}{1} = 0.99948$$

∠T = 45°1′

6. b. In right △ADB, DB = 0.96569, AD = 1.1303.
Compute ∠A:

$$\tan ∠A = \frac{DB}{AD} = \frac{0.96569}{1.1303} = 0.85437$$

∠A = 40°31′

In right △AED:

∠R = 90° − 40°31′ = 49°29′

  c. In right △AED, ∠A = 40°31′, AD = 1.1303.
Compute DE:

$$\sin 40°31′ = \frac{DE}{AD}$$

$$0.64967 = \frac{DE}{1.1303}$$

DE = 0.73432

In right △CDE, DC = 1, DE = 0.73432.
Compute ∠T:

$$\cot ∠T = \frac{DE}{DC} = \frac{0.73432}{1} = 0.73432$$

∠T = 53°43′

UNIT **69** (*continued*)

7. a.

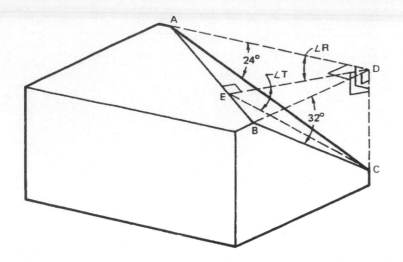

Make DC = 1

b. In right △DBC, DC = 1, ∠B = 32°.
Compute DB:

$$\cot 32° = \frac{DB}{DC}$$

$$1.6003 = \frac{DB}{1}$$

DB = 1.6003

In right △ADC, DC = 1, ∠A = 24°.
Compute AD:

$$\cot 24° = \frac{AD}{DC}$$

$$2.2460 = \frac{AD}{1}$$

AD = 2.2460

In right △ADB, DB = 1.6003, AD = 2.2460.
Compute ∠A:

$$\tan ∠A = \frac{DB}{AD} = \frac{1.6003}{2.2460} = 0.71251$$

∠A = 35°28.2′

7. b. In right △AED, ∠R = 90° − 35°28.2′ = 54°31.8′ = 54.53°

c. In right △AED, ∠A = 35°28.2′, AD = 2.2460.
Compute DE:

$$\sin 35°28.2′ = \frac{DE}{AD}$$

$$0.58028 = \frac{DE}{2.2460}$$

DE = 1.3033

In right △CDE, CD = 1, DE = 1.3033.
Compute ∠T:

$$\cot ∠T = \frac{DE}{DC} = \frac{1.3033}{1} = 1.3033$$

$$∠T = 37°29.9′ = 37.50°$$

UNIT **69**   *(continued)*

8. a.

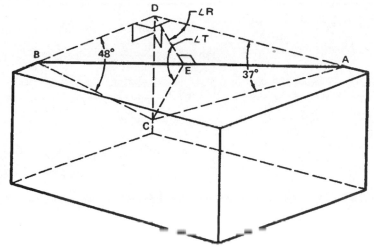

Make DC = 1

b. In right △DBC, DC = 1, ∠B = 48°.
Compute DB:

$$\cot 48° = \frac{DB}{DC}$$

$$0.90040 = \frac{DB}{1}$$

$$DB = 0.90040$$

In right △ADC, DC = 1, ∠A = 37°.
Compute AD:

$$\cot 37° = \frac{AD}{DC}$$

$$1.3270 = \frac{AD}{1}$$

$$AD = 1.3270$$

In right △ADB, DB = 0.90040, AD = 1.3270.
Compute ∠A:

$$\tan ∠A = \frac{DB}{AD} = \frac{0.90040}{1.3270} = 0.67852$$

$$∠A = 34°9'$$

8. b. In right △AED:

$$∠R = 90° - 34°9' = 55°51'$$

c. In right △AED, ∠A = 34°9', AD = 1.3270.
Compute DE:

$$\sin 34°9' = \frac{DE}{AD}$$

$$0.56136 = \frac{DE}{1.3270}$$

$$DE = 0.74492$$

In right △CDE, CD = 1, DE = 0.74492.
Compute ∠T:

$$\cot ∠T = \frac{DE}{DC} = \frac{0.74492}{1} = 0.74492$$

$$∠T = 53°19'$$

9. a. $\tan ∠R = \dfrac{\tan ∠B}{\tan ∠A} = \dfrac{\tan 44°}{\tan 39°} = \dfrac{0.96569}{0.80978} = 1.1925$

$∠R = 50°01'$

b. $\tan ∠T = \dfrac{\tan ∠A}{\cos ∠R} = \dfrac{\tan 39°}{\cos 50°01'} = \dfrac{0.80978}{0.64255} = 1.2603$

$∠T = 51°34'$

10. a. $\tan ∠R = \dfrac{\tan ∠B}{\tan ∠A}$

$\tan 46° = \dfrac{\tan 43°20'}{\tan ∠A}$

$1.0355 = \dfrac{0.94345}{\tan ∠A}$

$\tan ∠A = 0.91111$

$∠A = 42°20'$

UNIT **69** (*continued*)

10. b. $\tan \angle T = \dfrac{\tan \angle A}{\cos \angle R} = \dfrac{\tan 42°20'}{\cos 46°} = \dfrac{0.91111}{0.69466} = 1.3116$

 $\angle T = 52°41'$

11. a. $\tan \angle T = \dfrac{\tan \angle A}{\cos \angle R}$

 $\tan 52° = \dfrac{\tan 41.20°}{\cos \angle R}$

 $1.2799 = \dfrac{0.87543}{\cos \angle R}$

 $\cos \angle R = 0.68399$

 $\angle R = 46°51' = 46.84°$

 b. $\tan \angle R = \dfrac{\tan \angle B}{\tan \angle A}$

 $\tan 46°51' = \dfrac{\tan \angle B}{\tan 41.20°}$

 $1.0664 = \dfrac{\tan \angle B}{0.87543}$

 $\tan \angle B = 0.93356$

 $\angle B = 43°19' = 43.03°$

12. a. $\tan \angle R = \dfrac{\tan \angle B}{\tan \angle A} = \dfrac{\tan 23°10'}{\tan 19°} = \dfrac{0.42791}{0.34433} = 1.2427$

 $\angle R = 51°11'$

 b. $\tan \angle T = \dfrac{\tan \angle A}{\cos \angle R} = \dfrac{\tan 19°}{\cos 51°11'} = \dfrac{0.34433}{0.62683} = 0.54932$

 $\angle T = 28°47'$

13. a. $\tan \angle R = \dfrac{\tan \angle B}{\tan \angle A}$

 $\tan 22° = \dfrac{\tan 18°}{\tan \angle A}$

 $0.40403 = \dfrac{0.32492}{\tan \angle A}$

 $\tan \angle A = 0.80420$

 $\angle A = 38°48'$

 b. $\tan \angle T = \dfrac{\tan \angle A}{\cos \angle R} = \dfrac{\tan 38°48'}{\cos 22°} = \dfrac{0.80420}{0.92718}$

 $= 0.86736$

 $\angle T = 40°56'$

14. a. $\tan \angle T = \dfrac{\tan \angle A}{\cos \angle R}$

 $\tan 26.50° = \dfrac{\tan 15.60°}{\cos \angle R}$

 $0.49858 = \dfrac{0.27920}{\cos \angle R}$

 $\cos \angle R = 0.55999$

 $\angle R = 55°56.7' = 55.95°$

 b. $\tan \angle R = \dfrac{\tan \angle B}{\tan \angle A}$

 $\tan 55°56.7' = \dfrac{\tan \angle B}{\tan 15.60°}$

 $1.4795 = \dfrac{\tan \angle B}{0.27920}$

 $\tan \angle B = 0.41308$

 $\angle B = 22°26.7' = 22.45°$

UNIT **70** Computing Angles Made by the Intersection of Two Angular Surfaces

1. Make DE = 1

 a. In right △BDE, DE = 1, ∠B = 55°.
 Compute BD:

 $\cot 55° = \dfrac{BD}{DE}$

 $0.70021 = \dfrac{BD}{1}$

 $BD = 0.70021$

1. a. In right △ADE, DE = 1, ∠A = 42°.
 Compute DA:

 $\cot 42° = \dfrac{DA}{DE}$

 $1.1106 = \dfrac{DA}{1}$

 $DA = 1.1106$

UNIT **70** (*continued*)

1. a. In right △CBD, BD = 0.70021, BC = DA = 1.1106.

   Compute ∠R:

   $$\tan \angle R = \frac{BD}{BC} = \frac{0.70021}{1.1106} = 0.63048$$

   $$\angle R = 32°14'$$

   b. In right △CBD, ∠R = 32°14', BD = 0.70021.

   Compute DC:

   $$\sin 32°14' = \frac{BD}{DC}$$

   $$0.53337 = \frac{0.70021}{DC}$$

   $$DC = 1.3128$$

   In right △CDE, DE = 1, DC = 1.3128.

   Compute ∠C:

   $$\cot \angle C = \frac{DC}{DE} = \frac{1.3128}{1} = 1.3128$$

   $$\angle C = 37°18'$$

2. Make DE = 1

   a. In right △BDE, DE = 1, ∠B = 48°.

   Compute BD:

   $$\cot 48° = \frac{BD}{DE}$$

   $$0.90040 = \frac{BD}{1}$$

   $$BD = 0.90040$$

   In right △ADE, DE = 1, ∠A = 40°.

   Compute DA:

   $$\cot 40° = \frac{DA}{DE}$$

   $$1.1918 = \frac{DA}{1}$$

   $$DA = 1.1918$$

   In right △CBD, BD = 0.90040, BC = DA = 1.1918.

   Compute ∠R:

   $$\tan \angle R = \frac{BD}{BC} = \frac{0.90040}{1.1918} = 0.75550$$

   $$\angle R = 37°04'$$

   b. In right △CBD, ∠R = 37°4', BD = 0.90040.

   Compute DC:

   $$\sin 37°4' = \frac{BD}{DC}$$

   $$0.60274 = \frac{0.90040}{DC}$$

   $$DC = 1.4938$$

2. b. In right △CDE, DE = 1, DC = 1.4938.

   Compute ∠C:

   $$\cot \angle C = \frac{DC}{DE} = \frac{1.4938}{1} = 1.4938$$

   $$\angle C = 33°48'$$

3. Make DE = 1

   a. In right △BDE, DE = 1, ∠B = 61°40'.

   Compute BD:

   $$\cot 61°40' = \frac{BD}{DE}$$

   $$0.53920 = \frac{BD}{1}$$

   $$BD = 0.53920$$

   In right △ADE, DE = 1, ∠A = 50°10'.

   Compute DA:

   $$\cot 50°10' = \frac{DA}{DE}$$

   $$0.83415 = \frac{DA}{1}$$

   $$DA = 0.83415$$

   In right △CBD, BD = 0.53920, BC = DA = 0.83415.

   Compute ∠R:

   $$\tan \angle R = \frac{BD}{BC} = \frac{0.53920}{0.83415} = 0.64641$$

   $$\angle R = 32°53'$$

   b. In right △CBD, ∠R = 32°53', BD = 0.53920.

   Compute DC:

   $$\sin 32°53' = \frac{BD}{DC}$$

   $$0.54293 = \frac{0.53920}{DC}$$

   $$DC = 0.99313$$

   In right △CDE, DE = 1, DC = 0.99313.

   Compute ∠C:

   $$\cot \angle C = \frac{DC}{DE} = \frac{0.99313}{1} = 1.99313$$

   $$\angle C = 45°12'$$

4. Make DE = 1

   a. In right △BDE, DE = 1, ∠B = 52.70° = 52°42'.

   Compute BD:

   $$\cot 52°42' = \frac{BD}{DE}$$

   $$0.76179 = \frac{BD}{1}$$

   $$BD = 0.76179$$

UNIT **70** *(continued)*

4. a. In right △ADE, DE = 1, ∠A = 43.35° = 43°21′.
        Compute DA:

$$\cot 43°21′ = \frac{DA}{DE}$$

$$1.0593 = \frac{DA}{1}$$

$$DA = 1.0593$$

In right △CBD, BD = 0.76179, BC = DA = 1.0593.
Compute ∠R:

$$\tan ∠R = \frac{BD}{BC} = \frac{0.76179}{1.0593} = 0.71914$$

$$∠R = 35°43.3′ = 35.72°$$

4. b. In right △CBD, ∠R = 35°43.3′, BD = 0.76179.
        Compute DC:

$$\sin 35°43.3′ = \frac{BD}{DC}$$

$$0.58385 = \frac{0.76179}{DC}$$

$$DC = 1.3048$$

In right △CDE, DE = 1, DC = 1.3048.
Compute ∠C:

$$\cot ∠C = \frac{DC}{DE} = \frac{1.3048}{1} = 1.3048$$

$$∠C = 37°28′ = 37.47°$$

5. a.

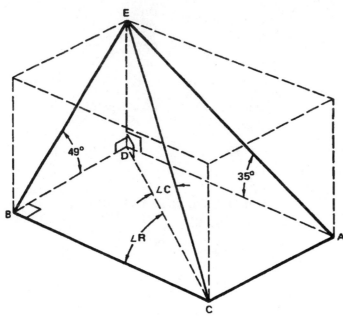

Make DE = 1

b. In right △BDE, DE = 1, ∠B = 49°.
    Compute BD:

$$\cot 49° = \frac{BD}{DE}$$

$$0.86929 = \frac{BD}{1}$$

$$BD = 0.86929$$

5. b. In right △ADE, DE = 1, ∠A = 35°.
        Compute DA:

$$\cot 35° = \frac{DA}{DE}$$

$$1.4282 = \frac{DA}{1}$$

$$DA = 1.4282$$

In right △CBD, BD = 0.86929, BC = DA = 1.4282.
Compute ∠R:

$$\tan ∠R = \frac{BD}{BC} = \frac{0.86929}{1.4282} = 0.60866$$

$$∠R = 31°20′$$

c. In right △CBD, ∠R = 31°20′, BD = 0.86929.
    Compute DC:

$$\sin 31°20′ = \frac{BD}{DC}$$

$$0.52002 = \frac{0.86929}{DC}$$

$$DC = 1.6716$$

In right △CDE, DE = 1, DC = 1.6716.
Compute ∠C:

$$\cot ∠C = \frac{DC}{DE} = \frac{1.6716}{1} = 1.6716$$

$$∠C = 30°53′$$

UNIT **70** (*continued*)

6. a.

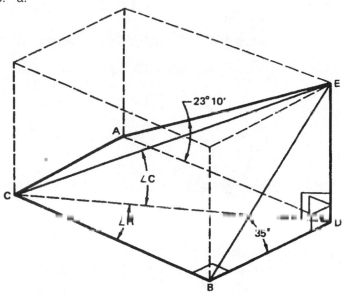

Make DE = 1

b. In right △BDE, DE = 1, ∠B = 35°.
Compute BD:

$$\cot 35° = \frac{BD}{DE}$$

$$1.4282 = \frac{BD}{1}$$

$$BD = 1.4282$$

6. b. In right △ADE, DE = 1, ∠A = 23°10′.
Compute DA:

$$\cot 23°10′ = \frac{DA}{DE}$$

$$2.3369 = \frac{DA}{1}$$

$$DA = 2.3369$$

In right △CBD, BD = 1.4282, BC = DA = 2.3369.
Compute ∠R:

$$\tan ∠R = \frac{BD}{BC} = \frac{1.4282}{2.3369} = 0.61115$$

$$∠R = 31°26′$$

c. In right △CDD, ∠R = 31°20′, BD = 1.4281.
Compute DC:

$$\sin 31°26′ = \frac{BD}{DC}$$

$$0.52151 = \frac{1.4282}{DC}$$

$$DC = 2.7386$$

In right △CDE, DE = 1, DC = 2.7386.
Compute ∠C:

$$\cot ∠C = \frac{DC}{DE} = \frac{2.7386}{1} = 2.7386$$

$$∠C = 20°4′$$

7. a.

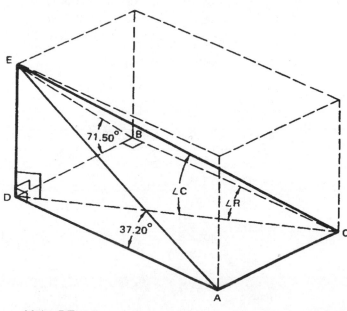

Make DE = 1

7. b. In right △BDE, DE = 1, ∠B = 71.50°.
Compute BD:

$$\cot 71.50° = \frac{BD}{DE}$$

$$0.33460 = \frac{BD}{1}$$

$$BD = 0.33460$$

In right △ADE, DE = 1, ∠A = 37.20° = 37°12′.
Compute DA:

$$\cot 37°12′ = \frac{DA}{DE}$$

$$1.3175 = \frac{DA}{1}$$

$$DA = 1.3175$$

In right △CBD, BD = 0.33460, BC = DA = 1.3175.
Compute ∠R:

$$\tan ∠R = \frac{BD}{BC} = \frac{0.33460}{1.3175} = 0.25397$$

$$∠R = 14°15′ = 14.25°$$

UNIT **70**   *(continued)*

7. c. In right $\triangle CBD$, $\angle R = 14°15'$, BD = 0.33460.
Compute DC:

$$\sin 14°15' = \frac{BD}{DC}$$

$$0.24615 = \frac{0.33460}{DC}$$

$$DC = 1.3593$$

7. c. In right $\triangle CDE$, DE = 1, DC = 1.3593.
Compute $\angle C$:

$$\cot \angle C = \frac{DC}{DE} = \frac{1.3593}{1} = 1.3593$$

$$\angle C = 36°20.4' = 36.34°$$

8. a.

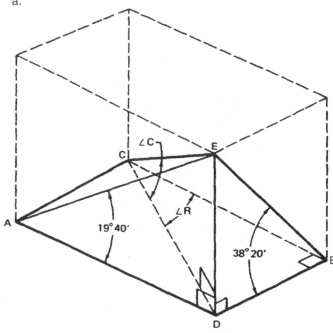

Make DE = 1

b. In right $\triangle BDE$, DE = 1, $\angle B = 38°20'$.
Compute BD:

$$\cot 38°20' = \frac{BD}{DE}$$

$$1.2647 = \frac{BD}{1}$$

$$BD = 1.2647$$

In right $\triangle ADE$, DE = 1, $\angle A = 19°40'$.
Compute DA:

$$\cot 19°40' = \frac{DA}{DE}$$

$$2.7980 = \frac{DA}{1}$$

$$DA = 2.7980$$

8. b. In right $\triangle CBD$, BD = 1.2647, BC = DA = 2.7980.
Compute $\angle R$:

$$\tan \angle R = \frac{BD}{BC} = \frac{1.2647}{2.7980} = 0.45200$$

$$\angle R = 24°19'$$

c. In right $\triangle CBD$, $\angle R = 24°19'$, BD = 1.2647.
Compute DC:

$$\sin 24°19' = \frac{BD}{DC}$$

$$0.41178 = \frac{1.2647}{DC}$$

$$DC = 3.0713$$

In right $\triangle CDE$, DE = 1, DC = 3.0713.
Compute $\angle C$:

$$\cot \angle C = \frac{DC}{DE} = \frac{3.0713}{1} = 3.0713$$

$$\angle C = 18°2'$$

9. a. $\tan \angle R = \dfrac{\cot \angle B}{\cot \angle A} = \dfrac{\cot 43°50'}{\cot 36°} = \dfrac{1.0416}{1.3764} = 0.75676$

$$\angle R = 37°7'$$

b. $\cot \angle C = \sqrt{\cot^2 \angle A + \cot^2 \angle B}$

$\cot \angle C = \sqrt{\cot^2 36° + \cot^2 43°50'}$

$\cot \angle C = \sqrt{1.3764^2 + 1.0416^2}$

$\cot \angle C = \sqrt{1.8944769 + 1.0849305}$

$\cot \angle C = \sqrt{2.9794074}$

$\cot \angle C = 1.7261$

$\cot \angle C = 30°5'$

10. a. $\tan \angle R = \dfrac{\cot \angle B}{\cot \angle A}$

$\tan 40° = \dfrac{\cot 48°10'}{\cot \angle A}$

$0.83910 = \dfrac{0.89515}{\cot \angle A}$

$\cot \angle A = 1.0668$

$\angle A = 43°9'$

UNIT **70** (*continued*)

10. b. $\cot \angle C = \sqrt{\cot^2 \angle A + \cot^2 \angle B}$

$\cot \angle C = \sqrt{\cot^2 43°9' + \cot^2 48°10'}$

$\cot \angle C = \sqrt{1.0668^2 + 0.89515^2}$

$\cot \angle C = \sqrt{1.1380622 + 0.8012935}$

$\cot \angle C = \sqrt{1.9393557}$

$\cot \angle C = 1.3926$

$\cot \angle C = 35°41'$

11. a. $\cot \angle C = \sqrt{\cot^2 \angle A + \cot^2 \angle B}$

$\cot 28° = \sqrt{\cot^2 31.60° + \cot^2 \angle B}$

$1.8807 = \sqrt{1.6255^2 + \cot^2 \angle B}$

$1.8807^2 = 1.6255^2 + \cot^2 \angle B$

$3.53703 = 2.64225 + \cot^2 \angle B$

$\cot^2 \angle B - 0.89478$

$\cot \angle B = 0.94593$

$\angle B = 46°35.4' = 46.59°$

b. $\tan \angle R = \dfrac{\cot \angle B}{\cot \angle A} = \dfrac{\cot 46°35.4'}{\cot 31.60°} = \dfrac{0.94598}{1.62548} = 0.58197$

$\angle R = 30°11.9' = 30.20°$

12. a. $\tan \angle R = \dfrac{\cot \angle B}{\cot \angle A} = \dfrac{\cot 25°}{\cot 17°40'} = \dfrac{2.1445}{3.1397} = 0.68303$

$\angle R = 34°20'$

b. $\cot \angle C = \sqrt{\cot^2 \angle A + \cot^2 \angle B}$

$\cot \angle C = \sqrt{3.1397^2 + 2.1445^2}$

$\cot \angle C = \sqrt{9.857716 + 4.5988802}$

$\cot \angle C = \sqrt{14.456596}$

$\cot \angle C = 3.8022$

$\cot \angle C = 14°44'$

13. a. $\tan \angle R = \dfrac{\cot \angle B}{\cot \angle A}$

$\tan 27°50' = \dfrac{\cot 31°}{\cot \angle A}$

$0.52798 = \dfrac{1.6643}{\cot \angle A}$

$\cot \angle A = 3.1522$

$\angle A = 17°36'$

b. $\cot \angle C = \sqrt{\cot^2 \angle A + \cot^2 \angle B}$

$\cot \angle C = \sqrt{\cot^2 17°36' + \cot^2 31°}$

$\cot \angle C = \sqrt{3.1522^2 + 1.6643^2}$

$\cot \angle C = \sqrt{9.936080 + 2.769860}$

$\cot \angle C = \sqrt{12.706259}$

$\cot \angle C = 3.5646$

$\cot \angle C = 15°40'$

14. a. $\cot \angle C = \sqrt{\cot^2 \angle A + \cot^2 \angle B}$

$\cot 14° = \sqrt{\cot^2 16.40° + \cot^2 \angle B}$

$4.0108 = \sqrt{3.3977^2 + \cot^2 \angle B}$

$4.0108^2 = 3.3977^2 + \cot^2 \angle B$

$16.086517 = 11.544365 + \cot^2 \angle B$

$\cot^2 \angle B = 4.542152$

$\cot \angle B = 2.1312$

$\angle B = 25°8.2' = 25.14°$

b. $\tan \angle R = \dfrac{\cot \angle B}{\cot \angle A} = \dfrac{2.1312}{3.3977} = 0.62725$

$\angle R = 32°5.88' = 32.10°$

UNIT **71** Computing Compound Angles on Cutting and Forming Tools

1. Make AB = 1

In right $\triangle ABD$, AB = 1, $\angle A = 30°$.

Compute BD:

$\tan 30° = \dfrac{BD}{AB}$

$0.57735 = \dfrac{BD}{1}$

$BD = 0.57735$

1. In right $\triangle CAB$, AB = 1, $\angle B = 15°$.

Compute CB:

$\cos 15° = \dfrac{AB}{CB}$

$0.96593 = \dfrac{1}{CB}$

$CB = 1.03527$

UNIT **71** (*continued*)

1. In right △CBD, BD = 0.57735, CB = 1.03527.
   Compute ∠C:

   $$\tan \angle C = \frac{BD}{CB} = \frac{0.57735}{1.03527} = 0.55768$$
   $$\angle C = 29°9'$$

2. Make AB = 1
   In right △ABD, AB = 1, ∠A = 26°.
   Compute BD:

   $$\tan 26° = \frac{BD}{AB}$$
   $$0.48773 = \frac{BD}{1}$$
   $$BD = 0.48773$$

   In right △CAB, AB = 1, ∠B = 12°.
   Compute CB:

   $$\cos 12° = \frac{AB}{CB}$$
   $$0.97815 = \frac{1}{CB}$$
   $$CB = 1.022338$$

   In right △CBD, BD = 0.48773, CB = 1.022338.
   Compute ∠C:

   $$\tan \angle C = \frac{BD}{CB} = \frac{0.48773}{1.022338} = 0.47707$$
   $$\angle C = 25°30'$$

3. Make AB = 1
   In right △ABD, AB = 1, ∠A = 27°.
   Compute BD:

   $$\tan 27° = \frac{BD}{AB}$$
   $$0.50953 = \frac{BD}{1}$$
   $$BD = 0.50953$$

   In right △CAB, AB = 1, ∠B = 11°.
   Compute CB:

   $$\cos 11° = \frac{AB}{CB}$$
   $$0.98163 = \frac{1}{CB}$$
   $$CB = 1.01871$$

   In right △CBD, BD = 0.50953, CB = 1.01871.
   Compute ∠C:

   $$\tan \angle C = \frac{BD}{CB} = \frac{0.50953}{1.01871} = 0.50017$$
   $$\angle C = 26°34'$$

4. Make AB = 1
   In right △ABD, AB = 1, ∠A = 30°.
   Compute BD:

   $$\tan 30° = \frac{BD}{AB}$$
   $$0.57735 = \frac{BD}{1}$$
   $$BD = 0.57735$$

   In right △CAB, AB = 1, ∠B = 24°.
   Compute CB:

   $$\cos 24° = \frac{AB}{CB}$$
   $$0.91355 = \frac{1}{CB}$$
   $$CB = 1.094631$$

   In right △CBD, BD = 0.57735, CB = 1.094631.
   Compute ∠C:

   $$\tan \angle C = \frac{BD}{CB} = \frac{0.57735}{1.094631} = 0.52744$$
   $$\angle C = 27°49'$$

5. a.

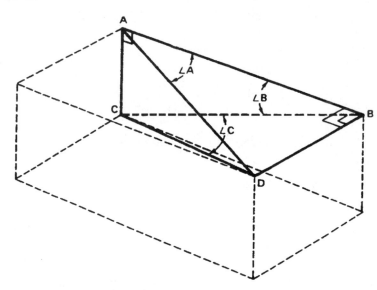

   b. Make AB = 1
      In right △ABD, AB = 1, ∠A = 24°.
      Compute DB:

      $$\tan 24° = \frac{BD}{AB}$$
      $$0.44523 = \frac{DB}{1}$$
      $$DB = 0.44523$$

UNIT **71**   *(continued)*

5. b. In right $\triangle CAB$, AB = 1, $\angle B = 15°$.
    Compute CB:

    $$\cos 15° = \frac{AB}{CB}$$

    $$0.96593 = \frac{1}{CB}$$

    $$CB = 1.035272$$

5. b. In right $\triangle CBD$, DB = 0.44523, CB = 1.035272.
    Compute $\angle C$:

    $$\tan \angle C = \frac{DB}{CB} = \frac{0.44523}{1.035272} = 0.43006$$

    $$\angle C = 23°16'$$

6. a.

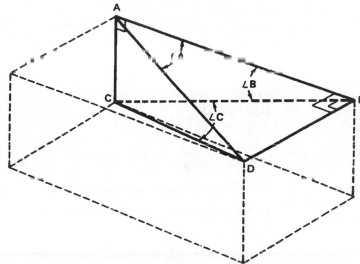

6. b. Make AB = 1

    In right $\triangle ABD$, AB = 1, $\angle A = 20°$.
    Compute DB:

    $$\tan 20° = \frac{DB}{AB}$$

    $$0.36397 = \frac{DB}{1}$$

    $$DB = 0.36397$$

    In right $\triangle CAB$, AB = 1, $\angle B = 8°$.
    Compute CB:

    $$\cos 8° = \frac{AB}{CB}$$

    $$0.99027 = \frac{1}{CB}$$

    $$CB = 1.009826$$

    In right $\triangle CBD$, DB = 0.36397, CB = 1.009826.
    Compute $\angle C$:

    $$\tan \angle C = \frac{DB}{CB} = \frac{0.36397}{1.009826} = 0.36043$$

    $$\angle C = 19°49'$$

7. a.

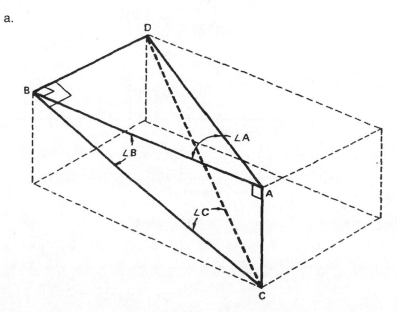

7. b.

    In right $\triangle ABD$, AB = 1, $\angle A = 30°$.
    Compute BD:

    $$\tan 30° = \frac{BD}{AB}$$

    $$0.57735 = \frac{BD}{1}$$

    $$BD = 0.57735$$

    In right $\triangle CAB$, AB = 1, $\angle B = 12°$.
    Compute CB:

    $$\cos 12° = \frac{AB}{CB}$$

    $$0.97815 = \frac{1}{CB}$$

    $$CB = 1.022338$$

UNIT 71 (*continued*)

7. b. In right △CBD, BD = 0.57735, CB = 1.022338.

Compute ∠C:

$$\tan \angle C = \frac{BD}{CB} = \frac{0.57735}{1.022338} = 0.56473$$

$$\angle C = 29°27'$$

8. a.

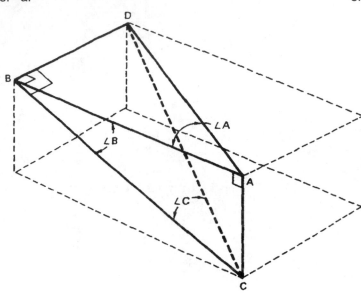

8. b. Make AB = 1

In right △ABD, AB = 1, ∠A = 23°.
Compute BD:

$$\tan 23° = \frac{BD}{AB}$$

$$0.42447 = \frac{BD}{1}$$

$$BD = 0.42447$$

In right △CAB, AB = 1, ∠B = 10°.
Compute CB:

$$\cos 10° = \frac{AB}{CB}$$

$$0.98481 = \frac{1}{CB}$$

$$CB = 1.015424$$

In right △CBD, BD = 0.42447, CB = 1.015424.
Compute ∠C:

$$\tan \angle C = \frac{BD}{CB} = \frac{0.42447}{1.015424} = 0.41802$$

$$\angle C = 22°41'$$

9.   tan ∠C = (tan ∠A)(cos ∠B)
    tan ∠C = (tan 33°)(cos 14°)
    tan ∠C = (0.64941)(0.97030)
    tan ∠C = 0.63012
      ∠C = 32°13'

10.   tan ∠C = (tan ∠A)(cos ∠B)
    tan 28°30' = (tan ∠A)(cos 10°)
     0.54296 = (tan ∠A)(0.98481)
      tan ∠A = 0.55133
        ∠A = 28°52'

11. tan ∠C = (tan ∠A)(cos ∠B)
    tan ∠C = (tan 26°)(cos 14°)
    tan ∠C = (0.48773)(0.97030)
    tan ∠C = 0.47324
      ∠C = 25°20'

12.   tan ∠C = (tan ∠A)(cos ∠B)
    tan 27.20° = (tan 28°)(cos ∠B)
     0.51393 = (0.53171)(cos ∠B)
      cos ∠B = 0.96656
        ∠B = 14°51.53' = 14.86°

13. Make AB = 1

In right △ABD, AB = 1, ∠A = 30°.
Compute BD:

$$\tan 30° = \frac{BD}{AB}$$

$$0.57735 = \frac{BD}{1}$$

$$BD = 0.57735$$

In right △ACB, AB = 1, ∠B = 10°.
Compute CB:

$$\cos 10° = \frac{CB}{AB}$$

$$0.98481 = \frac{CB}{1}$$

$$CB = 0.98481$$

In right △CBD, BD = 0.57735, CB = 0.98481.
Compute ∠C:

$$\tan \angle C = \frac{BD}{CB} = \frac{0.57735}{0.98481} = 0.58626$$

$$\angle C = 30°23'$$

UNIT **71**   (*continued*)

14. Make AB = 1

In right △ABD, AB = 1, ∠A = 28°.
Compute BD:

$$\tan 28° = \frac{BD}{AB}$$

$$0.53171 = \frac{BD}{1}$$

$$BD = 0.53171$$

In right △ACB, AB = 1, ∠B = 15°.
Compute CB:

$$\cos 15° = \frac{CB}{AB}$$

$$0.96593 = \frac{CB}{1}$$

$$CB = 0.96593$$

In right △CBD, BD = 0.53171, CB = 0.96593.
Compute ∠C:

$$\tan ∠C = \frac{BD}{CB} = \frac{0.53171}{0.96593} = 0.55046$$

$$∠C = 28°50'$$

15. Make AB = 1

In right △ABD, AB = 1, ∠A = 33°.
Compute BD:

$$\tan 33° = \frac{BD}{AB}$$

$$0.64941 = \frac{BD}{1}$$

$$BD = 0.64941$$

In right △ACB, AB = 1, ∠B = 11°.
Compute CB:

$$\cos 11° = \frac{CB}{AB}$$

$$0.98163 = \frac{CB}{1}$$

$$BD = 0.98163$$

In right △CBD, BD = 0.64941, CB = 0.98163.
Compute ∠C:

$$\tan ∠C = \frac{BD}{CB} = \frac{0.64941}{0.98163} = 0.66156$$

$$∠C = 33°29'$$

16. Make AB = 1

In right △ABD, AB = 1, ∠A = 25°.
Compute BD:

$$\tan 25° = \frac{BD}{AB}$$

$$0.46631 = \frac{BD}{1}$$

$$BD = 0.46631$$

In right △ACB, AB = 1, ∠B = 14°.
Compute CB:

$$\cos 14° = \frac{CB}{AB}$$

$$0.97030 = \frac{CB}{1}$$

$$CB = 0.97030$$

In right △CBD, BD = 0.46631, CB = 0.97030.
Compute ∠C:

$$\tan ∠C = \frac{BD}{CB} = \frac{0.46631}{0.97030} = 0.48058$$

$$∠C = 25°40'$$

17. a.

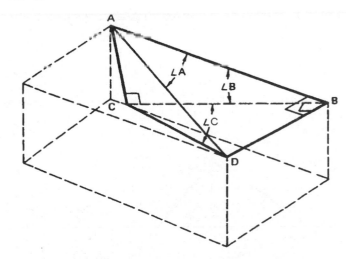

b. Make AB = 1

In right △ABD, AB = 1, ∠A = 30°.
Compute DB:

$$\tan 30° = \frac{DB}{AB}$$

$$0.57735 = \frac{DB}{1}$$

$$DB = 0.57735$$

UNIT **71**   *(continued)*

17. b. In right $\triangle$ACB, AB = 1, $\angle$B = 15°.
Compute CB:

$$\cos 15° = \frac{CB}{AB}$$

$$0.96593 = \frac{CB}{1}$$

$$CB = 0.96593$$

17. b. In right $\triangle$CBD, DB = 0.57735, CB = 0.96593.
Compute $\angle$C:

$$\tan \angle C = \frac{DB}{CB} = \frac{0.57735}{0.96593} = 0.59771$$

$$\angle C = 30°52'$$

18. a.

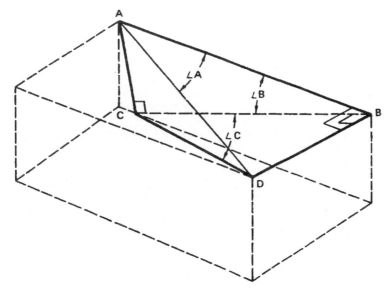

18. b. Make AB = 1

In right $\triangle$ABD, AB = 1, $\angle$A = 38°.
Compute DB:

$$\tan 38° = \frac{DB}{AB}$$

$$0.78129 = \frac{DB}{1}$$

$$DB = 0.78129$$

In right $\triangle$ACB, AB = 1, $\angle$B = 12°.
Compute CB:

$$\cos 12° = \frac{CB}{AB}$$

$$0.97815 = \frac{CB}{1}$$

$$CB = 0.97815$$

In right $\triangle$CBD, DB = 0.78129, CB = 0.97815.
Compute $\angle$C:

$$\tan \angle C = \frac{DB}{CB} = \frac{0.78129}{0.97815} = 0.79874$$

$$\angle C = 38°37'$$

19. a.

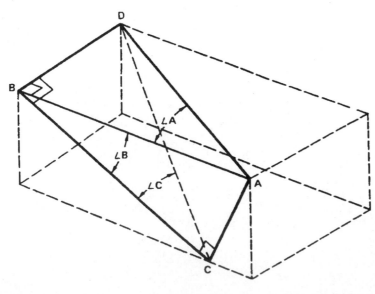

19. b. Make AB = 1

In right $\triangle$ABD, AB = 1, $\angle$A = 32°.
Compute DB:

$$\tan 32° = \frac{DB}{AB}$$

$$0.62487 = \frac{DB}{1}$$

$$DB = 0.62487$$

In right $\triangle$ACB, AB = 1, $\angle$B = 15°.
Compute CB:

$$\cos 15° = \frac{CB}{AB}$$

$$0.96593 = \frac{CB}{1}$$

$$CB = 0.96593$$

UNIT **71**   (*continued*)

19. b. In right $\triangle$CBD, DB = 0.62487, CB = 0.96593.

Compute $\angle$C:

$$\tan \angle C = \frac{DB}{CB} = \frac{0.62487}{0.96593} = 0.64691$$

$$\angle C = 32°54'$$

20. a.

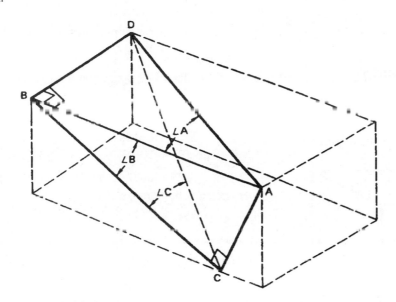

b. Make AB = 1

In right $\triangle$ABD, AB = 1, $\angle$A = 25°.
Compute DB.

$$\tan 25° = \frac{DB}{AB}$$

$$0.46631 = \frac{DB}{1}$$

$$DB = 0.46631$$

In right $\triangle$ACB, AB = 1, $\angle$B = 12°.
Compute CB:

$$\cos 12° = \frac{CB}{AB}$$

$$0.97815 = \frac{CB}{1}$$

$$CB = 0.97815$$

In right $\triangle$CBD, DB = 0.46631, CB = 0.97815.
Compute $\angle$C:

$$\tan \angle C = \frac{DB}{CB} = \frac{0.46631}{0.97815} = 0.47673$$

$$\angle C = 25°29'$$

21. $\tan \angle C - \dfrac{\tan \angle A}{\cos \angle B} - \dfrac{\tan 25°}{\cos 9°} = \dfrac{0.46631}{0.98769} = 0.47212$

$$\angle C = 25°16'$$

22. $\tan \angle C = \dfrac{\tan \angle A}{\cos \angle B}$

$$\tan 30°40' = \frac{\tan \angle A}{\cos 15°}$$

$$0.59297 = \frac{\tan \angle A}{0.96593}$$

$$\tan \angle A = 0.57277$$

$$\angle A = 29°48'$$

23. $\tan \angle C = \dfrac{\tan \angle A}{\cos \angle B} = \dfrac{\tan 34°}{\cos 8°} = \dfrac{0.67451}{0.99027} = 0.68114$

$$\angle C = 34°16'$$

24. $\tan \angle C = \dfrac{\tan \angle A}{\cos \angle B}$

$$\tan 28.60° = \frac{\tan 28°}{\cos \angle B}$$

$$0.54522 = \frac{0.53171}{\cos \angle B}$$

$$\cos \angle B = 0.97522$$

$$\angle B = 12°46.9' = 12.78°$$

UNIT **72** Achievement Review—Section Seven

1. a. $\tan \angle R = \dfrac{1.100}{1.900} = 0.57895$

    $\angle R = 30°4'$

    b. $\sin \angle R = \dfrac{1.100}{CB}$

    $\sin 30°4' = \dfrac{1.100}{CB}$

    $0.50101 = \dfrac{1.100}{CB}$

    $CB = 2.195565$

    $\tan \angle T = \dfrac{CB}{2.200} = \dfrac{2.195565}{2.200} = 0.99798$

    $\angle T = 44°57'$

Problem 1.

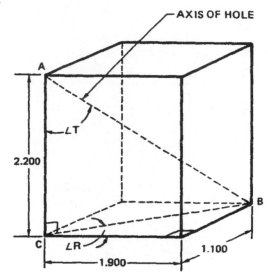

2. Solution by Formula

    a. $\tan \angle R = \dfrac{\tan \angle B}{\tan \angle A}$

    $\tan \angle R = \dfrac{\tan 22°}{\tan 37.30°}$

    $\tan \angle R = \dfrac{0.40403}{0.76180}$

    $\tan \angle R = 0.53036$

    $\angle R = 27.94°$

    b. $\tan \angle T = \sqrt{\tan^2 \angle A + \tan^2 \angle B}$

    $\tan \angle T = \sqrt{\tan^2 37.30° + \tan^2 22°}$

    $\tan \angle T = \sqrt{0.76180^2 + 0.40403^2}$

    $\tan \angle T = \sqrt{0.5803392 + 0.1632402}$

    $\tan \angle T = \sqrt{0.7435794}$

    $\tan \angle T = 0.86231$

    $\angle T = 40.77°$

3. Solution by Formula

    a. $\tan \angle R = \dfrac{\tan \angle B}{\tan \angle A}$

    $\tan \angle R = \dfrac{\tan 44.50°}{\tan 34°}$

    $\tan \angle R = \dfrac{0.98270}{0.67451}$

    $\tan \angle R = 1.4569$

    $\angle R = 55°32.1' = 55.54°$

    b. $\tan \angle T = \dfrac{\tan \angle A}{\cos \angle R}$

    $\tan \angle T = \dfrac{\tan 34°}{\cos 55°32.1'}$

    $\tan \angle T = \dfrac{0.67451}{0.56591}$

    $\tan \angle T = 1.1919$

    $\angle T = 50°0' = 50.00°$

4. Solution by Formula

    a. $\tan \angle R = \dfrac{\cot \angle B}{\cot \angle A}$

    $\tan \angle R = \dfrac{\cot 35°}{\cot 21°40'}$

    $\tan \angle R = \dfrac{1.4282}{2.5172}$

    $\tan \angle R = 0.56738$

    $\angle R = 29°34'$

    b. $\cot \angle C = \sqrt{\cot^2 \angle A + \cot^2 \angle B}$

    $\cot \angle C = \sqrt{\cot^2 21°40' + \cot^2 35°}$

    $\cot \angle C = \sqrt{2.5172^2 + 1.4282^2}$

    $\cot \angle C = \sqrt{6.3362958 + 2.0397552}$

    $\cot \angle C = \sqrt{8.376051}$

    $\cot \angle C = 2.8941$

    $\angle C = 19°4'$

5. Solution by Formula

    $\tan \angle C = (\tan \angle A)(\cos \angle B)$

    $\tan \angle C = (\tan 28°40')(\cos 9°20')$

    $\tan \angle C = (0.54673)(0.98676)$

    $\tan \angle C = 0.53949$

    $\angle C = 28°21'$

6. Solution by Formula

    $\tan \angle C = \dfrac{\tan \angle A}{\cos \angle B}$

    $\tan \angle C = \dfrac{\tan 27°}{\cos 15°}$

    $\tan \angle C = \dfrac{0.50953}{0.96593}$

    $\tan \angle C = 0.52750$

    $\angle C = 27°49'$

UNIT 73 **Introduction to Computer Numerical Control (CNC)**

1.

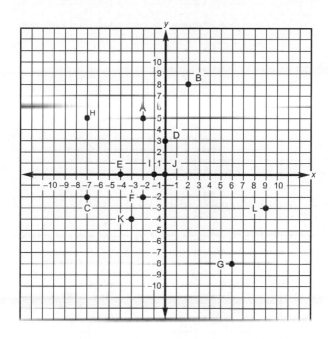

2.

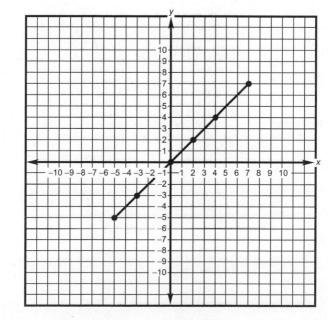

   a. A straight line is formed.

   b. An angle of 45° is formed with the x-axis.

UNIT 73   (*continued*)

3. A triangle is formed.

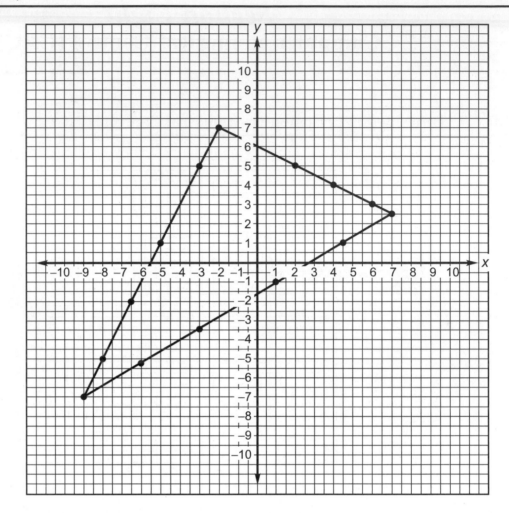

4. A (4, 3)   K (−9, 3)   T (−4, 4)   7 (−2, 8)   13 (5, 1)
    B (0, 7)   L (1, 5)   U (−4, −1)   8 (−9, −4)   14 (−8, −8)
    C (−7, 5)   M (−8, 0)   V (8, 0)   9 (8, −9)   15 (4, 9)
    D (0, −9)   N (−3, −4)   5 (9, −3)   10 (3, −6)   16 (7, 8)
    E (−2, −7)   P (4, −8)   6 (−5, −8)   12 (−8, 8)   17 (9, 3)
    F (1, −5)   Q (−7, −5)
    G (−5, 8)   R (6, −2)
    H (−4, 1)   S (−1, −1)
    J (9, 7)

5. Point locations to be sketched.

UNIT 74   Control Systems, Absolute Positioning, Incremental Positioning

1. a. Absolute Dimensioning

   Hole 1: $x = 4'' + 2.400'' = 6.400''$
   $y = 5'' - (1.520'' + 3.750'' + 2.100'') = -2.370''$

   Hole 2: $x = 6.400'' + 2.000'' = 8.400''$
   $y = 5'' - (2.320'' + 1.725'') = 0.955''$

   Hole 3: $x = 6.400''$
   $y = 5'' - 2.320'' = 2.680''$

   Hole 4: $x = 6.400'' + 6.050'' = 12.450''$
   $y = 5'' - (2.320'' - 0.800'') = 3.480''$

   Hole 5: $x = 6.400'' + 6.600'' = 13.000''$
   $y = 3.480'' - 3.750'' = 0.270''$

   Hole 6: $x = 13.000''$
   $y = -2.370''$

Hole	x	y
1	6.400″	−2.370″
2	8.400″	0.955″
3	6.400″	2.680″
4	12.450″	3.480″
5	13.000″	−0.270″
6	13.000″	−2.370″

   b. Incremental Dimensioning

   Hole 1: $x = 4'' + 2.400'' = 6.400''$
   $y = 5'' - (1.520'' + 3.750'' + 2.100'') = -2.370''$

   Hole 2: $x = 2.000''$
   $y = 2.100'' + 3.750'' - (0.800'' + 1.725'') = 3.325''$

   Hole 3: $x = -2.000''$
   $y = 1.725''$

   Hole 4: $x = 6.050''$
   $y = 0.800''$

   Hole 5: $x = 6.600'' - 6.050'' = 0.550''$
   $y = -3.750''$

   Hole 6: $x = 0$
   $y = -2.100''$

Hole	x	y
1	6.400″	−2.370″
2	2.000″	3.325″
3	−2.000″	1.725″
4	6.050″	0.800″
5	0.550″	−3.750″
6	0	−2.100″

2. a. Absolute Dimensioning

   Hole 1: $x = 6'' + 2.710'' = 8.710''$
   $y = 5'' - (1.380'' + 4.307'' + 2.416'') = -3.103''$

   Hole 2: $x = 8.710'' + 2.615'' = 11.325''$
   $y = 5'' - (2.300'' + 2.070'') = 0.630''$

   Hole 3: $x = 8.710''$
   $y = 5'' - 2.300'' = 2.700''$

   Hole 4: $x = 8.710'' + 6.475'' = 15.185''$
   $y = 5'' - 1.380'' = 3.620''$

   Hole 5: $x = 8.710'' + 7.010'' = 15.720''$
   $y = 5'' - (1.380'' + 4.307'') = -0.687''$

   Hole 6: $x = 15.720''$
   $y = -3.103''$

Hole	x	y
1	8.710″	−3.103″
2	11.325″	0.630″
3	8.710″	2.700″
4	15.185″	3.620″
5	15.720″	−0.687″
6	15.720″	−3.103″

   b. Incremental Dimensioning

   Hole 1: $x = 6'' + 2.710'' = 8.710''$
   $y = 5'' - (1.380'' + 4.307'' + 2.416'') = -3.103''$

   Hole 2: $x = 2.615''$
   $y = 8.103'' - (2.070'' + 2.300'') = 3.733''$

   Hole 3: $x = -2.615''$
   $y = 2.070''$

   Hole 4: $x = 6.475''$
   $y = 0.920''$

   Hole 5: $x = 7.010'' - 6.475'' = 0.535''$
   $y = -4.307''$

   Hole 6: $x = 0$
   $y = -2.416''$

Hole	x	y
1	8.710″	−3.103'
2	2.615²	3.733″
3	−2.615″	2.070″
4	6.475″	0.920″
5	0.535″	−4.307″
6	0	−2.416″

UNIT **74** (*continued*)

3. a. Absolute Dimensioning

Hole 1: $x = 100\text{ mm} + 60.00\text{ mm} = 160.00\text{ mm}$

$y = 100\text{ mm} - (30.84\text{ mm} + 92.24\text{ mm} + 52.30\text{ mm}) = -75.38\text{ mm}$

Hole 2: $x = 160\text{ mm} + 56.24\text{ mm} = 216.24\text{ mm}$

$y = 100\text{ mm} - (51.00\text{ mm} + 45.06\text{ mm}) = 3.94\text{ mm}$

Hole 3: $x = 160\text{ mm}$

$y = 100\text{ mm} - 51.00\text{ mm} = 49.00\text{ mm}$

Hole 4: $x = 160\text{ mm} + 132.32\text{ mm} = 292.32\text{ mm}$

$y = 100\text{ mm} - (51.00\text{ mm} - 20.16\text{ mm}) = 69.16\text{ mm}$

Hole 5: $x = 160\text{ mm} + 148.06\text{ mm} = 308.06\text{ mm}$

$y = 100\text{ mm} - (30.84\text{ mm} + 92.24\text{ mm}) = -23.08\text{ mm}$

Hole 6: $x = 308.06\text{ mm}$

$y = -75.38\text{ mm}$

Hole	x	y
1	160.00 mm	−75.38 mm
2	216.24 mm	3.94 mm
3	160 mm	49.00 mm
4	292.32 mm	69.16 mm
5	308.06 mm	−23.08 mm
6	308.06 mm	−75.38 mm

b. Incremental Dimensioning

Hole 1: $x = 100\text{ mm} + 60.00\text{ mm} = 160.00\text{ mm}$

$y = 100\text{ mm} - (30.84\text{ mm} + 92.24\text{ mm} + 52.30\text{ mm}) = -75.38\text{ mm}$

Hole 2: $x = 56.24\text{ mm}$

$y = 175.38\text{ mm} - (51.00\text{ mm} + 45.06\text{ mm}) = 79.32\text{ mm}$

Hole 3: $x = -56.24\text{ mm}$

$y = 45.06\text{ mm}$

Hole 4: $x = 132.32\text{ mm}$

$y = 20.16\text{ mm}$

Hole 5: $x = 148.06\text{ mm} - 132.32\text{ mm} = 15.74\text{ mm}$

$y = -92.24\text{ mm}$

Hole 6: $x = 0$

$y = -52.30\text{ mm}$

Hole	x	y
1	160.00 mm	−75.38 mm
2	56.24 mm	79.32 mm
3	−56.24 mm	45.06 mm
4	132.32 mm	20.16 mm
5	15.74 mm	−92.24 mm
6	0	−52.30 mm

4. a. Absolute Dimensioning

Hole 1: $x = 5.175'' - 10'' = -4.825''$

$y = 12.500'' - 8'' = 4.500''$

Hole 2: $\sin 42° = \dfrac{a}{5.500''} \qquad \cos 42° = \dfrac{b}{5.500''}$

$0.66913 = \dfrac{a}{5.500''} \qquad 0.74314 = \dfrac{b}{5.500''}$

$a = 3.680'' \qquad b = 4.087''$

$x = -4.825'' + 4.087'' = -0.738''$

$y = 4.500'' + 3.680'' = 8.180''$

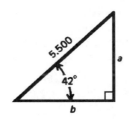

Hole 3: $\sin 42° = \dfrac{a}{11.250''} \qquad \cos 42° = \dfrac{b}{11.250''}$

$0.66913 = \dfrac{a}{11.250''} \qquad 0.74314 = \dfrac{b}{11.250''}$

$a = 7.528'' \qquad b = 8.360''$

$x = -4.825'' + 8.360'' = 3.535''$

$y = 4.500'' + 7.528'' = 12.028''$

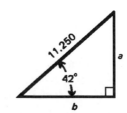

Hole 4: $\dfrac{360°}{5} = 72°$

$\sin 72° = \dfrac{a}{5.000''} \qquad \cos 72° = \dfrac{b}{5.000''}$

$0.95106 = \dfrac{a}{5.000''} \qquad 0.30902 = \dfrac{b}{5.000''}$

$a = 4.755'' \qquad b = 1.545''$

$x = -4.825'' + 14.250'' - 1.545'' = 7.880''$

$y = 4.500'' + 4.755'' = 9.255''$

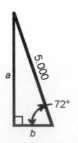

UNIT **74**   (*continued*)

4. a. Hole 5: $\sin 36° = \dfrac{a}{5.000''}$ $\cos 36° = \dfrac{b}{5.000''}$

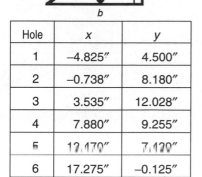

$0.58779 = \dfrac{a}{5.000''}$ $0.80902 = \dfrac{b}{5.000''}$

$a = 2.939''$ $b = 4.045''$
$x = -4.825'' + 14.250'' + 4.045'' = 13.470''$
$y = 4.500'' + 2.939'' = 7.439''$

Hole 6: $x = -4.825'' + 22.100'' = 17.275''$
$y = 4.500'' - 4.625'' = -0.125''$

Hole 7: x is the same as hole 5 = 13.470″
$y = 4.500'' - 2.939'' = 1.561''$

Hole 8: x is the same as hole 4 = 7.880″
$y = 4.500'' - 4.755'' = -0.255''$

Hole 9: $x = -4.825'' + 14.250'' - 5.000'' = 4.425''$
y is the same as hole 1 = 4.500″

Hole 10: $x = -4.825'' + 3.250'' = -1.575''$
$y = 4.500'' - 5.150'' = -0.650''$

Hole 11: $x = -4.825'' - 1.300'' = -6.125''$
$y = 4.500'' - 9.150'' = -4.650''$

Hole	x	y
1	−4.825″	4.500″
2	−0.738″	8.180″
3	3.535″	12.028″
4	7.880″	9.255″
5	13.470″	7.439″
6	17.275″	−0.125″
7	13.470″	1.561″
8	7.880″	−0.255″
9	4.425″	4.500″
10	−1.575″	−0.650″

b. Incremental Dimensioning

Hole 1: $x = 5.175'' - 10'' = -4.825''$
$y = 12.500'' - 8'' = 4.500''$

Hole 2: $x = 4.087''$
$y = 3.680''$

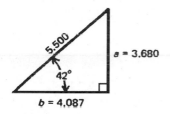

Hole 3: $x = 8.360'' = 4.087'' = 4.273''$
$y = 7.528'' - 3.680'' = 3.848''$

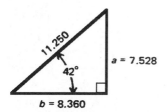

Hole 4: x distance from hole 1 to hole 3 = 8.360″
x distance from hole 1 to hole 4 = 14.250″ − 1.545″ = 12.705″
$x = 12.705'' - 8.360'' = 4.345''$
$-y = 7.528'' - 4.755'' = 2.773''$
$y = -2.773''$

Hole 5: $x = 1.545'' + 4.045'' = 5.590''$
$-y = 4.755'' - 2.939'' = 1.816''$
$y = -1.816''$

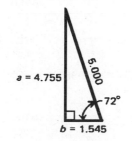

Hole 6: $x = 22.100'' - (14.250'' + 4.045'') = 3.805''$
$-y = 2.939'' + 4.625'' = 7.564''$
$y = -7.564''$

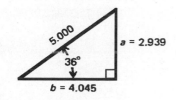

UNIT **74** *(continued)*

4. b. Hole 7: $x = x$ from hole 5 to 6 in the negative direction.

$x = -3.805''$
$y = 4.625'' - 2.939'' = 1.686''$

Hole 8: $-x = 4.045'' + 1.545''$
$x = -5.590''$
$-y = 4.755'' - 2.939'' = 1.816''$
$y = -1.816''$

Hole 9: $-x = 5.000'' - 1.545'' = 3.455''$
$x = -3.455''$
$y = 4.755''$

Hole 10: $-x = (14.250'' - 5.000'') - 3.250'' = 6.000''$
$x = -6.000''$
$y = -5.150''$

Hole 11: $-x = 1.300'' + 3.250'' = 4.550''$
$x = -4.550''$
$-y = 9.150'' - 5.150'' = -4.000''$
$y = -4.000''$

Hole	x	y
1	−4.825″	4.500″
2	4.087″	3.680″
3	4.273″	3.848″
4	4.345″	−2.773″
5	5.590″	−1.816″
6	3.805″	−7.564″
7	−3.805″	1.686″
8	−5.590″	−1.816″
9	−3.455″	4.755″
10	−6.000″	−5.150″
11	−4.550″	−4.000″

5. a. Absolute Dimensioning

Hole 1: $x = 5.250'' - 10'' = -4.750''$
$y = 12.750'' - 8'' = 4.750''$

Hole 2: $\sin 43° = \dfrac{a}{5.600''}$ $\qquad \cos 43° = \dfrac{b}{5.600''}$

$0.68200 = \dfrac{a}{5.600''}$ $\qquad 0.73135 = \dfrac{b}{5.600''}$

$a = 3.819''$ $\qquad\qquad b = 4.096''$

$x = -4.750'' + 4.096'' = -0.654''$
$y = 4.750'' + 3.819'' = 8.569''$

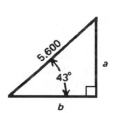

Hole 3: $\sin 43° = \dfrac{a}{11.300''}$ $\qquad \cos 43° = \dfrac{b}{11.300''}$

$0.68200 = \dfrac{a}{11.300''}$ $\qquad 0.73135 = \dfrac{b}{11.300''}$

$a = 7.707''$ $\qquad\qquad b = 8.264''$

$x = -4.750'' + 8.264'' = 3.514''$
$y = 4.750'' + 7.707'' = 12.457''$

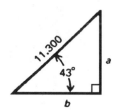

Hole 4: $\sin 72° = \dfrac{a}{5.100''}$ $\qquad \cos 72° = \dfrac{b}{5.100''}$

$0.95106 = \dfrac{a}{5.100''}$ $\qquad 0.30902 = \dfrac{b}{5.100''}$

$a = 4.850''$ $\qquad\qquad b = 1.576''$

$x = -4.750'' + 14.400'' - 1.576'' = 8.074''$
$y = 4.750'' + 4.850'' = 9.600''$

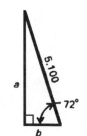

Hole 5: $\sin 36° = \dfrac{a}{5.100''}$ $\qquad \cos 36° = \dfrac{b}{5.100''}$

$0.58779 = \dfrac{a}{5.100''}$ $\qquad 0.80902 = \dfrac{b}{5.100''}$

$a = 2.998''$ $\qquad\qquad b = 4.126''$

$x = -4.750'' + 14.400'' + 4.126'' = 13.776''$
$y = 4.750'' + 2.998'' = 7.748''$

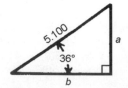

UNIT 74 *(continued)*

5. a. Hole 6: $x = -4.750'' + 22.250'' = 17.500''$
$y = 4.750'' - 4.850'' = -0.100''$

Hole 7: x is the same as x of hole 5 = 13.776″
$y = 4.750'' - 2.998'' = 1.752''$

Hole 8: x is the same as x of hole 4 = 8.074″
$y = 4.750'' - 4.850'' = -0.100''$

Hole 9: $x = -4.750'' + 14.400'' - 5.100'' = 4.550''$
y is the same as y of hole 1 = 4.750″

Hole 10: $x = -4.750'' + 3.562'' = -1.188''$
$y = 4.750'' - 5.270'' = -0.520''$

Hole 11: $x = -4.750'' - 1.412'' = -6.162''$
$y = 4.750'' - 9.375'' = -4.625''$

Hole	x	y
1	−4.750″	4.750″
2	−0.654″	8.569″
3	3.514″	12.457″
4	8.074″	9.600″
5	13.776″	7.748″
6	17.500″	−0.100″
7	13.776″	1.752″
8	8.074″	−0.100″
9	4.550″	4.750″
10	1.100″	0.520″
11	−6.162″	−4.625″

b. Incremental Dimensioning

Hole 1: $x = 5.250'' - 10.000'' = -4.750''$
$y = 12.750'' - 8'' = 4.750''$

Hole 2: $x = 4.096''$
$y = 3.819''$

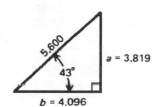
$a = 3.819$
5.600
43°
$b = 4.096$

Hole 3: $x = 8.264'' - 4.096'' = 4.168''$
$y = 7.707'' - 3.819'' = 3.888''$

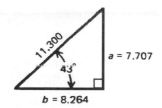
$a = 7.707$
11.300
43°
$b = 8.264$

Hole 4: x distance from hole 1 to hole 3 = 8.264″
x distance from hole 1 to hole 4 = 14.400″ − 1.576″ = 12.824″
$x = 12.824'' - 8.264'' = 4.560''$
$-y = 7.707'' - 4.850'' = 2.857''$
$y = -2.857''$

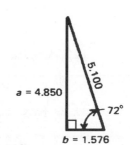
$a = 4.850$
5.100
72°
$b = 1.576$

Hole 5: $x = 1.576'' + 4.126'' = 5.702''$
$-y = 4.850'' - 2.998'' = 1.852''$
$y = -1.852''$

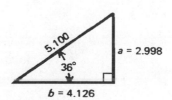
5.100
36°
$a = 2.998$
$b = 4.126$

UNIT 74 *(continued)*

5. b. Hole 6: $x = 22.250'' - (14.400'' + 4.126'') = 3.724''$
   $-y = 4.850'' + 2.998'' = 7.848''$
   $y = -7.848''$

   Hole 7: $x = x$ distance from hole 5 to 6 in a negative direction.
   $x = -3.724''$
   $y = 4.850'' - 2.998'' = 1.852''$

   Hole 8: $-x = 4.126'' + 1.576'' = 5.702''$
   $x = -5.702''$
   $-y = 4.850'' - 2.998'' = 1.852''$
   $y = -1.852''$

   Hole 9: $-x = 5.100'' - 1.572'' = 3.524''$
   $x = -3.524''$
   $y = 4.850''$

   Hole 10: $-x = (14.400'' - 5.100'') - 3.562'' = 5.738''$
   $x = -5.738''$
   $y = -5.270''$

   Hole 11: $x = -(1.412'' + 3.562'') = -4.974''$
   $-y = 9.375'' - 5.270'' = -4.105''$
   $y = -4.105''$

Hole	x	y
1	−4.750″	4.750″
2	4.096″	3.819″
3	4.168″	3.888″
4	4.560″	−2.857″
5	5.702″	−1.852″
6	3.724″	−7.848″
7	−3.724″	1.852″
8	−5.702″	−1.852″
9	−3.524″	4.850″
10	−5.738″	−5.270″
11	−4.974″	−4.105″

6. a. Absolute Dimensioning

   Hole 1: $x = 122.40$ mm $- 170$ mm $= -47.60$ mm
   $y = 249.30$ mm $- 130$ mm $= 119.30$ mm

   Hole 2: $41.75° = 41°45'$

   $$\sin 41°45' = \frac{a}{104\text{ mm}} \qquad \cos 41°45' = \frac{b}{104\text{ mm}}$$

   $$0.66588 = \frac{a}{104\text{ mm}} \qquad 0.74606 = \frac{b}{104\text{ mm}}$$

   $$a = 69.25\text{ mm} \qquad b = 77.59\text{ mm}$$

   $x = -47.60$ mm $+ 77.59$ mm $= 29.99$ mm
   $y = 119.30$ mm $+ 69.25$ mm $= 188.55$ mm

   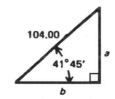

   Hole 3: $\sin 41°45' = \dfrac{a}{228.00\text{ mm}} \qquad \cos 41°45' = \dfrac{b}{228.00\text{ mm}}$

   $$0.66588 = \frac{a}{228.00\text{ mm}} \qquad 0.74606 = \frac{b}{228.00\text{ mm}}$$

   $$a = 151.82\text{ mm} \qquad b = 170.10\text{ mm}$$

   $x = -47.60$ mm $+ 170.10$ mm $= 122.50$ mm
   $y = 199.30$ mm $+ 151.82$ mm $= 271.12$ mm

   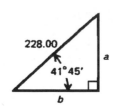

   Hole 4: $\sin 72° = \dfrac{a}{98.00\text{ mm}} \qquad \cos 72° = \dfrac{b}{98.00\text{ mm}}$

   $$0.95106 = \frac{a}{98.00\text{ mm}} \qquad 0.30902 = \frac{b}{98.00\text{ mm}}$$

   $$a = 93.20\text{ mm} \qquad b = 30.28\text{ mm}$$

   $x = -47.60$ mm $+ 300.40$ mm $- 30.28$ mm $= 222.52$ mm
   $y = 119.30$ mm $+ 93.20$ mm $= 212.50$ mm

   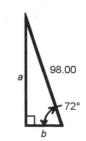

   Hole 5: $\sin 36° = \dfrac{a}{98.00\text{ mm}} \qquad \cos 36° = \dfrac{b}{98.00\text{ mm}}$

   $$0.58779 = \frac{a}{98.00\text{ mm}} \qquad 0.80902 = \frac{b}{98.00\text{ mm}}$$

   $$a = 57.60\text{ mm} \qquad b = 79.28\text{ mm}$$

   $x = -47.60$ mm $+ 300.40$ mm $+ 79.28$ mm $= 332.08$ mm
   $y = 119.30$ mm $+ 57.60$ mm $= 176.90$ mm

   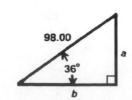

UNIT 74 *(continued)*

6. a. Hole 6: $x = -47.60$ mm $+ 450.00$ mm $= 402.40$ mm
    $y = 119.30$ mm $- 95.10$ mm $= 24.20$ mm

   Hole 7: x is the same as x of hole 5 = 332.08 mm
    $y = 119.30$ mm $- 57.60$ mm $= 61.70$ mm

   Hole 8: x is the same as x of hole 4 = 222.52 mm
    $y = 119.30$ mm $- 93.20$ mm $= 26.10$ mm

   Hole 9: $x = -47.60$ mm $+ 300.40$ mm $- 98.00$ mm $= 154.80$ mm
    y is the same as y of hole 1 = 119.30 mm

   Hole 10: $x = -47.60$ mm $+ 70.00$ mm $= 22.40$ mm
    $y = 119.30$ mm $- 108.70$ mm $= 10.60$ mm

   Hole 11: $x = -47.60$ mm $- 30.00$ mm $= -77.60$ mm
    $y = 119.30$ mm $- 187.30$ mm $= -68.00$ mm

Hole	x	y
1	−47.60 mm	119.30 mm
2	29.99 mm	188.55 mm
3	122.50 mm	271.12 mm
4	222.52 mm	212.50 mm
5	332.08 mm	176.90 mm
6	402.40 mm	24.20 mm
7	332.08 mm	61.70 mm
8	222.52 mm	26.10 mm
9	154.80 mm	119.30 mm
10	22.40 mm	10.60 mm
11	−77.60 mm	−68.00 mm

b. Incremental Dimensioning

   Hole 1: $x = 122.40$ mm $- 170.00$ mm $= -47.60$ mm
    $y = 249.30$ mm $- 130.00$ mm $= 119.30$ mm

   Hole 2: $x = 77.59$ mm
    $y = 69.25$ mm

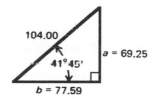

   Hole 3: $x = 170.10$ mm $- 77.59$ mm $= 92.51$ mm
    $y = 151.82$ mm $- 69.25$ mm $= 82.57$ mm

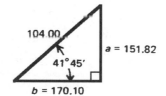

   Hole 4: x distance from hole 1 to hole 3 = 170.10 mm
    x distance from hole 1 to hole 4 = 300.40 mm $- 30.28$ mm $= 270.12$ mm
    $x = 270.12$ mm $- 170.10$ mm $= 100.02$ mm
    $-y = 151.82$ mm $- 93.20$ mm $= 58.62$ mm
    $y = -58.62$ mm

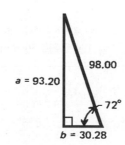

   Hole 5: $x = 30.28$ mm $+ 79.28$ mm $= 109.56$ mm
    $-y = 93.20$ mm $- 57.60$ mm $= 35.60$ mm
    $y = -35.60$ mm

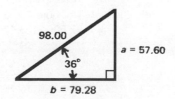

UNIT **74** *(continued)*

6. b. Hole 6: $x = 450.00\text{ mm} - (300.40\text{ mm} + 79.28\text{ mm}) = 70.32\text{ mm}$
$-y = 95.10\text{ mm} + 57.60\text{ mm} = 152.70\text{ mm}$
$y = -152.70\text{ mm}$

   Hole 7: $x = x$ from hole 5 to hole 6 in a negative direction.
$x = -70.32\text{ mm}$
$y = 95.10\text{ mm} - 57.60\text{ mm} = 37.50\text{ mm}$

   Hole 8: $-x = 79.28\text{ mm} + 30.28\text{ mm} = 109.56\text{ mm}$
$x = -109.56\text{ mm}$
$-y = 93.20\text{ mm} - 57.60\text{ mm} = 35.60\text{ mm}$
$y = -35.60\text{ mm}$

   Hole 9: $-x = 98.00\text{ mm} - 30.28\text{ mm} = 67.72\text{ mm}$
$x = -67.72\text{ mm}$
$y = 93.20\text{ mm}$

   Hole 10: $-x = (300.40\text{ mm} - 98.00\text{ mm}) - 70.00\text{ mm} = 132.40\text{ mm}$
$x = -132.40\text{ mm}$
$y = -108.70\text{ mm}$

   Hole 11: $-x = 70.00\text{ mm} + 30.00\text{ mm} = 100.00\text{ mm}$
$x = -100.00\text{ mm}$
$-y = 187.30\text{ mm} - 108.70\text{ mm} = 78.60\text{ mm}$
$y = -78.60\text{ mm}$

Hole	x	y
1	−47.60 mm	119.30 mm
2	77.59 mm	69.25 mm
3	92.51 mm	80.57 mm
4	100.02 mm	−58.62 mm
5	109.56 mm	−35.60 mm
6	70.32 mm	−152.70 mm
7	−70.32 mm	37.50 mm
8	−109.56 mm	−35.60 mm
9	−67.72 mm	93.20 mm
10	−132.40 mm	−108.70 mm
11	−100.00 mm	−78.60 mm

7. a. Absolute Dimensioning

   Center of circle: $x = -7.815''$
$y = 12.500''$

   Hole 1: $\sin 75°45' = \dfrac{a}{6.100''}$ $\cos 75°45' = \dfrac{b}{6.100''}$

   $0.96923 = \dfrac{a}{6.100''}$ $0.24615 = \dfrac{b}{6.100''}$

   $a = 5.912''$ $b = 1.502''$

   $x = (10.185'' - 1.502'') - 18'' = -9.317''$
$y = 5'' + 7.500'' + 5.912'' = 18.412''$

   Hole 2: $180° - (75°45' + 55°30') = 48°45'$

   $\sin 48°45' = \dfrac{a}{6.100''}$ $\cos 48°45' = \dfrac{b}{6.100''}$

   $0.75184 = \dfrac{a}{6.100''}$ $0.65934 = \dfrac{b}{6.100''}$

   $a = 4.586''$ $b = 4.022''$

   $x = -7.815'' + 4.022'' = -3.793''$
$y = 12.500'' + 4.586'' = 17.086''$

   Hole 3: $x = -7.815'' + 13.700'' = 5.885''$
$y = 12.500'' + 5.750'' = 18.250''$

   Hole 4: $x = -7.815'' + 19.215'' = 11.400''$
$y = 12.500'' + 4.250'' = 16.750''$

   Hole 5: $x = -7.815'' + 26.750'' = 18.935''$
$y = 12.500''$

   Hole 6: $x = x$ of hole 3 = 5.885''
$y = 12.500'' - 3.170'' = 9.330''$

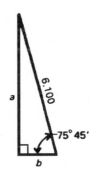

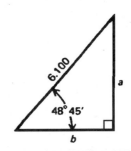

Hole	x	y
1	−9.317″	18.412″
2	−3.793″	17.086″
3	5.885″	18.250″
4	11.400″	16.750″
5	18.935″	12.500″
6	5.885″	9.330″
7	−3.616″	8.075″
8	−13.541″	10.397″

UNIT **74** *(continued)*

7. a. Hole 7: $(75°45' + 55°30' + 95°15') - 180° = 46°30'$

$$\sin 46°30' = \frac{a}{6.100''} \qquad\qquad \cos 46° 30' = \frac{b}{6.100''}$$

$$0.72537 = \frac{a}{6.100''} \qquad\qquad 0.68835 = \frac{b}{6.100''}$$

$$a = 4.425'' \qquad\qquad b = 4.199''$$

$x = -7.815'' + 4.199'' = -3.616''$
$y = 12.500'' + 4.425'' = 8.075''$

Hole 8: $\sin 20°10' = \dfrac{a}{6.100''} \qquad\qquad \cos 20°10' = \dfrac{b}{6.100''}$

$$0.34475 = \frac{a}{6.100''} \qquad\qquad 0.93869 = \frac{b}{6.100''}$$

$$a = 2.103'' \qquad\qquad b = 5.726''$$

$x = -7.015'' - 5.726'' = -13.541''$
$y = 12.500'' - 2.103'' = 10.397''$

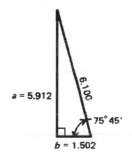

b. Incremental Dimensioning

Hole 1: $x = 10.185'' - 1.502'' - 18'' = -9.317''$
$ y = 5'' + 7.500'' + 5.912'' = 18.412''$

Hole 2: $x = 1.502'' + 4.022'' = 5.524''$
$ -y = 5.912'' - 4.586'' = 1.326''$
$ y = -1.326''$

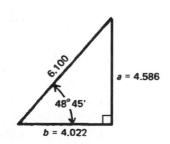

Hole 3: $x = 13.700'' - 4.022'' = 9.678''$
$ y = 5.750'' - 4.586'' = 1.164''$

Hole 4: $x = 19.215'' - 13.700'' = 5.515''$
$ -y = 5.750'' - 4.250'' = 1.500''$
$ y = -1.500''$

Hole 5: $x = 26.750'' + 19.215'' = 7.535''$
$ y = -4.250''$

Hole 6: $-x = 26.750'' - 13.700'' = 13.050''$
$ x = -13.050''$
$ y = -3.170''$

Hole	x	y
1	−9.317″	18.412″
2	5.524″	−1.326″
3	9.678″	1.164″
4	5.515″	−1.500″
5	7.535″	−4.250″
6	−13.050″	−3.170″
7	−9.501″	−1.255″
8	−9.925″	2.322″

UNIT **74** (*continued*)

7. b. Hole 7: $-x = 13.700'' - 4.199'' = 9.501''$
  $x = -9.501''$
  $-y = 4.425'' - 3.170'' = 1.255''$
  $y = -1.255''$

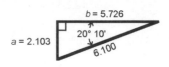

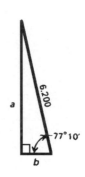

Hole 8: $-x = 5.726'' + 4.199'' = 9.925''$
  $x = -9.925''$
  $y = 4.425'' - 2.103'' = 2.322''$

8. a. Absolute Dimensioning

  Center of circle: $x = -8.480''$
    $y = 12.615''$

  Hole 1: $\sin 77°10' = \dfrac{a}{6.200''}$ $\cos 77°10' = \dfrac{b}{6.200''}$

    $0.97502 = \dfrac{a}{6.200''}$ $0.22212 = \dfrac{b}{6.200''}$

      $a = 6.045''$ $b = 1.377''$

  $x = -8.480'' - 1.377'' = -9.857''$
  $y = 12.615'' + 6.045'' = 18.660''$

  Hole 2: $180° - (77°10' + 57°15') = 45°35'$

    $\sin 45°35' = \dfrac{a}{6.200''}$ $\cos 45°35' = \dfrac{b}{6.200''}$

    $0.71427 = \dfrac{a}{6.200''}$ $0.69987 = \dfrac{b}{6.200''}$

      $a = 4.428''$ $b = 4.339''$

  $x = -8.480'' + 4.339'' = -4.141''$
  $y = 12.615'' + 4.428'' = 17.043''$

  Hole 3: $x = -8.480'' + 14.020'' = 5.540''$
    $y = 12.615'' + 5.912'' = 18.527''$

  Hole 4: $x = -8.480'' + 19.570'' = 11.090''$
    $y = 12.615'' + 4.508'' = 17.123''$

  Hole 5: $x = -8.480'' + 27.380'' = 18.900''$
    $y = 12.615''$

  Hole 6: $x = x$ distance of hole 3 = 5.540"
    $y = 12.615'' - 2.602'' = 10.013''$

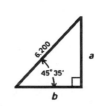

Hole	x	y
1	−9.857"	18.660"
2	−4.141"	17.043"
3	5.540"	18.527"
4	11.090"	17.123"
5	18.900"	12.615"
6	5.540"	10.013"
7	−4.318'	8.020"
8	14.469"	11.010"

  Hole 7: $(77°10' + 57°15' + 93°25') - 180° = 47°50'$

    $\sin 47°50' = \dfrac{a}{6.200''}$ $\cos 47°50' = \dfrac{b}{6.200''}$

    $0.74120 = \dfrac{a}{6.200''}$ $0.67129 = \dfrac{b}{6.200''}$

      $a = 4.595''$ $b = 4.162''$

  $x = -8.480'' + 4.162'' = -4.318''$
  $y = 12.615'' + 4.595'' = 8.020''$

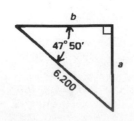

UNIT **74**   (*continued*)

8. a. Hole 8: $\sin 15° = \dfrac{a}{6.200''}$ $\cos 15° = \dfrac{b}{6.200''}$

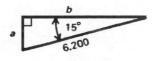

$0.25882 = \dfrac{a}{6.200''}$ $0.96593 = \dfrac{b}{6.200''}$

$a = 1.605''$ $b = 5.989''$

$x = -8.480'' - 5.989'' = -14.469''$
$y = 12.615'' - 1.605'' = 11.010''$

b. Incremental Dimensioning

Hole 1: $x = (10.520'' - 1.377'') - 19'' = -9.857''$
$y = 5'' + 7.615'' + 6.045'' = 18.660''$

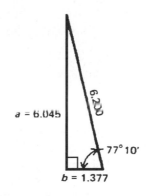

Hole 2: $x = 1.077'' + 4.039'' - 5.710''$
$-y = 6.045'' - 4.428'' = 1.617''$
$y = -1.617''$

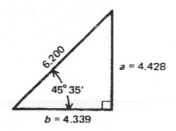

Hole 3: $x = 14.020'' - 4.339'' = 9.681''$
$y = 5.912'' - 4.428'' = 1.484''$

Hole 4: $x = 19.570'' - 14.020'' = 5.550''$
$-y = 5.912'' - 4.508'' = 1.404''$
$y = -1.404''$

Hole 5: $x = 27.380'' + 19.570'' = 7.810''$
$y = -4.508''$

Hole 6: $-x = 27.380'' - 14.020'' = 13.360''$
$x = -13.360''$
$y = -2.602''$

Hole	x	y
1	−9.857″	18.660″
2	5.716″	−1.617″
3	9.681″	1.484″
4	5.550″	−1.404″
5	7.810″	−4.508″
6	−13.360″	−2.602″
7	−9.585″	−1.993″
8	−10.151″	2.990″

Hole 7: $-x = 14.020'' - 4.162'' = 9.858''$
$x = -9.858''$
$-y = 4.595'' - 2.602'' = 1.993''$
$y = -1.993''$

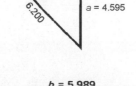

Hole 8: $x = 4.162'' + 5.989'' = 10.151''$
$x = -10.151''$
$y = 4.595'' - 1.605'' = 2.990''$

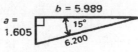

UNIT **74**   (*continued*)

9. a. Absolute Dimensioning

Center of circle: $x = -203.70$ mm

$y = 222.50$ mm

Hole 1: $72.67° = 72°40.2'$

$$\sin 72°40.2' = \frac{a}{112.00 \text{ mm}} \qquad \cos 72°40.2' = \frac{b}{112.00 \text{ mm}}$$

$$0.95461 = \frac{a}{112.00 \text{ mm}} \qquad 0.29787 = \frac{b}{112.00 \text{ mm}}$$

$$a = 106.92 \text{ mm} \qquad b = 33.36 \text{ mm}$$

$x = -203.70$ mm $- 33.36$ mm $= -237.06$ mm

$y = 222.50$ mm $+ 106.92$ mm $= 329.42$ mm

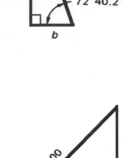

Hole 2: $180° - (72.67° + 61.50°) = 45.83° = 45°49.8'$

$$\sin 45°49.8' = \frac{a}{112.00 \text{ mm}} \qquad \cos 45°49.8' = \frac{b}{112.00 \text{ mm}}$$

$$0.71728 = \frac{a}{112.00 \text{ mm}} \qquad 0.69679 = \frac{b}{112.00 \text{ mm}}$$

$$a = 80.34 \text{ mm} \qquad b = 78.04 \text{ mm}$$

$x = -203.70$ mm $+ 78.04$ mm $= -125.66$ mm

$y = 222.50$ mm $+ 80.34$ mm $= 302.84$ mm

Hole 3: $x = -203.70$ mm $+ 225.00$ mm $= 51.30$ mm
$y = 222.50$ mm $+ 106.80$ mm $= 329.30$ mm

Hole 4: $x = -203.70$ mm $+ 378.34$ mm $= 174.64$ mm
$y = 222.50$ mm $+ 79.68$ mm $= 302.18$ mm

Hole 5: $x = -203.70$ mm $+ 521.40$ mm $= 317.70$ mm
$y = 222.50$ mm

Hole 6: $x = x$ distance of hole 3 $= 51.30$ mm
$y = 222.50$ mm $- 59.50$ mm $= 163.00$ mm

Hole	x	y
1	−237.06 mm	329.42 mm
2	−125.66 mm	302.84 mm
3	51.30 mm	329.30 mm
4	174.64 mm	302.18 mm
5	317.70 mm	222.50 mm
6	51.30 mm	163.00 mm
7	−136.30 mm	133.05 mm
8	−310.02 mm	187.28 mm

Hole 7: $(72.67° + 61.50° + 98.83°) - 180° = 53°$

$$\sin 53° = \frac{a}{112.00 \text{ mm}} \qquad \cos 53° = \frac{b}{112.00 \text{ mm}}$$

$$0.79864 = \frac{a}{112.00 \text{ mm}} \qquad 0.60182 = \frac{b}{112.00 \text{ mm}}$$

$$a = 89.45 \text{ mm} \qquad b = 67.40 \text{ mm}$$

$x = -203.70$ mm $+ 67.40$ mm $= -136.30$ mm

$y = 222.50$ mm $- 89.45$ mm $= 133.05$ mm

Hole 8: $18.33° = 18°19.8'$

$$\sin 18°19.8' = \frac{a}{112.00 \text{ mm}} \qquad \cos 18°19.8' = \frac{b}{112.00 \text{ mm}}$$

$$0.31449 = \frac{a}{112.00 \text{ mm}} \qquad 0.94926 = \frac{b}{112.00 \text{ mm}}$$

$$a = 35.22 \text{ mm} \qquad b = 106.32 \text{ mm}$$

$x = -203.70$ mm $- 106.32$ mm $= -310.02$ mm

$y = 222.50$ mm $- 35.22$ mm $= 187.28$ mm

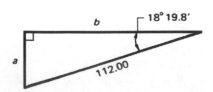

UNIT **74**   (*continued*)

9. b. Incremental Dimensioning

   Hole 1: x = (196.30 mm − 33.36 mm) − 400 mm = −237.06 mm
             y = 80 mm + 142.50 mm + 106.92 mm = 329.42 mm

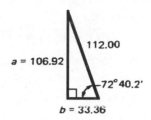

Hole 2: x = 33.36 mm + 78.04 mm = 111.40 mm
          $-y$ = 106.92 mm − 80.34 mm = 26.58 mm
          y = − 26.58 mm

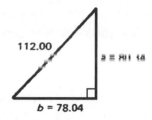

Hole 3: x = 225.00 mm − 78.04 mm = 176.96 mm
          y − 100.00 mm − 80.34 mm = 20.40 mm

Hole 4: x = 378.34 mm − 255.00 mm = 123.34 mm
          $-y$ = 106.80 mm − 79.68 mm = 27.12 mm
          y = − 27.12 mm

Hole 5: x = 521.40 mm − 378.34 mm = 143.06 mm
          $-y$ = 79.68 mm
          y = − 79.68 mm

Hole 6: $-x$ = 521.50 mm − 255.00 mm = 266.40 mm
          x = − 266.40 mm
          y = − 59.50 mm

Hole	x	y
1	−237.06 mm	329.42 mm
2	−125.66 mm	302.84 mm
3	51.30 mm	329.30 mm
4	174.64 mm	302.18 mm
5	317.70 mm	222.50 mm
6	51.30 mm	163.00 mm
7	−136.30 mm	133.05 mm
8	−310.02 mm	187.28 mm

Hole 7: $-x$ = 255.00 mm − 67.40 mm = 187.60 mm
          x = − 187.60 mm
          $-y$ = 89.45 mm − 59.50 mm = 29.95 mm
          y = − 29.95 mm

Hole 8: $-x$ = 67.40 mm + 106.32 mm = 173.72 mm
          x = − 173.72 mm
          y = 89.45 mm − 35.22 mm = 54.23 mm

UNIT 75 Binary Numeration System

1. $2(10^2) + 6(10^1) + 5(10^0)$
   200 + 60 + 5 = 265

2. $2(10^3) + 8(10^2) + 5(10^1) + 5(10^0)$
   2000 + 800 + 50 + 5 = 2855

3. $9(10^4) + 0(10^3) + 5(10^2) + 0(10^1) + 0(10^0)$
   90,000 + 0 + 500 + 0 + 0 = 90,500

4. $8(10^{-1}) + 0(10^{-2}) + 2(10^{-3})$
   0.7 + 0 + 0.004 = 0.704

5. $2(10^1) + 3(10^0) + 0(10^{-1}) + 2(10^{-2}) + 3(10^{-3})$
   20 + 3 + 0 + 0.02 + 0.003 = 23.023

6. $1(10^2) + 0(10^1) + 5(10^0) + 0(10^{-1}) + 0(10^{-2}) + 9(10^{-3})$
   100 + 0 + 5 + 0 + 0 + 0.009 = 105.009

7. $4(10^3) + 7(10^2) + 5(10^1) + 1(10^0) + 1(10^{-1}) + 0(10^{-2}) + 7(10^{-3})$
   4000 + 700 + 50 + 1 + 0.1 + 0 + 0.007 = 4751.107

8. $3(10^3) + 0(10^2) + 0(10^1) + 6(10^0) + 0(10^{-1}) + 2(10^{-2}) + 0(10^{-3}) + 4(10^{-4})$
   3000 + 0 + 0 + 6 + 0 + 0.02 + 0 + 0.0004 = 3006.0204

9. $1(10^2) + 6(10^1) + 3(10^0) + 0(10^{-1}) + 6(10^{-2}) + 4(10^{-3}) + 3(10^{-4})$
   100 + 60 + 3 + 0 + 0.06 + 0.004 + 0.0003 = 163.0643

10. 2_{10}

11. 1_{10}

12. 4_{10}

13. 5_{10}

14. 13_{10}

15. 15_{10}

16. 20_{10}

17. 11_{10}

18. 24_{10}

19. 21_{10}

20. 42_{10}

21. 53_{10}

22. 58_{10}

23. 0.5_{10}

24. 0.6875_{10}

25. 3.75_{10}

26. 3.25_{10}

27. 2.000_{10}

28. 15.75_{10}

29. 9.3125_{10}

30. 19.3125_{10}

31. 1110_2

32. 1100100_2

33. 1010111_2

34. 10111_2

35. 101011_2

36. 100_2

37. 1101001_2

38. 1100010_2

39. 1_2

40. 110_2

41. 110011_2

42. 100001110_2

43. 0.1_2

44. 0.001_2

45. 0.011_2

46. 1010.1_2

47. 1010001.11_2

48. 10011.0001_2

49. 1100101.01_2

50. 1.001_2

51. 10100011.111_2

UNIT 76 Achievement Review—Section Eight

1.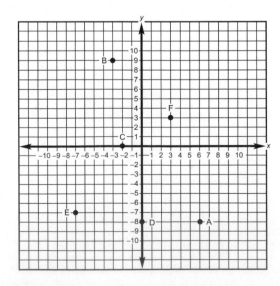

2. A = (5, 8) F = (1, −7) J = (−3, 0)
   B = (8, 3) G = (−9, −8) K = (−9, 9)
   C = (−4, 5) H = (−6, −6) L = (−2, −6)
   D = (−6, 1) I = (8, 0) M = (9, −9)
   E = (4, −1)

UNIT **76** *(continued)*

3. a. Absolute Dimensioning

    Hole 1: $x = 4'' + 2.272'' = 6.272''$
               $y = 3'' - 5.120'' = -2.120''$

    Hole 2: $x = 6.272'' + 1.900'' = 8.172''$
               $y = -2.120'' + 3.608'' = 1.488''$

    Hole 3: $x = 8.172'' + 5.029'' = 13.201''$
               y is the same as y of hole 2 = 1.488″

    Hole 4: $x = 13.201'' + 6.741'' = 19.942''$
               y is the same as y of hole 3 = 1.488″

    Hole 5: $x = 19.942'' + 1.090'' = 21.032''$
               $y = 1.488'' - 4.880'' = -3.392''$

    Hole 6: x is the same as x of hole 5 = 21.032″
               $y = -3.392'' - 2.115'' = -5.507''$

    Hole 7: $x = 21.032'' - 7.100'' = 13.903''$
               $y = -2.120'' - 2.119'' = -4.239''$

Hole	x	y
1	6.272″	−2.120″
2	8.172″	1.488″
3	13.201″	1.488″
4	19.942″	1.488″
5	21.032″	−3.392″
6	21.032″	−5.507″
7	13.903″	−4.239″

  b. Incremental Dimensioning

    Hole 1: $x = 4'' + 2.272'' = 6.272''$
               $y = 3'' - 5.120'' = -2.120''$

    Hole 2: $x = 1.900''$
               $y = 3.608''$

    Hole 3: $x = 5.029''$
               $y = 0$

    Hole 4: $x = 6.741''$
               $y = 0$

    Hole 5: $x = 1.090''$
               $y = -4.880''$

    Hole 6: $x = 0$
               $y = -2.115''$

    Hole 7: $x = -7.129''$
               $y = (4.880'' + 2.115'') - (2.119'' + 3.608'') = 1.268''$

Hole	x	y
1	6.272″	−2.120″
2	1.900″	3.608″
3	5.029″	0
4	6.741″	0
5	1.090″	−4.880″
6	0	−2.115″
7	−7.129″	1.268″

4. a. Absolute Dimensioning

    Hole 1: $x = -400 \text{ mm} + 90.00 \text{ mm} = -310.00 \text{ mm}$
               $y = 100 \text{ mm} + 171.10 \text{ mm} = 271.10 \text{ mm}$

    Hole 2: $x = -400 \text{ mm} + 240.00 \text{ mm} = -160 \text{ mm}$
               $y = 100 \text{ mm} + 284.36 \text{ mm} = 384.36 \text{ mm}$

    Hole 3: $x = -400 \text{ mm} + 352.17 \text{ mm} = -47.83 \text{ mm}$
               y is the same as y of hole 2, $y = 384.36$ mm

    Hole 4: $x = -400 \text{ mm} + 605.76 \text{ mm} = 205.76 \text{ mm}$
               y is the same as y of hole 3, $y = 384.36$ mm

Hole	x	y
1	−310.00 mm	271.10 mm
2	−160.00 mm	384.36 mm
3	−47.83 mm	384.36 mm
4	205.76 mm	384.36 mm
5	454.59 mm	286.67 mm
6	640.75 mm	380.99 mm
7	626.71 mm	192.13 mm
8	429.07 mm	234.14 mm
9	260.23 mm	220.00 mm

    Hole 5: $\sin 46° = \dfrac{a}{130.00 \text{ mm}}$ $\cos 46° = \dfrac{b}{130.00 \text{ mm}}$

                 $0.71934 = \dfrac{a}{130.00 \text{ mm}}$ $0.69466 = \dfrac{b}{130.00 \text{ mm}}$

                       $a = 93.51$ mm $b = 90.31$ mm

              $x = -400 \text{ mm} + 944.90 \text{ mm} - 90.31 \text{ mm} = 454.59 \text{ mm}$
              $y = 100 \text{ mm} + 193.16 \text{ mm} + 93.51 \text{ mm} = 386.67 \text{ mm}$

UNIT 76   (*continued*)

4. a. Hole 6:   42.50° = 42°30′

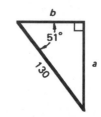

$$\sin 42°30′ = \frac{a}{130.00 \text{ mm}} \qquad \cos 42°30′ = \frac{b}{130.00 \text{ mm}}$$

$$0.67559 = \frac{a}{130.00 \text{ mm}} \qquad 0.73728 = \frac{b}{130.00 \text{ mm}}$$

$$a = 87.83 \text{ mm} \qquad\qquad b = 95.85 \text{ mm}$$

$x = -400 \text{ mm} + 944.90 \text{ mm} + 95.85 \text{ mm} = 640.75 \text{ mm}$

$y = 100 \text{ mm} + 193.16 \text{ mm} + 87.83 \text{ mm} = 380.99 \text{ mm}$

Hole 7:

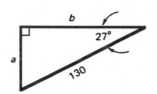

$$\sin 51° = \frac{a}{130.00 \text{ mm}} \qquad \cos 51° = \frac{b}{130.00 \text{ mm}}$$

$$0.77715 = \frac{a}{130.00 \text{ mm}} \qquad 0.62932 = \frac{b}{130.00 \text{ mm}}$$

$$a = 101.03 \text{ mm} \qquad\qquad b = 81.81 \text{ mm}$$

$x = -400 \text{ mm} + 944.90 \text{ mm} + 81.81 \text{ mm} = 626.71 \text{ mm}$

$y = 100 \text{ mm} - 193.16 \text{ mm} - 101.03 \text{ mm} = 192.13 \text{ mm}$

Hole 8:

$$\sin 27° = \frac{a}{130.00 \text{ mm}} \qquad \cos 27° = \frac{b}{130.00 \text{ mm}}$$

$$0.45399 = \frac{a}{130.00 \text{ mm}} \qquad 0.89101 = \frac{b}{130.00 \text{ mm}}$$

$$a = 59.02 \text{ mm} \qquad\qquad b = 115.83 \text{ mm}$$

$x = -400 \text{ mm} + 944.90 \text{ mm} - 115.83 \text{ mm} = 429.07 \text{ mm}$

$y = 100 \text{ mm} + 193.16 \text{ mm} - 59.02 \text{ mm} = 234.14 \text{ mm}$

Hole 9: $x = -400 \text{ mm} + 660.23 \text{ mm} = 260.23 \text{ mm}$

           $y = 100 \text{ mm} + 120.00 \text{ mm} = 220.00 \text{ mm}$

b. Incremental Dimensioning

Hole 1: $x = -400 \text{ mm} + 90.00 \text{ mm} = -310.00 \text{ mm}$

           $y = 100 \text{ mm} + 171.10 \text{ mm} = 271.10 \text{ mm}$

Hole 2: $x = 240.00 \text{ mm} - 90.00 \text{ mm} = 150 \text{ mm}$

           $y = 284.36 \text{ mm} + 171.10 \text{ mm} = 113.26 \text{ mm}$

Hole 3: $x = 352.17 \text{ mm} - 240.00 \text{ mm} = 112.17 \text{ mm}$

           $y = 0$

Hole 4: $x = 605.76 \text{ mm} - 352.17 \text{ mm} = 253.59 \text{ mm}$

           $y = 0$

Hole	x	y
1	−310.00 mm	271.10 mm
2	150.00 mm	113.26 mm
3	112.17 mm	0
4	253.59 mm	0
5	248.83 mm	2.31 mm
6	186.16 mm	−5.68 mm
7	−14.04 m	−188.86 mm
8	−197.64 mm	42.01 mm
9	−168.84 mm	−14.14 mm

.   Hole 5: $x = 944.90 \text{ mm} - 605.76 \text{ mm} - 90.31 \text{ mm} = 248.83 \text{ mm}$

              $y = 193.16 \text{ mm} + 93.51 \text{ mm} - 284.36 \text{ mm} = 2.31 \text{ mm}$

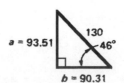

UNIT **76**   *(continued)*

4. b. Hole 6: $x = 90.31$ mm $+ 95.85$ mm $= 186.16$ mm
$y = 87.83$ mm $- 93.51$ mm $= -5.68$ mm

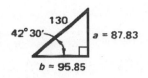

Hole 7: $x = 81.81$ mm $- 95.85$ mm $= -14.04$ mm
$y = -87.83$ mm $- 101.03$ mm $= -188.86$ mm

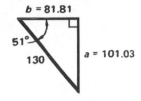

Hole 8: $x = -81.81$ mm $- 115.83$ mm $= -197.64$ mm
$y = 101.03$ mm $- 59.02$ mm $= 42.01$ mm

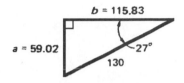

Hole 9: $x = 660.23$ mm $- (911.00$ mm $- 115.83$ mm$) = -168.84$ mm
$y = 59.02$ mm $- (193.16$ mm $- 120.00$ mm$) = -14.14$ mm

5. a. 1
b. 7
c. 21
d. 3.25
e. 9.5625

6. a. 111_2
b. 100000_2
c. 10011101_2
d. 0.001_2
e. 1001010.01_2